A NATURAL HISTORY OF CUMBERLAND ISLAND, GEORGIA

MERCER UNIVERSITY PRESS

Endowed by

TOM WATSON BROWN
and
THE WATSON-BROWN FOUNDATION, INC.

A NATURAL HISTORY

Wild ...

OF

Cumberland Island

GEORGIA

Carol

CAROL RUCKDESCHEL

MERCER UNIVERSITY PRESS | MACON, GEORGIA | 2017

"Occasional Publications of the Cumberland Island Museum, No. 4"

MUP/ P585

© 2019 Mercer University Press
First paperback edition
© 2017 by Mercer University Press (hardback)
Published by Mercer University Press
1501 Mercer University Drive
Macon, Georgia 31207

9 8 7 6 5 4 3 2 1

Books published by Mercer University Press are printed on acid-free paper
that meets the requirements of the American National Standard for
Information Sciences—Permanence of Paper for Printed Library Materials.

ISBN   978-0-88146-710-9
Cataloging-in-Publication Data is available from the Library of Congress

To C. R. Shoop for cheerfully sharing the load, his
wonderful sense of humor, and white peggies, and
V. J. Henry Jr., who made this book possible.

Contents

List of Tables   ix

List of Figures   x

Foreword   xii

Preface   xv

Acknowledgments   xvii

Abbreviations   xviii

Tables   xix

Naturalists: Observers and Collectors on Cumberland Island   1

Chapter 1: Geology   4

    Setting   4

    Geologic History   5

    Beach   7

    Shoreline   8

    Soils   9

    Freshwater   11

    Intracoastal Waterway   13

    Climate   15

    Precipitation   18

    Tide   18

Chapter 2: Modifications   20

    Archaeological Evidence   20

    Subsistence   22

      Fauna   23

      Flora   24

    Agriculture   25

    European Colonization   25

      Spanish   25

    Commerce   28

    Forest Products   32

Logging   35
Marsh and Waterways   36
Modern Agriculture   37
Carnegies   40
Other Endeavors   41
Fire   42
Chapter 3: Communities   46
  Beach/Dunes   46
    Beach   47
    Primary and Secondary Dunes 48
    Interdune   49
    Rear Dune   51
  Maritime Forest   52
  Pine   60
  Scrub   64
  Freshwater Communities   68
    Sloughs   68
      Wet Savanna   69
      Interdune Myrtle Slough 70
      Inland Slough 71
    Ponds   73
    Whitney Lake   76
    Hardwood Swamp   78
    Seep   81
  Salt Marsh   81
Chapter 4: Species Accounts   87
  Introduction   87
  This Presentation   88
  Fish   89
    Species Accounts   89
  Amphibians and Reptiles   93
    Introduction   93
    Amphibians   94

Species Accounts	94
Reptiles	106
Species Accounts	106
Birds	147
Introduction	147
Heronries	148
Species Accounts	150
Mammals	212
Introduction	212
Species Accounts	214
Feral Livestock	275
Impact	280
Personal Correspondence References	283
References	285
Appendix I. Vascular Plant List	299
Appendix II. Fish Species List	318
Appendix III. Amphibian and Reptile Species List	319
Appendix IV. Birds	322
A. Bird Species List	322
B. Avian Museum Species List	335
Appendix V. Mammal Species List	352
Appendix VI. Parasites	354
A. Amphibians and Reptiles	354
B. Birds	355
C. Mammals	357
Index	365

List of Tables

1. Classification of soil on Cumberland Island, Georgia, p. xix

2. Zooarcheological records from Cumberland Island, Georgia, p. xx.

3. Amphibians and reptiles on Cumberland Island and adjacent mainland, Camden Co., Georgia, p. xxi.

4. Sea turtle strandings on Cumberland Island, Georgia. 1981–2010, p xxiv.

5. Mammals on Cumberland Island and adjacent mainland, Camden County, Georgia, xxv.

6. Food of the Virginia opossum, *Didelphis virginiana*, on Cumberland Island, Georgia, xxvii.

7. Food of the coyote, *Canis latrans*, on Cumberland Island, Georgia, xxviii.

8. Food of the raccoon, *Procyon lotor*, on Cumberland Island, Georgia, xxix.

9. Food of the North American river otter, *Lontra Canadensis*, on Cumberland Island, Georgia, p. xxx.

10. Important food of bobcats, *Lynx rufus*, on Cumberland Island, Georgia, xxxi.

List of Figures

Chapter 1: Geology
1. Georgia barrier islands and Amelia Island, Florida.
2. Cumberland Island map.
3. Quaternary shorelines in Georgia.
4. Pleistocene remnant of Cumberland Island.
5. Rock jetty along the mouth of the St. Marys River.
6. Waterfall over humate.

Chapter 2: Modifications
7. McKinnon 1802 map of Cumberland Island.
8. Page and Meader 1898 map of Dungeness and Stafford Place, Cumberland Island.
9. Proposed development from High Point south to McIntosh Creek, Cumberland Island, 1894.
10. Cactus with cochineal insects, Dactylopiidae.

Chapter 3: Communities
11. Vegetation map.
12. Beach/dunes, Cumberland Island.
13. Amber snail, *Succinea campestris,* a member of the interdune community.
14. Temporary Pond.
15. Maritime forest on Cumberland Island.
16. Terminal oak twigs killed by abrading sand and salt, Cumberland Island.
17. Scrub habitat, Cumberland Island.
18. Parallel dunes and sloughs of Holocene origin, Cumberland Island, 1993.
19. Whitney Lake, 1987, Cumberland Island.
20. Linear wax myrtle thicket, *Myrica cerifera,* Cumberland Island, 2012.
21. Hardwood swamp, Cumberland Island.
22. Freshwater seep along the western side of the island.
23. Salt marsh and tidal creek.

Chapter 4: Species Accounts

24. American Aligator.
25. Tracks of alligator beneath nest tree out of water.
26. Sweetwater heronry, 1997.
27. For supper, Cumberland Island.
28. Eastern Mole burrow on ocean beach.
29. Fumigating the Carriage House, Dungeness, 1976.
30. White or piebald deer on island.
31. Cumberland Island "pocket gopher," *Geomys* sp.
32. Feral hog on Cumberland Island.
33. Cattle were numerous in 1974 and took refuge on the beach from biting flies.

Foreword

In July 2007, I first traveled up the narrow, bumpy sand road to Cumberland Island's north end to visit Carol Ruckdeschel at the Cumberland Island Museum. The museum is not what one might expect, that is, a place of meticulously clean exhibits with fancy signage illustrating various items of natural history. The CI Museum is a working museum: the office is small and cramped with narrow counter space, which is itself crammed with specimens, papers, and notes of all sorts. Towering shelves of books and science journals fill two walls. To the back is a room jam-packed with specimens of all sorts, from salvaged sea turtle and marine mammal bones to jars containing the gut contents of nearly every animal Carol has found through decades of collecting and cataloging Cumberland's fauna. In between are geological specimens and artifacts found along the beaches from shipwrecks and the refuse of early (and some not-so-early) inhabitants. This is not a haphazard collection, however, but a meticulously assembled chronicle of Cumberland's history gathered since Carol came to the island in 1973. Outbuildings serve as areas for work where rotten carcasses are cleaned and prepped. The visitor cabin is clean and well kept but with only a screen (no walls to speak of) separating the interior from the elements. To the south and west is Carol's cabin that she shares with her cat Possum, a beautiful garden, and her chicken coops that comprise her largely self-sustaining homestead.

Cumberland Island is a magical, natural place, despite its location along the very densely populated and trendy Georgia-Florida coast. It is easy to get lost mystically in its moss-draped oaks, open marshes, or along the wild, lonely, white beaches on its northeastern side. The entire island is either federally protected or in private ownership, and access is limited to ferry crossings and by private boats. Limited access has allowed the island to remain undeveloped, and, although by no means pristine, at least it has not suffered the ravages of most of the Southeastern barrier islands. Bouncing up the sand road, one might see American alligators, deer, raccoons, squirrels, and, if extremely lucky, an eastern diamondback rattlesnake. Still, Cumberland is by no means "safe." Through the years, there have been numerous proposals to increase tourism, build a causeway, and allow for certain developments and "improvements." Local politicians and congressmen cannot seem to leave the place alone, always in the process of finagling benefits for favored constituents at the expense of the natural barrier island ecosystem and its inhabitants. In an era when parks are seen as playgrounds or places where value is measured in visitor numbers, Cumberland Island is particularly vulnerable geographically and politically.

In order to biologically understand a place, one needs to address three general themes. First, one must know about the life history and evolution of its inhabitants; that is, the species that make up its fauna and flora. It is necessary to learn this on-site, inasmuch as the life histories of species are often quite variable, and it is inappropriate to extrapolate life histories from one region to another. Place matters. Second, one must understand an area's physical and biotic environment—the influences of physiography, hydrology, weather, climate, geological history, and community structure on its varied ecosystems. Third (and often overlooked), one must become a historian to understand the ways in which humans have modified or influenced the area. In the case of Cumberland Island, the historical record extends far into the past, back to when the first indigenous peoples crossed the narrow Cumberland Sound about 4,000 years ago, through the period of ownership by wealthy families, to the present management by the National Park Service. These prerequisites of exceptional natural history are met in *A Natural History of Cumberland Island, Georgia*.

A guide to the natural history of Cumberland Island could not have been written by a casual visitor, even one who has conducted meticulous research over a period of years. To understand a place, one must live there, as Carol has done for more than four decades. The information in this book is not based on casual observations, but on a detailed examination of the life history of species encountered, individual by individual, through the years. These results incorporate thousands of hours of field biology and laboratory observations, making the author a true natural historian (a person of nature and history) in the best sense of the discipline. Through the years it has been a privilege to know Carol, a person who is neither wild nor untamed, but one who has seemed to know all her life what her life is about and that she belongs in nature. Although this guide contains but a sliver of her knowledge of Cumberland Island, it is the fitting culmination of a lifetime spent in the pursuit of natural history and the protection of Southeastern biodiversity.

As the Senegalese environmentalist Baba Dioum has reminded us, "In the end, we will conserve only what we love. We will love only what we understand. We will understand only what we are taught." In *A Natural History of Cumberland Island, Georgia*, Carol Ruckdeschel has given us an outstanding account of the flora, fauna, human history, and management practices that have affected the island through the years. This book forms the basis for understanding the island's natural history and provides a foundation for conservation grounded on the continuance of ecosystem function. Ultimately, of course, I hope it also will lead to a love of our Southeastern barrier islands and a new will to conserve them and our remaining Southern natural heritage.

—C. Kenneth Dodd Jr., PhD
Department of Wildlife Ecology and Conservation,
University of Florida

Preface

Producing this book was not an original goal when I came to live on Cumberland Island in 1973. Rather, this book is a result of forty years of inquiry into the ecology of the island through rigorous analyses of observations and forays into the literature. In assembling the preliminary background information, I realized how widely scattered it had been and that it covered several disciplines and many time periods, so it was no surprise that it had not been pulled together before. To put my observations in context, I needed to research and attempt to resolve many questions, which required delving into historical collections, compiling pertinent material from scientific literature, and consulting numerous experts in various fields. My efforts were not always methodical. There are many areas into which I may have dug deeper than necessary, and probably many areas I slighted. Sifting past errors from facts, however, has been a consistent goal throughout this effort.

Surprisingly little recent literature exists on the natural history of the Georgia barrier islands. In part, this is due to the lack of accessibility of the islands for a long period due to private ownership and the need for a boat. The sections on geology and modifications are intended to provide a foundation for an understanding—from a natural history perspective—of how Cumberland Island physically came to be what it is today. With few exceptions, my focus has been on the ecology of the terrestrial and freshwater habitats of the island rather than its marine connections.

The emphasis here is on contemporary ecology. The island no longer functions as it did prior to human manipulation and introductions, and never will again. Cumberland's legacy is of usurpation, as is that of all the Georgia barrier islands. Historically, no value was placed on natural ecosystems, and all have suffered abuse from logging, agriculture, drainage, livestock, introductions, and selective cropping of some species. In 1972, the island and surrounding salt marshes were congressionally designated a national seashore to be administered by the National Park Service (NPS). Another layer of protection was added in 1982, when the northern portion of the island, from Stafford north, was officially designated a Wilderness, presumably to be managed by the NPS Wilderness guidelines. Some old fields are barely discernable now, and in one- to two-hundred years, further changes should be evident as vegetation and communities mature. The floral and faunal cast will continue to change, so this inquiry is but a glimpse in time, roughly 1970 to 2010, but provides a base of understanding for some of the relationships. Because feral animals (former livestock) are so pervasive in the island ecology, they are mentioned throughout and in conjunction with native fauna, not necessarily with qualification each time.

Place names are as dynamic as the ocean beach and tend to change with each era. Few island locality names derive from the Revolutionary period; most date to the Carnegie era. When changes occur contemporaneously with studies or biological observations, future confusion may result. I have noted these changes when possible. A map identifies the main features referenced in the text.

This book is what I wished I had when I began my island tenure. I hope the information strengthens future studies for a better understanding of the Cumberland Island ecology.

Acknowledgments

My introduction to the island was in the mid-1960s by Helen B. Jordan, a professor at Georgia State University. Sam O. Candler facilitated a position as caretaker for me and John Pennington in the early 1970s, which convinced me this would be a good place to study. C. Robert Shoop, a herpetologist at the University of Rhode Island, became involved in 1979, and he and I envisioned this book. Sadly, he died in 2003, but contributed much to it, not only in specimens, but in ideas, enthusiasm, and support. He was also prominent in the establishment of the Cumberland Island Museum (www.cimuseum.org), which supported the research for this book.

Ann Mahoney provided strategic support throughout the project in grammatical corrections, suggestions of content, and morale boosts when necessary. She deserves much credit. Many individuals commented in their field of expertise, including Chester J. Jackson, Joanne Sharpe, C. Kenneth Dodd, Joseph C. Mitchell, David W. Johnston, Sheila Willis, Robert Kenney, Peter Laurie, John O. Whitaker Jr., Bud Freeman, and those too numerous to individually mention who took time to reply to my never-ending questions. H. Joel Hutcheson and James W. Mertins, with the National Veterinary Services Lab, provided identification of many external parasites, as did Nixon Wilson, John O. Whitaker Jr., and Lance Durden. Linda Armstrong and Paula K. Eubanks provided expertise regarding photographs, and Sasha Greenspan contributed her time and computer skills during the final phase. I thank them all.

Island people freely shared observations and information. I worked closely with the Georgia Department of Natural Resources and thank them for their long-term support, and I thank the National Park Service for many courtesies, especially for those years they allowed me to have a collecting permit. Working with Dr. Marc Jolley, Marsha Luttrell, and the staff at Mercer University Press has been a pleasure. I thank them for their expertise, attention to detail, and patience with my writing. The book was improved because of their efforts.

Abbreviations

BP	before present
C	centigrade
cm	centimeter = 0.39 inch
DOB	dead on beach
DOR	dead on road
F	Fahrenheit
h	hour
kg	kilogram = 2.2046 pounds
km	kilometer = 0.6 miles
mm	millimeter = 0.039 inch
m	meter = 39.37 inches
mph	miles per hour
n.d.	no date

TABLES

Table 1

Classification of Soil on Cumberland Island, Georgia.

USDA Soil Conservation Service	Hillestad et al., 1975
Cainhoy Fine Sand	Lakeland Sand
Beach	Coastal Beach
Bohicket-Capers Association	Capers Soil
Fripp-Duckston Complex	Duckston Sand, Unstabilized Dunes, Fripp-Leon Fine Sand
Mandarin Fine Sand	Leon Fine Sand
Pottsburg Sand	Chipley Sand, Olustee Sand
Rutlege Fine Sand	Johnston Loam

Table 2

Zooarchaeological records from Cumberland Island, Georgia.
Deptford Phase Culture from 2400 BP – 200 BP

Taxon	Scientific Name	Common Name
FISH	Charcharhinidae	Requiem sharks
	Galeocerdo cuvieri	Tiger shark
	Sphyrnidae	Hammerhead sharks
	Dasytidae	Stingrays
	Myliobatidae	Eagle rays
	Arius felis	Hardhead catfish
	Bagre marinus	Gafftopsail catfish
	Archosargus sp.	Sheepshead
	Pogonias cromis	Black drum
	Scianops ocellatus	Red drum
REPTILES	Cheloniidae	Sea turtles
	Chrysemys sp.	Painted turtle
	Deirochelys reticularia	Chicken turtle
	Malaclemmys terrapin	Diamondback terrapin
	Terrapene carolina	Eastern box turtle
	Sternotherus sp.	Musk turtle
	Gopherus polyphemus	Gopher tortoise
	Apalone ferox	Florida softshell
BIRDS	*Mergus serrator*	Red-breasted merganser
MAMMALS	*Didelphis virginiana*	Virginia opossum
	Procyon lotor	Raccoon
	Monachus tropicalis	Caribbean monk seal
	Cetacean	Marine mammal
	Odocoileus virginianus	White-tailed deer
	Geomys sp.	Pocket gopher

Table 3

Amphibians and reptiles on Cumberland Island and adjacent mainland, Camden County, Georgia.
CUIS = Cumberland Island. CACO = Camden County.

Family Common name	Scientific name	CUIS	CACO
AMPHIBIANS			
Bufonidae			
Oak toad -	*Anaxyrus quericus*		•
Southern toad -	*Anaxyrus terrestris*	•	•
Hylidae			
Southern cricket frog -	*Acris gryllus*	•	•
Cope's gray treefrog -	*Hyla chrysocelis*	•	•
Green treefrog -	*Hyla cinerea*	•	•
Pine woods treefrog -	*Hyla femoralis*	•	•
Barking treefrog -	*Hyla gratiosa*	•	•
Squirrel treefrog -	*Hyla squirella*	•	•
Spring peeper -	*Pseudacris crucifer*	•	•
Southern chorus frog -	Pseudacris nigrita	•	•
Little grass frog -	Pseudacris ocularis	•	•
Ornate chorus frog -	*Pseudacris ornata*		•
Eleutherodactylidae			
Greenhouse frog -	*Eleutherodactylus planirostris*		•
Microhylidae			
Eastern narrow-mouthed frog	*Gastrophryne carolinensis*	•	•
Pelobatidae			
Eastern spadefoot -	*Scaphiopus holbrookii*	•	•
Ranidae			
Green frog -	*Lithobates clamitans*		•
Pig frog -	*Lithobates grylio*	•	•
Southern leopard frog -	*Lithobates sphenocephalus*	•	•
Ambystomatidae			
Marbled salamander -	*Ambystoma opacum*		•
Mole salamander -	*Ambystoma talpoideum*	•	•
Amphiumidae			
Two-toed amphiuma -	*Amphiuma means*	•	•

Family / Common name	Scientific name		
Plethodontidae			
Southern dusky salamander -	*Desmognathus auriculatus*	•	•
Two-lined salamander -	*Eurycea bislineata*		•
Dwarf salamander -	*Eurycea quadridigitata*	•	•
Slimy salamander -	*Plethodon glutinosus*		•
Mud salamander -	*Pseudotriton montanus*		•
Salmandridae			
Striped newt -	*Notophthalmus perstriatus*		•
Eastern newt -	*Notophthalmus viridescens*	•	•
Sirenidae			
Northern dwarf siren -	*Pseudobranchus striatus*		•
Lesser siren -	*Siren intermedia*		•

REPTILES

Family / Common name	Scientific name		
Aligatoridae			
American alligator -	*Alligator mississippiensis*	•	•
Anguidae			
Island glass lizard -	*Ophisaurus compressus*	•	•
Eastern glass lizard -	*Ophisaurus ventralis*	•	•
Phrynosomatidae			
Eastern fence lizard -	*Sceloporus undulatus*	•	•
Polychrotidae			
Green anole -	*Anolis carolinensis*	•	•
Brown anole -	*Anolis sagrei*		•
Scincidae			
Mole skink -	*Plesiodon eregius*	•	•
Five-lined skink -	*Plestiodon fasciatus*		•
Southeastern Five-lined skink -	*Plestiodon inexpectatus*	•	•
Broad-headed skink -	*Plestiodon laticeps*	•	•
Ground skink -	*Scincella lateralis*	•	•
Teidae			
Six-lined racerunner -	*Aspidoscelis sexlineata*	•	•
Colubridae			
Scarlet snake -	*Cemophora coccinea*	•	•
Northern black racer -	*Coluber constrictor*	•	•
Southern ring-necked snake -	*Diadophis punctatus*	•	•
Eastern indigo snake -	*Drymarchon couperi*		•
Corn snake -	*Pantherophis guttatus*	•	•
Yellow ratsnake -	*Pantherophis obsoletus*	•	•
Eastern mud snake -	*Farancia abacura*	•	•
Rainbow snake –	*Farancia erytrogramma*		•
Eastern hognose snake -	*Heterodon platirhinos*		•
Southern hog-nosed Snake -	*Heterodon simus*		•

Common name	Scientific name		
Eastern kingsnake	*Lampropeltis guttatus*	•	•
Scarlet kingsnake	*Lampropeltis elapsoides*	•	•
Eastern coachwhip	*Masticophis flagellum*	•	•
Southern banded watersnake	*Nerodia fasciata*	•	•
Brown watersnake	*Nerodia taxispilota*		•
Rough green snake	*Opheodrys aestivus*	•	•
Pine woods littersnake	*Rhadinaea flavilata*	•	•
Florida red-bellied snake	*Storeria occipitomaculata*	•	•
Eastern ribbon snake	*Thamnophis sauritus*	•	•
Common garter snake	*Thamnophis sirtalis*	•	•

Elapidae

Eastern coral snake	*Micrurus fulvius*		•

Viperidae

Cottonmouth	*Agkistrodon piscivorus*	•	•
Eastern diamondback rattlesnake	*Crotalus adamanteus*	•	•
Timber/Canebrake rattlesnake	*Crotalus horridus*	•	
Pygmy rattlesnake	*Sistrurus miliarius*		•

Cheloniidae

Loggerhead sea turtle	*Caretta caretta*	•	•
Green sea turtle	*Chelonia mydas*	•	•
Hawksbill sea turtle	*Eretmochelys imbricate*	•	•
Kemp's ridley sea turtle	*Lepidochelys kempii*	•	•

Dermochelidae

Leatherback sea turtle	*Dermochelys coriacea*	•	•

Chelydridae

Snapping turtle	*Chelydra serpentina*	•	•

Emydidae

Chicken turtle	*Deirochelys reticularia*	•	•
Diamond-backed terrapin	*Malaclemys terrapin*	•	•
Florida red-bellied cooter	*Pseudemys nelsoni*	•	•
Eastern box turtle	*Terrapene carolina*		•
Yellow-bellied pond slider	*Trachemys scripta*	•	•

Kinosternidae

Eastern mud turtle	*Kinosternon subrurum*	•	•
Striped mud turtle	*Kinosternon baurii*	•	

Testudinidae

Gopher tortoise	*Gopherus polyphemus*	•	•

Trionchidae

Florida softshell	*Apalone ferox*	•	•

Table 4

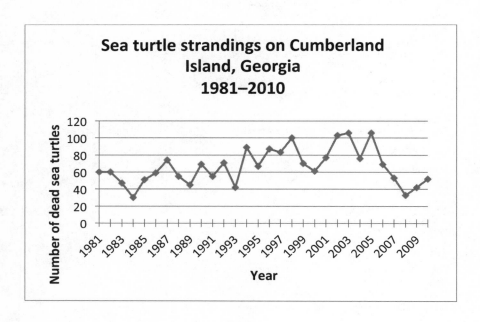

Table 5

Mammals on Cumberland Island (CUIS) and the adjacent mainland (CACO),Camden County, Georgia.

* Introduced
† Extirpated or temporary resident

Family

Common name – Scientific name	CUIS	CACO
Didelphidae		
Virginia opossum - *Didelphus virginiana* *	•	•
Dasypodidae		
Nine-banded armadillo - *Dasypus novemcinctus*	•	•
Talpidae		
Eastern mole - *Scalopus aquaticus*	•	•
Soricidae		
Southern short-tailed shrew - *Blarina carolinensis*	•	•
Southeastern shrew - *Sorex longirostris*		•
Least shrew - *Cryptotis parva*		•
Canidae		
Coyote - *Canis latrans* •		•
Gray fox - *Urocyon cinereoargentatus*		•
Ursidae		
American black bear - *Ursus americanus* * †	•	•
Procyonidae		
Raccoon - *Procyon lotor*	•	•
Mustilidae		
American mink - *Neovison vison*	•	•
Long-tailed weasel - *Mustela frenata*		•
North American river otter - *Lontra canadensis*	•	•
Striped skunk - *Mephitis mephitis*		•
Felidae		
Bobcat - *Lynx rufus* *	•	•
Equidae		
Feral horse - *Equus caballus* *	•	
Suidae		
Feral swine - *Sus scrofa* *	•	•
Cervidae		
White-tailed deer - *Odocoileus virginanus*	•	•
Sciuridae		
Eastern gray squirrel - *Sciurus carolinensis*	•	•
Eastern fox squirrel - *Sciurus niger*		•
Flying squirrel - *Glaucomys volans*		•
Geomyidae		
Southeastern pocket gopher - *Geomys pinetis* †	•	•
Castoridae		
American beaver - *Castor canadensis* †	•	•

	Col 1	Col 2
Cricetidae		
Marsh oryzomys - *Oryzomys palustris*	•	•
Harvest mouse - *Reithrodontomys humulis*		•
Cotton deermouse - *Peromyscus gossypinus*	•	•
Golden mouse - *Ochrotomys nuttalli*		•
Hispid cotton rat - *Sigmodon hispidus*	•	•
Eastern woodrat - *Neotoma floridana*		•
Round-tailed muskrat - *Neofiber alleni*		•
Muridae		
House mouse - *Mus musculus*		•
Norway rat - *Rattus norvegicus*		•
Roof rat - *Rattus rattus* †	•	•
Leporidae		
Marsh rabbit - *Sylvilagus palustris*	•	•
Cottontail rabbit - *Sylvilagus floridana*		•

Table 6

Food of the Virginia Opossum on Cumberland Island, Georgia
N = 35

Food Item	% Volume		% Frequency
VERTEBRATES	31.8		206
Fish		0.11	8.6
Lizard		2.1	11.4
Snake		6.0	11.4
Bird		15.5	64.7
Mole		2.3	5.7
Hair		17.0	94.3
Unid. mammal		1.9	5.7
Unid. vertebrate		3.9	5.7
INVERTEBRATES	26.4		106
Insect		22.5	88.6
Mollusk		0.1	5.7
Crab		1.3	8.6
Unid. invertebrate		2.4	2.9
VEGETATION	23.6		91.4
UNIDENTIFIED	1.1		2.9
PLASTIC	0.03		2.9

Table 7

Food of the Coyote on Cumberland Island, Georgia

N = 105

Food Item	% Volume	% Frequency		
MAMMALS	43.7		77.1	
Feral swine		18.2		28.6
White-tailed deer		13.1		17.1
Raccoon		6.6		8.6
Marsh rabbit		3.6		11.4
Armadillo		0.9		3.8
Eastern gray squirrel		0.4		2.8
Marsh oryzomys		0.4		0.9
Hispid cotton rat		0.08		0.9
Unidentified mammal		0.3		2.8
BIRDS (UNIDENTIFIED)	3.2		12.4	
REPTILES	0.05		2.9	
Unidentified snakes		0.03		1.9
Unidentified turtle		0.03		1
INSECTS	5.0		62.8	
DIPLOPODA	0.06		1.9	
CRUSTACEA (CRABS)	0.7		7.6	
PLANTS	46.7		157.0	
Diospyros sp.		20.7		31.4
Serenoa sp.		7.3		10.5
Sideroxylon sp.		6.7		13.3
Vitaceae		2.8		9.5
Grass		1.1		22.8
Sabal sp.		0.9		0.9
Vaccineum sp.		0.6		1.9
Ilex sp.		0.6		0.9
Miscellaneous incidental		5.9		65.7

Table 8

Food of the Raccoon, *Procyon lotor*, on Cumberland Island, Georgia
N = 103

Common Name	Scientific Name	Number
VEGETATION (74% FREQUENCY)		77
Oak acorns	*Quercus* sp.	11
Tough buckthorn	*Sideroxylon* sp.	11
Green briar	*Smilax* sp.	10
Palmetto	*Serenoa* sp.	6
Grapes	*Vitis* sp.	5
Dewberry	*Rubus trivialis*	4
Cabbage palm	*Sabal palmetto*	4
American holly	*Ilex opaca*	4
Black cherry	*Prunus serotina*	4
Inkberry	*Ilex glabra*	3
Peppervine	*Ampelopsis* sp.	2
Blackberry	*Rubus cunefolius*	2
Red cedar	*Juniperus sp.*	2
Persimmon	*Diospyros* sp.	2
Yaupon	*Ilex vomitoria*	1
Blueberry	*Vaccinium* sp.	1
Pine	*Pinus* sp.	1
American olive	*Osmanthus* sp.	1
Hackberry	*Celtis* sp.	1
Red bay	*Persea* sp.	1
Fibrous plant material		1
INVERTEBRATES (31.1% FREQUENCY)		32
Crayfish	*Procambarus* sp.	11
Fiddler crab	*Uca* sp.	11
Insects		6
Ghost crab	*Ocypode* sp.	3
Mussel	*Geukensia* sp.	1
VERTEBRATES (10.7% FREQUENCY)		11
Bird	Aves	4
Frog	Amphibia Anuran	2
Hair	Mammal	2
Fish	Pices	1
Lizard	Reptilia Lacertilia	1
Snake	Reptilia Serpentes	1

Table 9

Food of North American River Otter, *Lutra canadensis*, on Cumberland Island, Georgia

	% Volume		% Frequency	
Crustacea	60.4		78.8	
Crayfish		56.3		71.2
Mud crab		1.5		1.5
Fiddler crab		1.4		1.5
Marine crab		1.2		4.5
Fish	26.5		50	
Amphibians	4.5		25.8	
Amphiuma		3.9		13.6
Anuran		0.4		6.1
Unidentified		0.2		6.1
Insects	4.0		63.6	
Unidentified		3.2		46.9
Odonate larvae		0.7		15.2
Water bug		0.05		1.5
Vegetation	2.4		71.2	
Reptiles	1.6		13.6	
Snake		1.6		12.1
Unidentified		0		1.5
Bird	0.46		3.0	
Mollusca	0.06		6.1	

Table 10

Important Food of Bobcats (*Lynx rufus*) from Cumberland Island, Georgia. N=128.

Food Item	Percent Volume	Percent Frequency
Marsh rabbit - *Sylvilagus palustris*	21.2	75.0
Hispid cotton rat - *Sigmodon hispidus*	19.8	68.0
Eastern gray squirrel - *Sciurus carolinensis*	14.8	64.8
Wild boar - *Sus scrofa*	14.6	44.5
Aves - Bird	7.9	63.3
Cotton deermouse - *Peromyscus gossypinus*	5.9	70.3
White-tailed deer - *Odocoileus virginianus*	5.1	8.6
Marsh oryzomys - *Oryzomys palustris*	3.7	46.1
Miscellaneous vegetation	2.5	50.8
Nine-banded armadillo - *Dasypus novemcinctus*	1.6	18.8
Raccoon - *Procyon lotor*	1.5	2.3
Unknown	0.6	1.5
Grass	0.5	18.0

James C. Greenway Jr.

Helen B. Jordan

Naturalists
Observers and Collectors on Cumberland Island

During the 1600 and 1700s, the New World held species of plants and animals unknown to Europeans. Linne's system of binomial nomenclature was just being formulated, and there was enthusiasm to name all species. The Royal Society of London, founded in 1662, supported explorations with the requirement that seeds and specimens be sent back to England. A common thought at that time was that every country produced plants especially suited to cure diseases of the area, promoting a utilitarian aspect to the collecting. Countries wanted to increase their wealth and provide more food for their people and fodder for livestock while also potentially acquiring new spices, dyes, and medicines. Natural history per se was in its infancy. Specimens of plants and animals collected at that time serve as baseline data for studies today. Distributions of flora and fauna have been inexorably scrambled by other than natural factors, but without early collections and records, much of that information might have been lost.

Since the early 1800s, access to Cumberland Island has been somewhat limited, requiring permission of the landowners. Both the Greene/Miller family and Carnegies granted access to many naturalists and supported their endeavors.

Some of the more notable naturalists whose work had an impact on Cumberland Island or science in general are included on this list. In 1774, **William Bartram** (1739–1823) set foot on the island during his patron's sponsored expeditions to the Southeast. He was instructed to keep a field journal, make drawings, collect and ship plants to London, and generally note all aspects of natural history. He made no in-depth study of the flora and fauna of Cumberland Island.

The botanist **Andre Michaux** (1746–1802) made a brief stop at Cumberland Island in the late 1700s, while observing the forests, plants, and natural history of the Southeast.

In 1803, plant collector and nurseryman **John Lyon** (?–1814) collected on Cumberland Island and established a holding garden at Dungeness, located at the southern end of the island, for species he collected elsewhere, primarily in Florida. The plants would ultimately be shipped to Philadelphia and beyond for horticultural purposes.

William Baldwin (1779–1819) received his medical degree in 1807, but his passion was botany. He practiced medicine in St. Marys, Georgia, for a while, and visited Cumberland Island as a guest of island landowner Catherine Miller in 1813. He made fast friends with Catherine and her daughter, Louisa Shaw. Louisa shared Baldwin's interest in botany, collecting and drawing many island plants for identification. Baldwin communicated with H. E. G. Muhlenberg (1753–1815), a well-known botanist in his later years. The beautiful pink muhly grass, seen on the Cumberland Island interdune area, bears his name.

In 1818, renowned naturalist **Thomas Say** (1787–1834) spent time on the Georgia Sea Islands and collected a new species of terrestrial snail in Shaw's garden at Dungeness. The crinkled amber snail, *Succenia campestris* Say, 1818, is common in the interdune area.

In 1896, after the arrival of the Carnegies, **Outram Bangs** (1863–1932), ornithologist and curator of birds at the Museum of Comparative Zoology (MCZ) at Harvard, also worked with mammals, and along with William Brewster, trapped on the island for pocket gophers, *Geomys* sp., which occurred on no other Georgia barrier island. Bangs named the island species *G. cumberlandius*.

Working for Bangs was field collector **Wilmot W. Brown** (ca. 1869–death date unknown), who collected for various museums between 1890 and 1953. He reportedly augmented Bangs's Cumberland Island collection, adding 100 mammals and 50 birds in twelve days.

Thaddeus Surber (1871–1949) collected along the Georgia coast for the Field Museum in Chicago between 1899 and 1901. He requested permission to collect on Cumberland but was denied. He did collect at St. Marys, Georgia.

The botanist **Roland Harper** (1878–1966), brother of Francis, worked for the Bureau of Plant Industry, US Department of Agriculture, and identified himself as an "expert in botanical investigations and experiments." He was on Cumberland Island briefly in 1902.

A local (St. Marys) naturalist, **Isaac F. Arnow** (1869–1957), postmaster of St. Marys for fifteen years, collected birds in the vicinity of Cumberland in 1903 and 1904.

Between 1902 and 1905, **Arthur Helme** (1860–1947) made the most comprehensive bird collections on the island. Helme had a degree in veterinarian science but became a professional ornithologist and worked at the Brooklyn Museum and the American Museum of Natural History in New

York. He preserved well over 450 bird specimens from Cumberland Island, which are now scattered among several museums but greatly facilitating research even today.

Willis W. Worthington (1861–1940), an ornithologist and taxidermist, was employed by private ornithologists to collect from Pennsylvania to Florida, Mexico, Central America, and Puerto Rico. He collected a few birds on Cumberland Island in 1916 and in 1921.

Gilbert Pearson (1873–1943), with the Audubon Society, visited Cumberland Island from 2 to 6 May 1921 and recorded ninety-seven species of birds. He produced the first formal avian species list for Cumberland Island (1922).

James C. Greenway Jr. (1903–1989) was Curator of Birds at the Museum of Comparative Zoology at Harvard from 1932 to 1960, then went to the American Museum of Natural History, where he was a research associate in ornithology. Greenway is the author of the classic *Extinct and Vanishing Birds of the World* (1958) and was a personal friend of the Carnegies. He collected a few birds on the island.

For a week in April 1932 and again in April 1933, **Alexander Sprunt Jr.** (1898–1973) visited Cumberland Island as a guest of the Carnegies. He recorded 149 species of birds in the roughly two-week period he combed the island.

J. Kenneth Doutt (1923–2008), a mammalogist with the Carnegie Museum of Natural History and personal friend of the Carnegies, was on the island for three collecting trips between 1957 and 1959, collecting mostly mammals.

Helen B. Jordan (1907–1993) had a PhD in protozoology from the University of California at Berkeley and was a professor at Georgia State University specializing in lizard malaria. She did much research on the island in the 1960s through the 1980s and published on some Cumberland Island lizard parasites.

1

Geology

Setting

Cumberland Island stands out as the largest and southernmost in the chain of major Georgia barrier islands along the coast of Georgia (Fig. 1). It also has the most diverse flora and fauna on these islands and contains the largest natural body of freshwater, Whitney Lake. It is separated five to eight miles from the Georgia mainland by a network of tidal rivers and salt marshes. The ontogeny (birth and development) of the islands is complex; most are composed of both Pleistocene and Holocene elements. Wide sand beaches on the Atlantic Ocean or easterly side of these islands absorb incessant pounding surf and abuse from storms, and thus the islands offer protection to the interior, low-lying mainland coast. The length of the island varies seasonally and annually due to accretion and erosion of the beach; however, the average length is about 17 contiguous miles, and the maximum width is about 3 miles (Fig. 2).

The island covers about 15,000 hectares (37,000 acres), 4,639.5 hectares (11,464.3 acres) of which are uplands, with a strip of beach/dunes on the east and abutted by salt marsh and/or tidal rivers to the west. A salt marsh separates Cumberland and Little Cumberland islands, with Little Cumberland Island forming the northern tip of the complex. Large rivers originating in the Georgia Coastal Plain incise deep channels that separate Little Cumberland Island from Jekyll Island to the north and Cumberland Island from Amelia Island, Florida, to the south.

Elevation of most of the Georgia barrier islands reaches about 8 meters (25 feet) above sea level, but places on the northwest end or "High Point" of Cumberland Island are over 15 meters (50 feet; Johnson et al., 1974) and areas mid-island reach 12 meters (40 feet). South of Stafford, the relief is more uniform and generally not over 8 meters (25 feet) above sea level. Little Cumberland is less than eight meters in elevation except for the large dunes on the north end, which are influenced by prevailing winds and can reach well over 10 meters (30 feet).

Geologic History

Knowledge of the geologic history of the island helps in understanding some factors affecting the current biological composition. For the complete story, according to the presently accepted theory, we must go back in time to the Pleistocene Epoch, between 25,000 and 50,000 years ago. The Pleistocene was a time of great climatic flux and featured several dramatic changes in sea level. As global temperatures increased, ice at the polar caps melted, raising sea level. Dunes and shoreline features developed along the dynamic land-sea interface when temperature and sea level were stable long enough to permit sand to accumulate. Relatively stable warm climatic periods were apparently followed each time by rapidly decreasing temperatures; snow and ice accumulation at the poles caused the sea to retreat, leaving high and dry a broken chain of ridges or terraces that once had been barrier islands. This sequence of events, repeated several times during the Quaternary Period (Pleistocene and recent epochs; Fig. 3), left discrete shoreline complexes abandoned by the sea in coastal Georgia, which were mapped and named in the twentieth century (Cooke, 1939; Huddlestun, 1988).

At least 40,000 years ago, during the last stable climatic period, designated "Silver Bluff," the terrace or ridge that would later become the major part of Cumberland Island was formed. The Silver Bluff shoreline and associated features extend along the Georgia coast in approximately the same position as the modern shoreline. During earlier interglacial periods, sea level had been significantly higher.

When global temperatures plummeted again, the sea level dropped to approximately 100 meters (328 feet) below the present level. The established Silver Bluff shoreline was left high and dry, and the active shoreline moved roughly 125 kilometers (78 miles) east of its present location. The gently sloping area (1 meter per 1.5 kilometer, about 3 feet per mile) that is now the continental shelf off the Georgia coast became dry land. The vast area exposed by the retreating sea facilitated access for neotropical species by reducing the distance between Georgia and Central America and providing suitable habitat between them. Webb (1974) speculated that the predominant habitats of this broad, new coastal plain were flat grassland and savanna. Fossil evidence shows that this Gulf Atlantic Coast savanna corridor periodically supported species that inhabited arid western grasslands, such as the pocket gopher, ground squirrel, primitive horse, and bison. Fossils of these species have been recovered from Georgia Pleistocene sediments (Frey and Voorhies, 1975). During this period of extremely low sea level, the Silver Bluff shoreline became an undistinguished part of the mainland except for its relief in an otherwise flat area. Over time, climatic forces changed the dynamic island terrain to a more uniform topography stabilized by upland vegetation. The rivers, estuaries, and tidal creeks surrounding the original island became freshwater environments. For probably 15,000 years, sea level had little effect on the terrestrial environment of the ancient island remnant, which is now Cumberland Island, as it weathered and blended into its new inland surroundings far from the sea.

The last (most recent) interglacial or warming period began about 12,000 years ago and marked a transition to the Holocene period. Ice melted, sea level rose, and the broad Pleistocene coastal fringe was again inundated. Sea level stabilized before reaching the old Silver Bluff shoreline about 3,000 to 5,000 years ago, and the present theory is that a new shoreline system of dunes and high ground began to form there. Rivers slowed when they encountered the sea and deposited silt and suspended organic material behind this newly formed shoreline. Soon the area of deposition was exposed at low tides and marsh vegetation became established. The sea level continued to rise, forcing the new shoreline-dune system to retreat to the west; the new sands finally abutted the ancient Silver Bluff formation, then an erosional remnant island, with its appearance noticeably different from the newly formed beach-ridge island approaching from the east.

From the marriage of these two genetically independent systems, the present Cumberland Island was born. All the beach, dune, interdune, and back-barrier salt marsh habitats on Cumberland Island are of Holocene age (Fig. 4). As sea level continues to creep higher, now and in the future, the new composite shoreline will inexorably retreat westward, but for the last 125 years the Cumberland Island shoreline has remained dynamically stable (McLemore et al., 1981; Griffin and Henry, 1984). Occasionally, periods of localized beach erosion expose Pleistocene sediments on the east side.

Archaeological evidence suggests that for perhaps the last 4,500 years the sea has influenced the terrestrial animal and plant communities on Cumberland Island (DePratter and Howard, 1977). Because the parent Silver Bluff island was an integral part of the mainland prior to the last rapid rise in sea level, we can surmise that it supported a representative floral and faunal complement at the time of isolation. If, in its dynamic stability, sea level repeatedly fluctuated between one and three meters during that time, as has been suggested (Tanner, 1992), colonization opportunities would have been extended. Island size, interactions between life forms, habitat restrictions, and species mobility would have modified the original biotic assemblage, but the Holocene also marked a period of noticeable change in floral communities of the Southeast during which some of the ecosystems we recognize today may have become established (Watts, 1971). The degree of isolation or type of environment between the island and the mainland, deliberate modifications by man, including introductions of various species, along with the above-listed factors, continue to affect island species composition today.

The relatively high-relief, beach dune-like topography of Little Cumberland Island is clearly evident and in dramatic contrast with the more level, eroded, older terrain of Cumberland Island, but similar to the Holocene dune-interdune topography on Cumberland. The variety of habitats and species are reduced on the smaller island, and its land use, while probably similar to that of other Georgia Holocene islands, such as Little St. Simons and Blackbeard islands, has been quite different from that of larger Cumberland Island.

Beach

Besides physically protecting the interior forest from a rising sea, a functional dune system provides a reservoir of sand that it shares with offshore bars paralleling the beach. These bars are quite changeable depending upon the energy of the waves. During the frequent, severe winter storms, sand eroded from the upper beach and dunes accumulates on the offshore bar. The augmented bar causes large waves to break before reaching the shore and thus reduces their effect on the upper beach and dunes. The steeper winter beach profile also helps dissipate wave energy. During summer, the milder, fewer storms reverse the pattern, with sand from the bars moving toward and onto the beach, leveling the profile, and rebuilding the eroded dunes. Low, unvegetated areas frequently breached or flooded in the winter become more stable with the increased amount of sand in the summer beach profile and are frequently used as nesting areas for several species of shorebirds. The summer beach profile may not become established on Cumberland Island until late April.

Shoreline

In their youth, Thomas Carnegie's grandchildren played on skeletons of live-oak trees that littered the eroded beach from Stafford southward (N. C. Rockefeller, pers. comm.). A visitor to the island in 1902 recalled an old resident pointing out to sea and reminiscing about the fields he used to plow "way out there" and the tree he used to rest his oxen under, all of which had washed away (J. W. Sanders, 1979, pers. comm.). An 1898 survey confirms that recollection. A look at the documented historical changes in that shoreline shows that the mid-1800s beach south of Stafford roughly corresponded to the line of high rear dunes in the area today. McLemore et al. (1981) speculated that between 1843 and 1876, prior to construction of the rock jetty (Fig. 5) between 1881 and 1903, a "flood-dominated funnel channel" scoured the beach south of Stafford, eroding into the uplands. Further north this erosion did not occur. The dune line continued broken north of Stafford, with dune and interdune areas forming to the east. The beach east of Duckhouse was fairly stable from 1857 to 1974 (Griffin and Henry, 1984). The jetty altered tidal flow patterns and, coupled with a predominantly southern longshore current, caused accretion of sand and the establishment of a functional dune system from Stafford southward. Prior to the elimination of herds of free-roaming cattle on the island (last fresh sign noted in August 1987), substantial primary dunes were absent south of Duckhouse Road, and the wide area of sand accretion immediately north of the jetty was atypically flat. Lack of dunes and parallel ridges on the accreted sand were likely the result of the impact of cattle and feral horses grazing and trampling the stabilizing beach vegetation. With no vegetation to hold sand in place, the wind moves it and ridges are soon flattened. Accretion continues today. Despite seemingly significant shoreline wanderings and a rising sea level, the dominant trend for the Cumberland Island ocean beach system for over one hundred years has been relative stability to accretion (Cofer-Shabica, 1993; Jackson, 2006).

The back-barrier, or west shoreline, of the island is also dynamic, experiencing variable change over its existence. Between 1875 and 2002, nearly 70% of that shoreline suffered net erosion (Jackson, 2006). Factors contributing to the changes included sea-level rise, migrating and general tidal channel dynamics, grazing, boat wakes, and storms. The orientation of the land face with regard to prevailing wind guarantees erosion in some areas and accretion in others.

Soils

Geologic evidence indicates the island did not start with a clean biotic slate in the Holocene period, but more likely with a representation of isolated mainland communities. The marriage of the old and new shorelines to form Cumberland Island further complicates speculation on the types of communities initially available. In augmenting the size of the older terrain, the young sediments provided additional, although generally less hospitable, habitats. Quartz sands of the older Pleistocene island had had time to accumulate organics and thus provided greater variety and soil development than recent deposits. The soils of both periods are primarily acidic, tough, quartz sands, which resist weathering and decomposition and have a poor water-holding capacity. Water passes quickly through the sandy soil to the groundwater table, carrying with it many valuable nutrients that would be lost to the adjacent communities were it not for special plant adaptations (Hillestad et al., 1975). The several soil types described for Cumberland Island are delineated in part by elevation (Rigdon and Green, 1980) and support characteristic plant communities (Table 1).

Island soils of special interest include clay deposits, heavy minerals, and soils in areas of potentially arable land, all of which have the potential for commercial exploitation. Clay from the marshes and small sand beaches on the western side of the island is derived from suspended organic and mineral material in tidal waters of the Holocene salt marshes (McLemore et al., 1981). Island deposits of "good clay" have been described as "practically inexhaustible" (Hunter Tract Prospectus, 1894). These deposits were no doubt mined by aboriginals for the manufacture of pottery, and the name "Brickhill River" (originally Brick Kiln) indicates an early brick-making enterprise. Seibert (1966) noted the establishment of "a large brickkiln just south of High Point" (probably south of Terrapin Point) on Cumberland Island that shipped bricks all over the world. The precise location of the deposits mined cannot be determined from existing soil surveys, and the specific site of the kiln has not been located. Discrete balls or chunks of clean, gray clay frequently occur on the north beach of Little Cumberland Island, a thick layer of beautiful gray clay underlies the Terrapin Point marsh, and clay is visible along the river at Brickhill Bluff. In 1785, Maxwell related the following regarding the south end of Cumberland Island: "No, I did not observe any place where clay has been dug to make bricks, tho I look'd very attentively for it" (Lockey et al., 1949).

Along with the sparkling white quartz sands of the beach, significant amounts of dark, heavy minerals occur. Selectively sorted by water and wind, ribbons of titanium minerals (ilmenite, leucoxene, and rutile), zirconium, and rare earth minerals are frequently visible, sandwiched between beds of white sand in eroded dune faces. Heavy minerals have accumulated in downdrift directions from river mouths, and commercially valuable ore grade deposits of heavy minerals are located on ancient and modern barrier island complexes (Pirkle et al., 1993), including Cumberland Island.

Humate is a dark-brown-to-black organic-rich material consisting of sand cemented by water rich in humic material. This water is derived from leaching of decaying plant material on the surface but precipitates under ground by a physical-chemical mechanism when combined with dissolved ions such as aluminum, iron, and magnesium, which are common in sea water (Swanson and Palacas, 1965; Thom, 1967). It is usually found in layers of varying thickness in Pleistocene-aged deposits. On Cumberland Island, a layer is regularly exposed at low tide between Sea Camp and Dungeness on the river side. Humate is also known as hardpan, which may perch water tables, influencing the availability of groundwater. It underlies the north end scrub community and contributes to its character. Many species on the island take advantage of humate, such as swallows that excavate burrows in it, alligators that construct dens in it, and species of crayfish that require subsurface groundwater and shun open water. Humate even provides Cumberland Island with a waterfall when there is enough water for streams to flow (Fig. 6).

The sometimes strange configurations and locations of former agricultural fields and their absence from other seemingly appropriate areas may be partially explained by overlaying a map of the 1898 fields of Cumberland Island (Page and Meader, map of 1898; Fig. 9) on a map delineating soil types. Most, if not all, fields in 1898 were on Lakeland and Chipley soils, with the exception of Swamp Field (Johnson loam), which had been drained. Lakeland and Chipley soils compose 40% of the potentially arable uplands on the island (Hillestad et al., 1975). One soil type avoided in agricultural pursuits was Leon or Mandarin fine sand. This type is poorly drained and low in organic matter and nutrients, with a low capacity for holding water, which gives it poor potential for row crops (Rigdon and Green, 1980). Leon fine sands comprise 47.2% of the interior land. Some inland wetlands (11.2%) and Olustee sands (.8%) may have been partially cultivated. The main agricultural period on Cumberland Island was over by 1898, so all land once cleared and farmed may not have been represented on the 1898 Page and Meader map. Based on soil types, probably about half of the interior forest of Cumberland Island was cleared and farmed. A supporting description was provided by White (1849): "More than half the island is worthless as far as cultivation is concerned."

Freshwater

The Pleistocene sediments of Cumberland Island are slightly more than 15 meters (50 feet) thick, composed primarily of fine-grained quartz sand, and underlain by clays from relic marsh sediments, which form an aquiclude or water barrier. Rainwater percolates quickly through the sand and accumulates as a freshwater lens beneath the island. This layer is different from the underlying Pliocene-Miocene aquifer that is separated by impermeable strata. Weight of freshwater is less than that of saltwater, which results in a buoying up and containment of the freshwater by surrounding seawater. A continual seep of freshwater from the periphery of the island prevents intrusion of saltwater and provides the most reliable, dispersed source of freshwater for wildlife. Since rainwater is the only natural replenishing source of freshwater on the island, the water table fluctuates considerably, as seen in the changes in water levels of the many temporary ponds and sloughs. In 1981, during a severe drought and natural forest fire, only a small portion of Whitney Lake contained water, and there was only a puddle at Willow Pond; all other ponds and sloughs were dry. The only other freshwater available at that time was in temporary pond basins and accessed by following alligator holes down to the water table. Seeps at the edge of the island were minimal. Similar conditions apparently existed in 1954 when the Carnegie caretaker wrote, "The ponds are all dry, which makes Whitney Lake the only duck stopover place," and in 1932, "All ponds dry except Whitney Lake" (Georgia Division of Archives and History [GDAH]). Whitney Lake is the largest natural body of freshwater on any of the Georgia barrier islands, which emphasizes the ephemeral nature of freshwater and the potential for it to be a critical limiting resource on the barrier islands.

When the ponds and sloughs of the island begin to fill, runoff may be expected to flow from at least two "outlets" across the ocean beach: one in the vicinity of Stafford Shoals and the other, known as the Whitney outlet, near South Fraser Road. The latter drains a much larger area and flows more often.

On US Geological Survey topographic maps, the freshwater slough complex running from Willow Pond north to Whitney Lake is identified as Sweetwater Lake. The name apparently originated with the cartographer as a practical description, since none of the 1975 island people were familiar with the term. The topography of the Sweetwater Lake complex shows broken, parallel Holocene ridges separated by valleys or open lowlands (sloughs). During periods of normal precipitation, these contain water much of the time. The elevation and continuity of the large dune ridge east of the complex helps confine the freshwater and provide effective separation between beach and inland habitats. The one breach in the large dune line that permits drainage is the Whitney outlet. Drainage of Whitney Lake occurs only at times of very high water, and the outflow must pass through the Sweetwater complex before it reaches the outlet and the sea. The Whitney outlet primarily drains many kilometers of the Sweetwater slough system, Sweetwater Lake on topographic maps.

The other major freshwater outlet on the east side of the island, in the Stafford Shoals area, drains a smaller, more recent slough system, referred to by the early Carnegies as "Big Slough." Through a misinterpretation by Hillestad et al. (1975) the area is presently referred to as Retta Lake. A large interdune area, which holds freshwater much of the year, developed between the old dune ridge and the accreting beach. Drainage for this "Big Slough" low relief system is more intermittent than the Whitney outlet since it drains considerably less area. During exceptionally high tides, seawater may invade parts of the "Big Slough" system.

Of the numerous temporary freshwater ponds, very few naturally drain to the edge of the island. When the ponds fill they simply overflow into the surrounding, poorly drained terrain. Two ponds on the south tip of the island do have a shallow, two-way interface with the edge of the island and periodically receive saltwater (Kozel, 1991). Judging from a map drawn in 1802 (Fig. 8), Swamp Field was one of the few ponds that apparently had natural, one-way drainage not flooded with saltwater. Shortly thereafter ditches were dug to drain the area. Together they altered the natural water regime and allowed the fertile wetland to be farmed. The deep northern channel is presently influenced by tides, and the north end of the pond supports brackish water flora and fauna. There is also a wooded swamp associated with this drainage. The canal on the south end has filled over time and no longer drains the pond, but it may affect drainage on adjacent land between the Swamp Field and the marsh, including Heron (Nightingale) Pond.

On the west side of Cumberland Island, three other major freshwater streams all head in wooded swamps. Many small, temporary ponds are imperceptibly associated with the swamps, except during periods of high water when sheet-overflow may be followed to the swamps and ultimately to the streams.

Early wells were dug or driven into the shallow water table to provide water for human use, but the water had to be manually dipped or pumped from these sources. A well in the Settlement on the north end of Cumberland Island, where the elevation is greater than nine meters (30 feet), measures 5.9 meters (18 feet) deep and 4.1 meters (13 feet) to the water table. A well of this type, referred to as a driven well, could be "sunk" in one day and would produce excellent water (Humphries, 1991). On St. Simons Island, in 1735, freshwater was found "in all places where they have tried" within 9 feet of the surface (Moore, 1983), and in Liberty County, Georgia, Harden (1845) reported the deepest well to be 10 to 20 feet. Not until 1881 were any successful artesian wells drilled in Georgia (Warren, 1944). The first on Cumberland Island was in 1887 (McCallie, 1898). Freshwater in the deep Floridian aquifer is under pressure and when tapped produces a free-flowing "artesian" water supply. Using this water supply, hydraulic ram pumps filled large wooden tanks mounted more than 50 feet high on metal scaffolding to provide an unlimited water supply under constant gravity pressure to dwellings at Dungeness, Greyfield, Stafford, Plum Orchard, and the hotel on the north end of the island. The Carnegies had several artesian wells drilled specifically to provide water for herds of cattle on the island. Sometimes far from human habitation, these man-made sources of freshwater served wildlife as well. People also modified several of the temporary ponds on the island by deepening them, damming small streams, or adding artesian water as an incentive to attract ducks during hunting season or for aesthetic purposes.

Intracoastal Waterway

The degree of Cumberland Island's isolation from the mainland is of paramount importance to island species composition. Whether plant or animal, resident, colonizer, recolonizer, or visitor, access is a significant factor. Distance determines which seeds or spores, birds or mammals can easily access the island, and in conjunction with water currents, dictates the odds on what might arrive alive as flotsam, but it is the intervening terrain that critically isolates the island. If, during the last 5,000 years, sea level fluctuated enough to periodically provide a terrestrial connection between the island and the mainland, amphibians, reptiles, small mammals, and terrestrially bound invertebrates would have had additional chances to become established in the changing communities of the island, or to contribute to an already-present gene pool, further reducing the likelihood of endemic species on Cumberland and other Georgia barrier islands.

A valley or continuous lowland corridor between the Georgia barrier islands and the mainland developed as part of a freshwater drainage system when the sea retreated from the ancient shoreline during the last glacial period, about 20,000 years ago. In 1742, Bartram suggested that the salt marshes adjoining the coast of the mainland were formerly high swamps of firm land (Harper, 1958), and Lyell (1849) noticed buried stumps of cypress and pine below sea level at the mouth of the Altamaha River. A rising sea level backed up rivers and encouraged sediment deposition bordering the valley drainage. Vegetation changed, and the resulting natural waterway west of the barrier islands was flanked with wide, flat marshlands and lesser tidal creeks, providing an uninterrupted, protected water route along the coast of Georgia and an impediment to species exchange between the islands and the mainland. While the vast salt marshes may be lethal to some species (amphibians, some reptiles, and some small mammals), the width and especially the depth of the river, the type of bottom it had (firm sand or soft, deep mud), and the type of adjacent marsh could limit or support the arrival of larger species.

Aborigines traveled tidal rivers and creeks by dugout. Plantation owners had sailboats. But it was not until the 1870s that the volume of traffic and size of vessels demanded improvements be made to the waterway west of Cumberland and the other barrier islands in order to permit travel at all tidal stages. Concern over the possibility of a military blockade also influenced the governmental decision to survey the route in 1876, with the optimal channel being about two meters (6 feet) deep and 33 meters (100 feet) wide at low tide. Areas of concern were mainly midway behind barrier islands where tides from north and south met (or divided, "the dividings") and caused shoaling. When tidal flow slowed, sediment was deposited forming shoals, which hindered navigation. In 1938, depth to 12 feet was authorized. Easements in the marsh for disposing of the dredge material were acquired by the state and transferred to the US Army Corps of Engineers. Between 1884 and 1932, 51,797,991 cubic yards of sediment were dredged for the Intracoastal Waterway in Georgia, and some of the disposal sites have become significant marsh islands with appropriate flora and fauna. Initially, the dredging was primarily an economic issue, whereas today, the majority of use of the waterway is by recreational boaters.

The tidal "dividings," with associated shoals and sandbars, existed in all major rivers behind the coastal barrier islands, and those points were undoubtedly recognized and used by roving mammalian predators and early human inhabitants, especially if the area could be traversed on foot at low tide. I. F. Arnow (1950–1953), a naturalist from St. Marys, wrote of the mouth of Crooked River, "It is my understanding that this sandbar was used as the only fording place between the mainland and Cumberland Island." The US Army Corps of Engineers now maintains the Cumberland River section of the Intracoastal Waterway by dredging it to a depth of 3.66 meters (12 feet).

Climate

"Thermometer several degrees below zero. The creek at the bridge...frozen across strong enough to bear a man's weight. Eggs frozen—pitchers broken by ice—oranges frozen as hard as cannon balls, & a keen wind from the N.W." (Floyd, 1835). Even the moderating waters surrounding Cumberland Island were not enough to ameliorate the cold spell C. R. Floyd described for the mainland opposite the island. "The frost of 1835 destroyed the fine forests of orange trees" on Cumberland Island (White, 1849), but they either resprouted or were replanted, because by 1846 oranges were plentiful enough for export (Torres, 1977).

Coastal Georgia winters are usually described as moderate and of short duration, with temperatures averaging from 40 to 60 degrees. While temperature extremes are usually of short duration, large temperature fluctuations are frequent. In conjunction with the mild average temperature, they present a threat to cold-blooded vertebrates. During two consecutive winters, 1983–1984 and 1984–1985, temperatures in single digits were recorded on the north end of Cumberland Island with little snow for protection. Ponds froze, water pumps burst, and ice formed along the edges of the Whitney outlet on the beach, and elsewhere. Following the severe freezes, several species of amphibians and reptiles were found dead, presumably frozen in their ill-chosen abodes. The wonderful sour orange trees that were scattered about the north end of the island were also killed and never resprouted.

Summer temperatures average in the 80s during the day, and rarely do extremely high temperatures (>95°F) last for longer than three days. Afternoon thundershowers, onshore breezes, and the water surrounding the island are moderating influences. Ocean surf temperature is in the low 80s in the summer and the mid-50s in the winter, providing a cooling effect during hot weather and warming effect during cold. Just as on the mainland, distance from the shoreline reduces the moderating effect of the water temperature, and since Cumberland Island is up to 4.8 kilometers (3 miles) wide, the temperature in different locations may vary greatly depending on vegetation type and prevailing winds.

Relative humidity is usually high on islands and near the coast. The average mid-afternoon relative humidity in Camden County, as calculated by the National Climatic Center, is about 60%, and at dawn 90% (Rigdon and Green, 1980). Heavy dew and seasonally thick fog are common.

While the warmer water temperature of the Gulf Stream has a limited effect on our local climate because of predominantly northwest winds over the United States, it does influence the paths taken by tropical storms. A corridor of light, warm air flows above the warm surface water of the Gulf Stream as it passes through the Straits of Florida and hugs the edge of the continental shelf north to near Cape Hatteras, North Carolina. The areas of cooler water on each side of the Gulf Stream support cooler, heavier air above them, which confines the warm air above the Gulf Stream, forming a long, natural corridor of low air pressure for hurricanes to follow. Since the Gulf Stream and its low-pressure corridor flow along the edge of the continental shelf, which is between 112 and 128 kilometers (70 to 80 miles) off the present Georgia coast, few hurricanes move into the wide, adjoining high-pressure area between this corridor and the Georgia mainland (Gibson, 1948). Rather, they usually forsake the stream south or north of Georgia, where it runs much closer to the coast and a much narrower band of high pressure facilitates departure.

Storms along the coast, especially hurricanes and tornadoes, have the potential to greatly modify island communities. Tight canopies of tough live oak may be suddenly ripped open, offering understory species sunlight and a chance to compete. Saltwater may flood freshwater and normally terrestrial upland areas, killing many of the established plants and providing opportunities for others. High winds and water are major factors in the temporal remodeling of shoreline features and communities, and also provide the potential for transport of biota to and from the island.

Some of the most powerful hurricanes to affect Cumberland Island and vicinity occurred in 1804, 1813, 1824, 1898, and 1964. Early accounts relate grim scenes. "The water was the principal instrument of destruction," wrote Aaron Burr in a letter describing the 1804 hurricane on St. Simons Island (Lovell, 1933). "The flood was about seven feet above the height of an ordinary tide. This has been sufficient to inundate a great part of the coast, to destroy all the rice, to carry off most of the buildings which were in the low lands, and to destroy the lives of many blacks" (Lovell, 1933). The 1813 storm was confined to the area between Darien, Georgia, and north of St. Augustine, Florida. Houses were blown down on Amelia Island, Florida, thousands of trees were prostrate, and "nearly the whole forest was under water and in some places up to the saddle" (Darlington, 1969). Catherine Greene Miller described effects of the hurricane on Dungeness in a letter to a friend: "The roof of my house blew off—and can you believe it, those large timbers went from the south side of the house quite over it, and lodged two to three hundred feet on the north side." Almost all the buildings were blown down (Torres, 1977). Sapelo Island was said to be in the "very vortex" of the 1824 storm. "The island was in part overflowed, and heavy losses were incurred by the drowning of horses, cattle, and other stock" (Lovell, 1933). The center of the 1898 hurricane struck north of Brunswick and flooding was widespread. The city of Brunswick suffered much damage, as did the adjacent islands.

All sections of Georgia experience tornadoes, but the highest frequency is over the Coastal Plain. Most Georgia tornadoes occur in the spring and move from southwest to northeast ahead of strong frontal activities. While the size and intensity of tornadoes varies, the average swath of ground affected is about 300 yards (Plummer and Purvis, 1991). Tornadoes are the most violent and destructive atmospheric phenomenon, as evidenced by the impact on large live-oak trees.

During a severe storm on 3 March 1991, an estimated 150 meter-wide (500 feet) swath across Little Cumberland Island was cleared of most standing vegetation. Branches were twisted and torn from large, apparently healthy live oaks, leaving a scene of devastation. The track of the storm was from southwest to northeast, with most of the downed trees and limbs aligned north-south, having fallen to the north. Workmen on the island reported many dead gulls. Another unseen, probable tornado touched down at Hickory Hill on Cumberland Island in 2000 or 2001. Live oaks there were no match for the fury of the wind. Numbers of trees and limbs fell, leaving large openings in the canopy that changed the character of the area.

Precipitation

Annual rainfall for the lower coast of Georgia averages 135 centimeters (53 inches; National Oceanic and Atmospheric Administration). As for most of the South, summer rainfall is associated with afternoon thunderstorms or tropical storms rather than cold-front activity. Records from the north end of Cumberland Island for seven years (1987–1993) average 111.76 centimeters (44 inches), with 1990 the driest year (93.85 centimeters, 36.95 inches) and 1991 the wettest (145.36 centimeters, 57.23 inches). Months of lowest precipitation during that seven-year period include March, November, and December, with August and September representing the highest, but individual years vary greatly. Based on the fire history of the island (S. Turner, n.d. ~1984), the drought cycle, which predisposes large areas of vegetation to lightning ignition, is 25 to 30 years. Minor droughts have been recorded with more frequency. Major fluctuations of surface water characterize the Georgia barrier islands and are an important aspect of the ecology.

Tide

Tidal cycles, much a part of coastal life, are influenced by the position of the moon. Two high tides a day along the Georgia coast are 12 hours 25 minutes apart, making the high tide approximately an hour later each day. The timing is a result of the speed at which the moon revolves around the earth combined with the rotation of the earth on its axis, and is 50 minutes longer than the 24-hour solar day. High tides result from the gravitational pull of the sun and the moon on the fluid surfaces of the earth, and two high and two low tides occur somewhere on the planet at all times. Of the two bodies, the moon has more influence because of its proximity to earth, but twice a month the sun and moon combine their efforts and produce "spring tides." Spring tides refer to tides higher than usual that occur at the full- and new-moon cycles when the sun, moon, and earth are aligned. Perigean spring tides produce the highest astronomical tides and occur when, in its elliptical orbit, the moon is nearest the earth. The highest spring tide is usually during the new moon when the sun and moon are pulling together. During the full moon, each force is independent but not conflicting. Along the Georgia coast, spring tides average 2.5 meters (8 to 9 feet) and reach 60 to 80 kilometers (40 to 50 miles) up the Satilla and 104 kilometers (65 miles) up the St. Marys rivers. The lowest tides of the cycle, "neap tides," occur during the first- and third-quarter phases of the moon when the pull of the sun and pull of the moon conflict at right angles. By knowing the phase of the moon, the position of the tide may be roughly judged. On Cumberland Island, high tide occurs about an hour after moonrise. The full and new moons rise in the early evening, bringing the tide high an hour afterwards. Neap tides are high at midday, and without easterly winds, rarely reach the dunes. The average range of neap tides along the Georgia coast is 1.6 meters (5 to 6 feet). Velocity and direction of the wind have great influence on the magnitude of the tide regardless of the cycle stage. Neap tides may be pushed as high as spring tides by strong easterly winds, and, conversely, spring tides may be restrained by westerly winds.

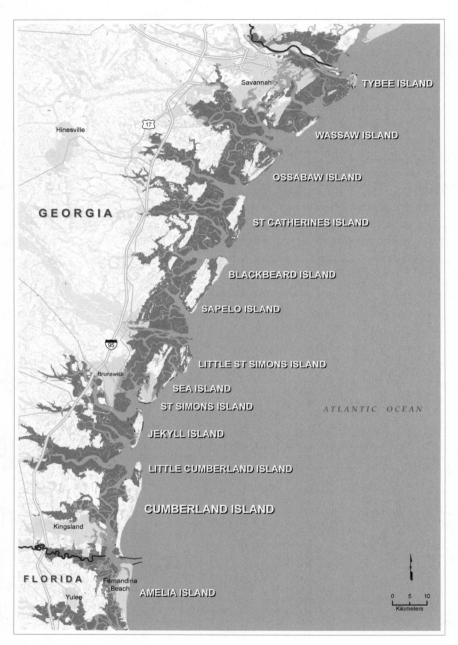

Figure 1
Georgia barrier islands and Amelia Island, Florida.
(C. J. Jackson)

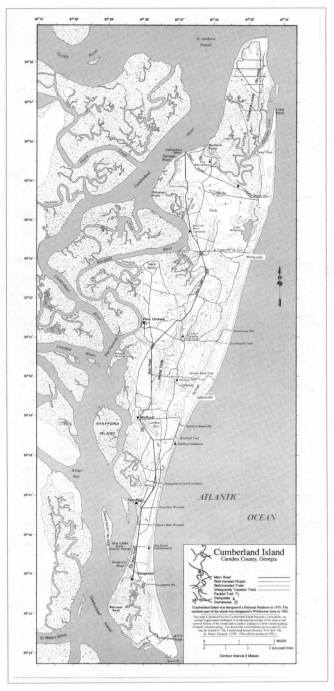

Figure 2
Cumberland Island, Georgia.
(Cumberland Island Museum)

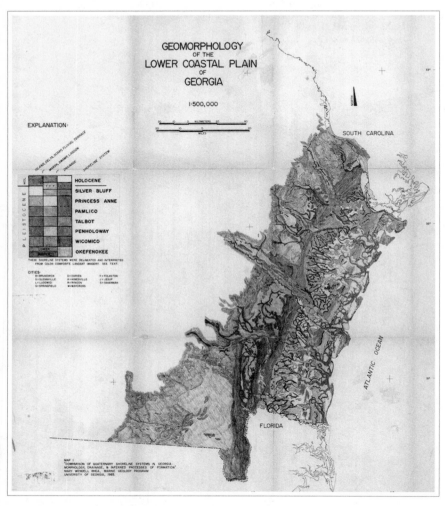

Figure 3

Quaternary shorelines in Georgia.

(Mary Rhea, University of Georgia, 1986)

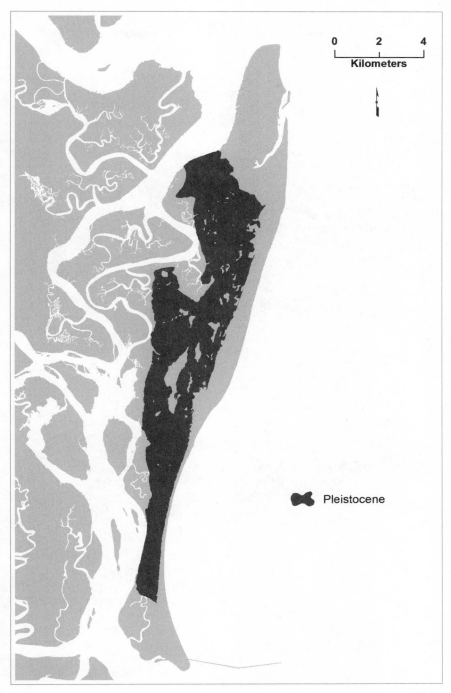

Kilometers

0 2 4

Pleistocene

Figure 4
Pleistocene remnant of Cumberland Island, Georgia.
(National Park Service)

Figure 5
North rock jetty along the mouth of the St. Marys River, Georgia.

Figure 6

Waterfall over humate.

2

Modifications

Archaeological Evidence

Early human effects on the environment might be expected to have influenced present island biota, such as the composition of island flora and fauna, therefore, a brief recount of archaeological and historic evidence of human occupation and potential and known impacts is in order. Based on archaeological work on Amelia Island, Florida, to the south (Hemmings and Deagan, 1973) and on the Georgia barrier islands (Larsen, 1982), the present coastal area has been occupied by humans since at least 2200 BC—more than four millennia. Considering the fickle nature of the coastline during the last 5,000 years, many archaeological sites have likely been submerged and obliterated by rising sea level, limiting the available information. Pleistocene megafauna (ground sloths, mastodons, and mammoths) occupied the coastal area at lower sea levels (DePratter and Howard, 1980).

The Spanish included Cumberland Island in the Indian "Province of Timucua," the island forming the northern coastal border of that area, which comprised the northern third of the Florida peninsula (Bushnell, 1994). The number of Eastern Timucua, those inhabiting southeast Georgia and northeast Florida, prior to European contact has been conservatively estimated at 15,000 to 20,000 (Deagan, 1978). Early people inhabiting Cumberland Island and environs left no evidence to suggest that their methods of subsistence differed markedly from other contemporary coastal groups, and it might be expected that they "fully exploited most of the animal (and plant) life their environment had to offer" (Hudson, 1976). Milanich (1973) listed the vertebrate species recovered from two Deptford archaeological sites (2400 to1300 BP) on Cumberland Island, which are the only prehistoric sites that have been excavated by professional archaeologists. Individual species will be addressed later in this book, but the important thing to notice here is the great variety of remains of both terrestrial and marine species, which suggests long-term occupancy of the sites.

Subsistence

Archaeological evidence from the Georgia coast prior to 850 BP suggests hunting and gathering was the primary method of aboriginal subsistence (Larsen, 1980). Whether settlements were permanent, seasonally used, or temporary camps usually depended in part upon the availability and diversity of local resources (Yesner, 1980). If subsistence was provided by numerous resources, as may have been the case on Cumberland Island, the overexploitation or failure of a single resource would not be cause to shift location. Early human groups (AD 500 to 400 BC) on Cumberland Island were relatively small, with five or so dwellings in a camp occupied by nuclear families of five to six people each (Milanich, 1973). It is possible that deer were tamed and even milked (Swanton, 1922), but the only animal known to be domesticated by southeastern groups, and sometimes eaten (Lowery, 1911), was the dog. Two varieties of dog, one large and one small, have been documented from preceramic sites in Florida (Neill et al., 1956). Due to the abundance of the resources per capita and the tools involved, the hunting-and-gathering method of subsistence probably had a low environmental impact. Traps and snares were used on vertebrates, and weirs erected to trap fishes, but direct capture or hunting was likely the primary method used. There is no evidence to suggest fire drives were employed as a hunting technique in this area (Larson, 1980).

Faunal remains identified from aboriginal and historic sites can provide information on species occurrence, but even these are subject to interpretation and should be evaluated. For example, if a species is represented by unusually low numbers of individuals, it may be that the animal was brought as a gift by visitors or bartered rather than a component of the local fauna. Since my emphasis here is on the terrestrial vertebrates of the island, the zooarchaeological record of not only Cumberland Island but also other Georgia barrier islands, Amelia Island, Florida, and the adjacent mainland is relevant, and, when available, that information is integrated into the discussion of individual species.

Fauna

In general, what were the food resources available on Cumberland Island? Probably all available animals of suitable size and abundance were, at one time or another, eaten as food by local aboriginals (Table 2). Immobile species, such as clams and oysters, were easily accessible either from banks, by wading the hard-bottomed tidal creeks, or by canoe. Contrary to Larson's comments (1980), oysters and clams are frequently collected here from the same general locations in small tidal creeks. Optimum habitat for both species is naturally ever-changing, resulting in new colonies being established as others decline, even with no human depredation. This characteristic would help defend against overexploitation. Ribbed mussels abound in the high salt marsh and would have been easy to collect. Mussel populations must also respond to continually changing environmental conditions and because of that necessary resilience also have a degree of protection from overexploitation.

Also available in the tidal creeks, on river beaches, or, after high winds, on ocean beaches are large gastropods, such as whelks. Native people consumed the animals and used the colorful shells for decorative jewelry, cups, and tools. Following strong winter winds, thousands of whelks of several species wash ashore alive on the ocean beach, a regular event that is unlikely to have gone unnoticed by foraging peoples. Several species of crabs and shrimp are also available in the tidal creeks. Both are easily captured, with shrimp availability being more seasonal than the crabs.

Fish are easily trapped in tidal creeks and were consumed by local aboriginals. During cool weather, a catch of mullet is nearly always guaranteed, while in the summer more effort is sometimes needed as the fish seek deeper, cooler water. An indication of the importance of fish in the Timucan diet was the custom that during menstruation and pregnancy, women abstained from eating fish (Milanich and Sturtevant, 1972). Many species of marine fish are found along the Georgia coast and many species are reported from coastal aboriginal middens; however, preparation techniques may influence the number and kind of fish remains. Native freshwater fish do not presently occur on the island in sizes or abundance to be considered a human food resource.

Among the reptiles, alligators and sea turtles are the largest species locally available. Besides constituting delicious fare, alligators presented a threat to aboriginal children and dogs and were likely removed from the vicinity of villages and camps. Alligator fidelity to specific habitats in creeks and ponds would assure fresh meat in times of food shortage. Sea turtles seasonally nest along the ocean and river beaches from May through August. Adult females are easily captured when they emerge to nest, and the 100 to 150 eggs they each deposit in two-week intervals are easily gathered. During different climate regimes, more or fewer turtles might have nested on Cumberland Island. The diamondback terrapin and several species of freshwater turtles are also available in limited numbers.

The seasonality of various avian species provides a nearly continuous dietary resource. Colonial nesting species, which would be the easiest to acquire, along with their eggs, are available during spring and early summer while migratory species arrive in early spring and the fall and many remain through the cool months.

The white-tailed deer was the most popular terrestrial mammal consumed by early Florida inhabitants, with raccoon ranked second, and opossum third (Neill et al., 1956). The same holds true for Cumberland Island, then and now, excluding the introduced Virginia opossum. Food, clothing, and tools were obtained from deer. Raccoons are numerous, and, although the island population numbers fluctuate, individuals can usually be found. Rabbits, squirrels, and various small rodents were also available. Of the large mammalian predators, only black bear have been documented on Cumberland Island, from middens and in recent times. Highly mobile predators likely journeyed to and from the island seasonally or opportunistically in search of prey, but only very low numbers of those individuals could have been maintained as full-year residents. Smaller predators, such as otter, mink, bobcat, and opossum, presently have population numbers modified by human intervention.

Marine mammals may seem like unreasonable prey for primitive humans, but the remains of at least two species have been cataloged from middens on Cumberland Island, and marine mammals are represented in other coastal middens. Larson (1980) provided a summary of early descriptions of Florida aboriginal people hunting "whales." As well as actively hunting marine mammals, opportunistic use could have been made of those animals found stranded in tidal pools or in other shallow water, or dead on the beach. Some New England natives owned the rights to whales that stranded on certain sections of beach, and they retained those rights as they sold the land to the English, indicating the importance of the resource in that locality (Little and Andrews, 1982). Manatees have been observed in tidal creeks around the island, and several species of cetaceans frequent the adjacent sounds, rivers, and sea.

Flora

Vegetables known to have been incorporated into the aboriginal diet are few. Plant material is unlikely to be preserved as well as bones and teeth; consequently, most of our knowledge derives from early historical accounts. Acorns and roots satisfied those early people living on Cumberland Island, according to Laudonniere (Lanning, 1935), but it is safe to assume that early people consumed all edible berries, fruits, nuts, roots, and leaves. It is difficult for us to judge the edible quality of native species due to our frame of reference. Pure sugar is our baseline for sweet, and hardly a day goes by that some sugar is not incorporated in each American diet. Deliberately eliminate all sugar from your diet for a few weeks or months and then try some of the less popular fruits the native people were known to have eaten. Surprise! Otherwise bland or strange-tasting fruits become eminently acceptable. Even palmetto berries, which Dickenson described as tasting like "rotten cheese steep'd in tobacco" (Andrews and Andrews, 1985), are pleasantly sweet.

One item in the aboriginal diet we can appreciate is the tea that was made from the roasted leaves of yaupon holly, a common shrub on Georgia barrier islands. The drink is quite pleasant and contains caffeine for stimulation. The specific name, *I. vomitoria*, was erroneously applied when it was thought this plant contributed the emetic properties associated with the ceremonial "black drink." The plant is abundant on Cumberland Island.

One early observation made on the native diet was most certainly misconstrued. Father Pareja, a missionary who had been on Cumberland Island, reported that along with coal, dirt, and broken pottery, the people ate fleas and lice (Milanich and Sturtevant, 1972). Animals have but a few ways to rid themselves of vermin, and it has been my observation that following capture under a fingernail or with a moistened finger, execution by incisor is the most reliable method. With experience, a flea or tick can be captured, bitten, and killed without disruption of conversation or thought. It has also been my personal misfortune to have been misinterpreted as eating ticks when, in fact, I only killed and disposed of them. Fleas and lice are not the problem they were in earlier times, but it is interesting to note that Father Pareja made no special mention of ticks and may have categorized them as insects.

Agriculture

Maize became an important part of the diet of coastal people about 850 BP, influencing settlement patterns and the impact on local environments (Larsen, 1980). Settlements became larger as a result of a regular, storable food supply, and more permanent due to agricultural needs. Maize, pumpkins, squash, and beans added variety to the early diet, but at a cost. Dental caries and periosteal disease apparently rose concomitantly (Larsen, 1980). During this period the first land was cleared for fields. Fewer than 400 years later, the first European contact with aboriginal peoples in south Georgia and Florida was made. With the early European explorers came livestock, more efficient weapons, and a greater ability to alter/impact the environment. The full extent of early fields on Cumberland Island is unknown.

European Colonization

European colonization began during the mid-1500s with the French, Spanish, and English vying for rights along the southeastern coast. Forts and missions were slowly established on Cumberland Island, and as the native people succumbed to war and introduced diseases, the advanced European technology took a lasting grip. Untempered by religious constraints regarding the environment—in fact, bolstered by their own credo—the Europeans began serious modifications of Cumberland Island that have continued for centuries.

Spanish

The Spanish established the garrison town of St. Augustine in 1565 as a base of operations for their contest of the east coast of North America. The aggressive nature of the early Spanish efforts precluded any success by missionaries in subduing and converting the natives. It was not until the king established a system of royal support for Florida's soldiers and friars (1570) and changed the method of conquest to one of "peaceful advances and voluntary conversions" (1573) that control over the local indigenous people was facilitated (Bushnell, 1994). Through gifts, the missionaries enticed the natives and slowly converted them to Christianity. The stronger the commitment to Christianity, the more numerous the gifts and more elaborate the religious accoutrements of the local missions and settlements. Once converted, locals were required to provide labor and provisions to the missions and the Spanish cause. Local people expanded their own system for community support to include the missions, and they planted large fields of wheat for church needs and greatly increased corn production, with extra fields exclusively for church use and general service of the Spanish crown. By 1670, produce from the ever-enlarging aboriginal fields of corn and beans was even being exported to St. Augustine and Havana (Bushnell, 1994).

San Pedro, located in the vicinity of the Dungeness wharf on Cumberland Island, was a sizeable native settlement, originally inhabited by Timucuans who were later replaced by Yamasse Indians. In 1595, San Pedro was reported to be "a town of many Christian Indian men and women" (and a detachment of Spaniards), whose cacique, don Juan, was described as Hispanicized, having been nurtured from childhood by Father Lopez (Bushnell, 1994). A church constructed on Cumberland Island during that period was reported to be "as large and capacious as the one in St. Augustine" (Bushnell, 1994). From the apparent size of the village and mission and its proximity to St. Augustine, we must assume a considerable amount of land in the vicinity of San Pedro was cleared and farmed by native people.

Another mission, Puturiba, was established on the north end of Cumberland Island by 1587 and may have been located on Brickhill Bluff (Walker, 1985). Several fragments of Spanish olive jars and shards of native pottery have been found at the base of the eroding bluff, suggesting a settlement. Much of the adjacent land is suited for agriculture and supported fields in the 1880s and no doubt for the native people much earlier. Since Cumberland Island was the site of several early villages and Spanish missions (Deagan, 1978), it is likely that areas were cleared for agriculture by the mid-1500s and continued to be enlarged for a century and a half.

The pre-Spanish and Spanish fields in the Dungeness area may have been the first land farmed on Cumberland Island, and that locale has been almost continuously occupied since. Native people cultivated beans and pumpkins as well as maize, which they sowed twice a year and grew to maturity in three months. They reportedly burned the weeds from six-month fallow fields just before planting (Swanton, 1922), and because of rapid nutrient depletion of the sandy soil, abandoned fields after only a few seasons (Larson, 1980).

Horses, cattle, hogs, and sheep were available to early Spanish friars and soldiers, but there was a suggestion they refrained from introducing cattle, concerned that the animals would raid the local cornfields and also be easy targets for poaching (Lanning, 1935). However, on St. Catherines Island in 1680, during a Spanish raid to remove the English-allied Yamassees near the end of the mission period, both cattle and hogs were reportedly killed (Worth, 1995). Excavations of two coastal mission sites in the province of Guale (between St. Catherines Island and St. Andrews Sound) revealed few domestic animal remains and a heavier reliance on native resources (Reitz, 1991). Later sixteenth-century mission settlements did not generally have horses; however, at least one horse was recorded on Cumberland Island by the end of the sixteenth century (1597), the property of Chief don Juan, a luxury even for most Spaniards in Florida at that time (Hann, 1996). Gifts of horses were occasionally made to compliant chiefs (Lanning, 1935). During Oglethorpe's fortifications of the coast (1736–1742), fifty to sixty horses were stabled at Fort St. Andrews on the north end of the island, and horses were probably associated with island residents thereafter, although that particular group of animals was slain (Ivers, 1974). Adaptable, prolific hogs arrived on the US Gulf Coast with de Soto in 1539 and were provided to French explorers by northeastern Florida natives in 1560 (Hanson and Karstad, 1959), substantiating that feral hogs occurred in the area by that time. Descriptions of Cumberland Island in 1785 and 1788 both mention hogs as an asset and extol the capacity of the island to support many free-ranging animals.

By 1600, the number of indigenous people recruited to Christianity by the Spanish missionaries on Cumberland Island was reported to be 500 to 800 (Lanning, 1935). Fifty years later, the Eastern Timucua population had been decimated by "epidemics of pestilence," and those with other cultural affinities had moved into the area (Deagan, 1978). By 1681, the total native population on Cumberland Island, residing in two or three settlements, had dropped to about 135 individuals (Milanich, 1972; Worth, 1995). Shortly after the turn of the century (1700), the mission system was destroyed. Between pestilence and slave raids, however, the Eastern Timucua culture perished, and the few remaining who had adopted Christianity had deserted their parishes along the entire East Coast.

In summary, the occupation of the island by indigenous people, through the evolution of subsistence techniques to the arrival of Europeans, had an impact on local biota, but it is unlikely that populations of plants and animals taken for food were permanently impaired or limited by the relatively low numbers of resident aboriginals. The hundreds of Christian converts that the missions reportedly produced no doubt included mainland groups.

Nevertheless, large areas on the island were cleared for fields to support Spanish interests. Clearing and burning land for agricultural purposes and settlements would have had lasting impacts; however, any such impacts were subsequently overshadowed by the larger fields cleared later by Europeans, grazing livestock, and other manipulations by early colonists. Disturbances to the salt marsh, such as mining clay for pottery manufacture, would have been obliterated by storms, which perpetually modify the edge of the island. Fish weirs and traps would have created temporary modifications due to the lack of rocks or long-lasting material with which to divert or obstruct waterways. Unusual pressure was placed on some resources following early European explorations. Locals collected items for barter, including sassafras, myrtle, and deerskins. The extent of use or export of various resources of interest to Europeans is not known, although the potential for environmental impact existed.

Commerce

Sassafras was of interest to the French and Spanish and was among the first articles exported from La Florida. In Virginia in 1590, sassafras was listed as a merchantable commodity "of most rare vertues in phisick for the care of many diseases" (Harriot, 1972). Natives made sassafras tea, and the Europeans desired the plant for its stimulant and diaphoretic effects as well as its use as a flavoring agent. The Spanish used it in treatment of syphilis and rheumatism (Porcher, 1970), the bark was used in dying, and the mucilaginous quality of the leaves was recognized. In the north, where the tree appears to grow larger, the aromatic wood was used for bedposts and hen-roosts to discourage vermin (*Peter Kalm's Travels in North America*, 1966).

In 1603, the Spanish governor of Florida urged young Cacica doña Ana of Cumberland Island "to foster the sassafras trade" (Ross, 1926). Early people collected sassafras roots for European trade from apparently abundant sources from New England southward. Sassafras was the dominant species in the forest behind the secondary dune system on Fire Island, New York, in 1974, and in Georgia and Florida it has been described as "common" (Duncan and Duncan, 1987) and "occasional" (Wunderlin and Hansen, 2011). Brown (1945) referred to sassafras in Louisiana as "formerly a large tree" with records of 36-inch diameters. Another source stated that while specimens of five-foot diameter had been recorded in Pennsylvania, in the Carolinas the plant rarely got over two feet in diameter (Coker and Totten, 1934).

The forest on St. Simons Island was described in 1735 as being "chiefly live oak, water oak, laurel, bay, cedar, gum and sassafras" (Moore, 1983). Sassafras "no bigger than [one's] thigh" was reported in an old field on Ossabaw Island (McPherson, 1962). An earlier name for Cumberland Island was Missoe (White, 1849) or Wissoe (Moore, 1983), meaning sassafras and suggesting abundance, yet the plant is far from abundant on the island today. What happened?

To comfort would-be sassafras foragers, Ewell Gibbons (1962) advised, "Don't be afraid that you might exterminate the plant by pulling up a few small saplings to gather the roots. Sassafras is very tenacious, and has the ability to put up new plants for every one you take. Unless you carefully grub out every root, gathering sassafras seems to make the clump thrive." Today sassafras is abundant in more northern states, suggesting that early economic pressure did not have a long-term negative impact on the species.

While most sources describe the preferred habitat of sassafras as open woods on moist but well-drained soils, which also fits the description of prime agricultural land on the island, it is unlikely that the impact of the original clearing of vegetation for fields is responsible for the scarcity of the plant today due to its prodigious reproductive ability. More likely, it is the number and species of feral animals on Cumberland Island, coupled with its intolerance of fire, that have restricted the plant. Even light fires reportedly kill small saplings (Fowells, 1965). Sassafras is known to be eagerly consumed by deer, and most things that deer will eat, cattle will eat. As a result, sassafras is a species that might be expected to increase in abundance when feral livestock is eliminated from the island.

As the European foothold along the southeast coast became more secure, reports of potentially valuable resources began to appear. One of the most regularly and enthusiastically described discoveries was the occurrence of the "prickly-pear shrub" or cactus of the genus *Opuntia*. Two species of this cactus are common along the Georgia coast, primarily in sandy, open habitats. Neither the edible purple fruit nor the succulent leaves held much interest for Europeans, but they did seek a tiny insect that fed upon the cactus. Those who have handled the prickly-pear fruit are aware of the rich, royal scarlet color the fruit imparts, and so it is with the insect. The cochineal insect, *Dactylopius coccus*, long used by the Aztecs, was discovered by the Spanish in Mexico in the early 1500s and exported to Europe as a source of crimson dye, cochineal. Most of the early observers in Georgia and Florida suggested the local species of cochineal insect was not the "true cochineal" but that the true species might do well if introduced.

Cochineal insects are of the order Hemiptera, family Dactylopiidae, and are scale insects, similar to mealybugs in appearance and habits. They are difficult to recognize as insects on the broad cactus leaves, because they cover themselves with a white, cottony, wax secretion in which they lay eggs (Fig. 7. Individuals, less than a quarter of an inch long, sometimes group together, forming cotton tufts. Only the males have wings and die shortly after fertilizing the females. For the manufacture of dye, mature females are brushed from the cacti, killed, and dried. The red pigment, carminic acid, is obtained from their tiny, dried, pulverized bodies. Approximately 70,000 are required to compose one pound of cochineal. The cochineal industry reached its peak between 1831 and 1847, after which it was replaced by synthetic dyes. Cochineal insects are still in demand today for coloring food products since, depending on changes in acidity, they hold their color for years. Only recently, in January 2011, did the Food and Drug Administration require that cochineal extract be included on a label if present.

The myrtle family includes many notable species, all of which contain aromatic volatile oils. Ripe fruit of the local myrtle—southern bayberry or wax-myrtle—were of commercial interest for the wax enveloping the fruit, which was used to make fragrant candles. The small fruits were dumped into a hot bath and the wax skimmed from the top after cooling. Whatever amount of commercialization this plant was subject to does not seem to have affected its abundance. It is extremely common on Cumberland Island and occupies a variety of habitats, especially the interdune area, now that there are no longer feral cattle on the island.

The great interest in new plants found in the American colonies also encouraged a lively traffic in seeds and plants to Europe, and one of the plant hunters and nurserymen engaged in this commerce was John Lyon. Because transportation was difficult in the early 1800s, Mr. Lyon established a "holding garden" in 1803 on Cumberland Island for plants he collected in Florida and on the island itself. The garden was at Dungeness on the property of Phineas Miller, planted in March and recovered at the end of January 1804. Not only exotic plants, but invertebrates as well could have been incidentally introduced to the island at that time. The groves of fruit trees maintained at Dungeness also may have been brought to the island in soil, potentially introducing exotics.

Skins of fur-bearing animals became important trade items during the colonization period. Beyond meeting their own demands, locals bartered and sold an enormous number of deer hides. Between 1699 and 1715, nearly 54,000 skins annually were sent to England from Carolina (Crane, 1928). The encroachment of Europeans increased the demand for mammal hides, and the pressure on deer populations and their environment continued until deer all but disappeared in the Eastern US by the late 1800s (Jenkins, 1953). Hunting regulations and a restocking program, mainly in the mountains, restored the population in Georgia, but out-of-state deer were introduced to accomplish it. Out-of-state deer were introduced on Cumberland Island, but for other reasons.

With English occupation in the early 1700s came construction of Fort St. Andrew at Terrapin Point and Fort Prince William on the extreme south end adjacent to the St. Marys River. Plans for Fort St. Andrew included barracks for 200 men, and in 1738 there is a reference to eighty women and children associated with the soldiers living on the island (Torres, 1977). Whether a settlement remained is not known. In 1757, a group of about 200 people under the leadership of Edmund Gray settled on Cumberland Island, but that number dwindled to seventy or eighty by 1766 (Torres, 1977). "Gray's Gang" was apparently self-sufficient and cultivated "fields of Rye which grow there in great plenty" (Torres, 1977). Because of the unsettled ownership of the coastal area and the continuing conflict over it between Spain and England, plantations and nonmilitary settlements on the island were few. No civil law presided, so residents were at the mercy of a multitude of unsavory characters until the Treaty of Paris in 1763 decided the fate of the region, giving control of what is now the Georgia coast to England. Influential people immediately petitioned for land on Cumberland Island, some with the intention to settle, some merely as speculation (Gallay, 1989). English Crown grants for land on Cumberland Island were issued beginning in 1760 and apparently stipulated that within three years the grantee clear and work three acres for every fifty granted or clear and drain three acres of swamp or marsh. An accounting of the sufficiency of the improvements was apparently to be made and forfeiture was the stated price for not meeting the requirements. Still, the coastal islands were described as thinly inhabited. In 1774, William Bartram suggested that most were owned by wealthy rice planters who installed "poor families on their insular estates" to "rear stocks of horned cattle, horses, swine and poultry and protect game for their proprietors." Island inhabitants, he observed, were vulnerable to "invasion and ravages of pirates, and in case of war, to incursions from their enemies [*sic*] armed vessels, in which case they must either remove with their families and effects to the main, or be stripped of all their movables, and their houses laid in ruins" (Harper, 1958). Historic documents and deeds from 1763 to the present provide an outline of subsequent major events and suggest when large-scale land modifications began. There is no evidence to suggest that any land granted by the crown was ever forfeited for failure of the owner to make the stipulated "improvements" (Cadle, 1991).

Forest Products

In 1783, Revolutionary War hero Nathanael Greene purchased an undivided one-half interest in land on Cumberland Island which supported buildings, gardens, and orchards (Torres, 1977). Greene's interest in the island apparently stemmed from the value of the magnificent live-oak trees, so in demand at the time for shipbuilding and the growing international trade. In 1784, Greene learned that two- or three-hundred people from Florida were illicitly harvesting his live oak and shipping it off (Torres, 1977). The extent of oak cut by Greene himself is unclear, but in 1784 he reported the entire island, except for a few old fields, covered with the best of live-oak and red-bay timber, and only twenty settled families (Torres, 1977). In 1786, Greene met his untimely end, and the live-oaking business, one of the first commercial ventures on the island, was put on hold. An advertisement to sell part of the island in 1788 described the Greene property as "covered with large quantities of the live oak timber" (Torres, 1977), suggesting not much logging had been accomplished. Apparently not until Greene's widow, Catherine, married Phineas Miller was any appreciable amount of timber cutting undertaken. The first frigates of the American navy were launched in 1797, and thereafter the naval demand for live oak was insatiable. In 1800, Miller had a contract with the US Navy to supply an amount of timber he was unable to procure on Cumberland Island alone. He had 240-plus men and over fifty grain-fed oxen working and delivered 120,076 cubic feet (Bullard, 1986). Besides providing as much of the timber for the contract as possible, the island served as a base for shipping operations. Having to resort to adjacent land in Florida and South Carolina at fifty or sixty different landings to fulfill his timber contract (Wood, 1981) suggested that a substantial amount of live oak was harvested from Cumberland Island.

Despite the amount of timbering reported, a government survey of southern coastal land from 1815 to 1817 provided reports of Cumberland Island's oak resources that could be interpreted as contradictory. One member of the team thought there were "quantities of large growth timber and thriving forests of young oak," while the other surveyor remarked that "contractors had cut off all the large trees and that frames for only two sloops were available" (Wood, 1981). Those trees may have been the timber referred to in an 1832 newspaper advertisement by P. M. Nightingale: "Live oak timber for sale on Cumberland Island. The proprietor of this timber wishing to clear the lands on which it stands, will dispose of it on very reasonable terms. It is believed the frames of a frigate and a sloop of war and about 30,000 feet of timber suitable for merchant vessels might be readily obtained here" (*Georgian*, 18 October 1832). This also suggested that more than selective cutting was done for live oak. Amelia Island too had been plundered, and in 1823, Vignoles (1979) reported that while considerable quantities of fine oak had been obtained there at various periods, almost all the timber fit for large vessels of war was gone.

In 1840, steam-powered vessels were becoming popular, and following events in the Civil War involving ironclad steam vessels, it became obvious that the era of wooden warships was over.

By 1883, Congressional acts had been passed requiring the construction of steel ships for the US Navy. Because of its tough, twisted grain and irregular growth form, live oak is of little commercial value today and is regaining its place of ecological dominance in the island maritime forest.

Besides general logging operations for live-oak and pine timber, other forest-related endeavors, involving primarily longleaf and slash pines, revolved around the manufacture of tar, pitch, and turpentine, collectively known as naval stores. Tar is pine resin extracted from dead wood by heating, and pitch is tar further reduced by more heating. Turpentine is distilled from resin, the material exuded by living pines to heal their wounds. Of these, tar was the most important early commodity as wooden sailing ships used large quantities of it for sealing. Other uses included the treatment of rope aboard ships, lubrication of axles, as a paint to protect wood from decay and insects, and even to prevent infection in wounds of animals (Herndon, 1968). The political situation in Florida and Georgia discouraged commercial naval-stores production until late in the nineteenth century, but Georgia was exporting a limited amount in the late 1700s.

The primary indication that there was at least one tar kiln on Cumberland Island is a road by that name, which parallels Main Road to the east between New Duckhouse Road and the north leg of Lost Road. There is not enough detail to show Tar Kiln Road on early maps, nor even those produced in 1800 or 1802, but it is shown on a survey of the property of Lucy C. Carnegie done by Page and Meader in January 1898. At that time, it was shorter, running only from Duckhouse Road to Main Road.

The location of Tar Kiln Road is quite reasonable for a tar kiln, being situated in an area that was pine forest in 1801 and is a longleaf pine forest today. It is also an area with varying relief, which would facilitate construction of a kiln. Tar was made exclusively from dead pine, those resin-laden parts of the tree known as lightwood, lightered, or fat wood that resist decay. Kilns were assembled on locations near a wood supply. The sites of some early tar kilns in Florida have been examined in the last couple of decades and described as "similar to aboriginal burial mounds" but containing charcoal (Bond, 1987). One site in Duval County, Florida, measured 4 feet high and 40 feet in diameter. The vicinity of Cumberland Island's Tar Kiln Road has been explored, especially to investigate the higher elevations for signs of a kiln, but none have been found. One prime area has been severely disturbed by a bulldozer in connection with the possible sale by the Carnegies of mineral rights to Glidden Paint Company in the 1950s (J. B. Peeples, pers. comm.). The site of the kiln was possibly destroyed at that time.

The impact of a tar kiln on the forest community was relatively low compared with turpentine or logging operations, but the woods were soon cleared of dead pine. Live longleaf and slash pines were next utilized, and the labor-intensive collection of turpentine began. The "faces" of the trees needed weekly scrapings, and the "boxes" had to be emptied every ten days to two weeks (Bond, 1987). "Face" was used to describe that part of the tree from which the bark was removed and the outer wood injured to stimulate the flow of protective resin from the tree. As resin covered the wounded area and its production slowed, another scrape above the previous one restimulated the flow. Opposing streaks or wounds were made which formed a wide V that eventually resembled cat whiskers, and in south Georgia the faces are referred to as cat-faces. A "box" was chopped in the tree below the cat-face at the lower point of the V to catch the oozing resin or gum.

A particularly characteristic cat-faced pine snag was recovered from the edge of the salt marsh on Terrapin Point in 1988. For years the tree stood, dead but imposing; unquestionably too heavy to move. Finally winds toppled it but fortunately it was caught and held by vines until discovered. Had it been solid, it would have been too heavy to move, but it was hollow. Its weight was estimated at 600 pounds, as three people labored an entire day to salvage a section of it with the cat-face and boxes (there are two) intact. Other boxed trees, some obviously second-growth timber, can still be found along Main Road in the area of the oak-pine forest east of Terrapin Point and elsewhere on Cumberland Island.

When did the turpentine operation take place? Raw gum obtained from living trees was of no value to the maritime industry, and the collection of it required a commitment in equipment and personnel that would conflict with agricultural pursuits. Raw gum was of little commercial value in this area prior to the introduction of the copper-distilling apparatus in 1834 (Blount, 1993), and the serious production of naval stores did not begin in Georgia until 1875 (Dyer, 1963), but continued into the twentieth century. In McIntosh County to the north (Sapelo Island, Darien), naval-stores activities came to be important sources of income only from 1870 on (Sullivan, 1990). Mary Miller, born in 1903 and intimately associated with the north end of Cumberland Island, remembered no "boxing" of pines on the island (interview, 1995) nor did O. H. Olsen Jr. (pers. comm.). The extent of turpentining on Cumberland Island is unknown.

Logging

In the late 1930s, an area on Cumberland Island of virgin longleaf pine that had been there at least seventy-five years, well prior to Carnegie ownership, was determined to have a dense understory of nearly 100% hardwoods, and, consequently, no pine reproduction (Heyward, 1939). In 1947, an area of approximately 2,000 acres, possibly some of the same area observed by Heyward, "occupying the higher central portion of the island" was examined, and increment borings of the pines revealed ages that ran from 100 to 200 years (Stoddard, 1947).

The area was probably the vicinity of Yankee Paradise.

Pine lumbering operations were undertaken during World War II by the Carnegies and covered the area from a little south of Plum Orchard north, but not as far as Brickhill. The longleaf timber was old and many trees had the characteristic red-heart disease (L. McCullough, pers. comm.) caused by the fungus *Phellinus pini,* which penetrates the heartwood of primarily old trees, causing rot and facilitating its use by certain native species.

A sawmill was set up in the middle of the island (Yankee Paradise), but it was found too costly to get the lumber out, so they ended up taking entire trees to the landing and rafting them up Crooked River to a sawmill. Many of the trees were cut full size and shipped to Tampa to fill US government needs. The logging crew left trees standing that were within 25 feet of the road, and even had to go back and cut any stumps visible from the road to satisfy the elder Carnegies.

Another Carnegie logging operation in 1954 followed a high fire season, and much of the work was done to salvage timber possibly impaired by fire. Wanting to establish new stands of pine timber, the Carnegies planted approximately 400,000 pine seedlings acquired from the state and elsewhere. Most were slash pine, but at least 100,000 were loblolly, and they were distributed in "the old burn near Plum Orchard, the burn near Whitney Lake, and Hickory Hill and Skeet Field" (GDAH). Since much of the work during the war had been done with crosscut saws, the early logging may have been somewhat selective. Priorities change with time, and during one of the later Carnegie operations, all the pines deliberately left adjacent to the road were cut, their stumps plainly visible today, especially in the area around Yankee Paradise.

A sawmill was set up on the north end at the Candler compound in the 1940s to cut lumber for a new house being built at that time. That mill was later moved to the west side of the island to cut lumber for maintenance of the wharf. O. H. Olsen Sr. set up another mill in the scrub on the north end, just west of the Candler compound, in the early 1960s, to cut lumber for his new house (O. H. Olsen Jr., pers. comm.).

Marsh and Waterways

Anthropogenic impacts to the Cumberland salt marshes, past and present, are numerous and serious. The names Brickhill River and Brickhill Bluff (a corruption of Brick Kiln) refer to the manufacture of bricks, the clay for which was mined from adjacent or nearby salt marshes. The firm clay underlying the fluff mud and organic material is what would have been used, and such mining would have at least temporarily destroyed the overlying marsh ecosystem. Little is known of the operation on Cumberland Island. Bricks have been manufactured from clay deposits on other barrier islands (Zeigler, 1973).

Another abuse to the marsh was the digging of marsh mud for use as fertilizer on potato and cotton land. Capping the more dense clay underlying the salt marsh is about 20 centimeters (8 inches) of silty clay loam, ranging from slightly acid to moderately alkaline. In the early 1800s, it was discovered that this mud was the cheapest and one of the most profitable manures for exhausted cotton fields. Wagonloads of rich mud were distributed over depleted, overworked fields to increase productivity. On a plantation in South Carolina, slaves went out in the marsh in boats, loaded the mud, and returned to unload it into carts or baskets to be taken to the field (Johnson, 1930). Salt mud was applied at the rate of about 41 cartloads to the acre, and if a cartload averaged 4.5 cubic yards, as has been suggested (M. Thrift, 1994, pers. comm.), the appreciation to the fields would have been enormous, as would the potential to alter the marsh.

Marsh grass was cut for horse and cattle fodder, and livestock was grazed in the high marsh, although a "strong, rancid, and peculiar smell" apparently affected the animals' breath, milk, butter, and even flesh when they fed upon marsh grass (Porcher, 1970). Prime marsh for pasture adjacent to Cumberland Island was indicated on maps as late as 1881.

The depth of water in the Cumberland River at the dividings in 1890 was about 1.7 meters (5.5 feet) at mean low water, and there was an island in the middle of the river opposite the mouth of Brickhill "Creek." The bottom sediments were sand and mud or sand and clay and quite firm, providing a potential access point, especially for large animals. As commercial boat traffic increased, so did the need for reliably deeper water on the protected inland route, as boats frequently had to be towed across the shallow area at low tide. In 1939, Congress authorized the river, part of the Intracoastal Waterway, to be deepened to a uniform depth of 3.7 meters (12 feet) at mean low water, and so it is maintained today. Now, foot access at even low water would require much swimming.

In 1881, construction of the rock jetty bordering the entrance channel to the St. Marys River initiated major changes in the local shoreline and southern Cumberland Island dune system. (See section on "Shoreline" in the geology chapter.)

Modern Agriculture

Major land clearing for commercial agricultural purposes was first undertaken along the Georgia coast for the culture of rice. Rice was being grown in South Carolina in 1690, and by 1700 that state was producing more than could be transported. Plantation development in Georgia was delayed by the political situation, but by 1765 productive rice plantations had been established along the Satilla River in Camden County (Smith, 1985). The first rice grown along the coast was on inland swamps rather than along river floodplains. A successful rice crop depended upon the correct amount of freshwater at appropriate times, so reservoirs were constructed upstream from the cleared and diked inland swamps to meter the flow. Saltwater, even brackish water, is lethal to growing rice, which restricted production to specialized habitats.

Cumberland Island was considered "unsuitable for rice production" (Gallay, 1989). Rice was not grown commercially on the Sea Islands due to an unreliable supply of freshwater; however, there are references to a "small rice field" on St. Simons in 1787 (Sullivan, 1990), a recollection after forty-one years, and a "slough planted in rice" on Sapelo (McMichael, 1977), another recollection. Folklore of Cumberland Island maintains that rice was grown in Swamp Field, a large, temporary pond/freshwater wetland in the center of the island south of Plum Orchard. In 1802, that wetland was described as a natural sawgrass pond (McKinnon map, 1802), and subsequently it was ditched down the center with connecting lateral drains. In 1839, the area was described in an advertisement for its sale as part of a much larger tract as containing 400 acres, 200 of which were "cleared and drained and in perfect order" (Torres, 1977). Significant drainage was ultimately provided at each end of the field via canals leading directly to the salt marsh. The natural drainage pattern, now known as Plum Creek on the north end of the pond, was channelized, but the canal at the south end was an entirely new feature, bisecting a twenty-foot ridge. The only way rice could have been commercially grown there was for reservoirs to have been constructed on the many small watersheds that direct intermittent flows into the wetland. For cultivating rice, there would have been no need to construct a canal at the southern end of the pond since there was drainage already; in fact, it would have been counterproductive. A southern canal served best as general drainage for row crops. As further confirmation that rice was not grown on the island in any quantity, no rice processing equipment was inventoried among the effects of the Greene heirs or Robert Stafford, the largest planter on Cumberland Island. Nor did Stafford ever report any rice on his agricultural censuses. Also, the north half of Swamp Field or "Old Swamp Field" reportedly had corn growing on it in 1839 (Torres, 1977).

The rich, organic soil of the drained wetlands did produce vegetables in abundance and corn enough to feed livestock, but it was the uplands of

Cumberland Island that proved valuable for commercial agriculture. The optimum place to grow cotton was described in 1828 as "such high lands of a light brown or yellow complexion, as were covered by an original growth of hickory, laurel, and red bay, interspersed with the live oak and white oaks, and the towering palmetto" (Elliott, 1828). Plant communities on Cumberland Island fitting that description are the oak-pine and mixed-oak hardwood associations that occur on Lakeland and Chipley soils (Bozeman, 1975) and cover about half of the island. In 1802, there were relatively few residents on the island but cotton fields were being cleared and planted. A fairly detailed map of the island made in 1802 provides the location of these fields (Fig. 8). Island cotton production increased until most suitable land was under cultivation, probably around the mid-1830s. The Civil War (1861–1865) abruptly ended the cotton era on the island, and in 1876 reportedly not an acre was under cultivation (Torres, 1977). Most of the old cotton fields have been fallow since that time.

Some indigo was apparently grown on Cumberland Island in the 1780s, based on a reference in county records to "the indigo fields of Cumberland Island," but no evidence has been found to suggest it was produced in large quantities (Bullard, 2003). No special requirements are necessary for growing the plant, as it grows on most sites as long as they are not wet (Porcher, 1970) and requires no fences, for neither horses nor cattle will eat it (Belt, 1985). It had ceased to be grown in Savannah in 1817, but farther south it had become naturalized (feral) and was growing around houses (Darlington, 1969). The only indigo documented on Cumberland Island now is the native Carolina indigo and false indigo.

To expand productive acreage and make use of the rich lowlands for commercial agriculture, ditches were dug for drainage and dikes constructed at the edge of the salt marsh. The dikes kept saltwater out, and the ditches drained excess freshwater. To find ditching in lowlands is not surprising but most island fields, even those seemingly high and dry, were frequently circumscribed by ditches. The Colonial Records (Coleman, 1985) showed that the Trustees had recommendations about ditches: "The Trustees are of the opinion the best fences to every plantation will be ditches, especially as good drains may be made into these from the lands. And on the tops of the ditches, to plant the prickly pear or the royal palmetto." As well as quickly removing any excess rainwater, these ditches definitively marked the boundary of the field and may have also been useful in eliminating tree roots and the spread of palmetto into the field. Regular maintenance was required to keep the drains open, and most island low ditches are no longer efficient due to an accumulation of debris; they probably no longer significantly affect the local water table. The dikes, located at various points around the island salt marsh, are mostly intact but with minor ecological impact due to the lack of the wooden water-control mechanisms, which rotted away. Freshwater streams now flow unimpeded to the high salt marsh through these breaches in the dikes, and at times of spring tides, saltwater floods into the area behind the dikes. These dikes in the high salt marsh, which may have been for personal rice plots, now provide special habitat for wildlife on Cumberland Island.

Carnegies

Thomas M. Carnegie acquired a large portion of Cumberland Island in 1881, and though no commercial agriculture was pursued, when on the island, the family was quite self-sufficient. As the Carnegie family grew, staff, livestock, and gardens in proximity to the dwellings also grew to keep pace. An 1898 map shows the extent of old fields at that time (Fig. 9). By 1921, most of the old fields were covered with bushes and second-growth trees (Pearson, 1922), and in 1947 were described as having "grown up in live oak jungle" (Stoddard, 1947).

A potentially remunerative venture T. M. Carnegie Jr. undertook was growing tung, *Aleurites fordii*, a native of China. Oil pressed from the seeds of this species is used in various paints and varnishes for its drying properties. At least three fields of tung trees were experimentally planted on Cumberland Island after Lucy C. Carnegie's death in 1916; one in the open area at the Dungeness dock, one in Beach Field at Dungeness, and the other in the vicinity of Stafford. For whatever reason, the venture was not pursued commercially, but some of the trees remain and do reproduce via seeds. The plants do not do well beneath the forest canopy, although they will sprout in shade, so distribution is restricted even with minimal impact from local mammals.

After the Civil War, accommodations for guests were provided on the north end of Cumberland Island. Expansion of the facilities was soon promoted by newly established railroads and steamboat service to the islands, ushering in the resort era. By 1891, the hotel, as it had become, could accommodate 350 guests and frequently hosted conventions and large groups such as the Georgia Teacher's Association, the Georgia Farmer's Association, and the Georgia Dental Society (Miller, 1990). The number of people and permanent staff roaming about the island and on the beach would have had an impact on the wildlife and especially the shorebirds.

Fishing and hunting were popular pastimes in season. Hunting was especially popular with the Carnegies on the south end of the island. They tallied the game killed between Christmas 1885 and January 1911, with the caveat that "many deer, turkey and ducks killed [were] not recorded; also snakes, hawks, etc." They recorded 3,109 ducks, 775 deer, 339 turkeys, 101 doves, 59 squirrels, 47 alligators, 31 raccoons, 27 snipe, 24 marsh hens, 14 rattlesnakes, 8 feral hogs, 6 bear, 3 wildcats, 2 geese, 2 eagles, 2 larks, and "often" rabbit, mink, moccasins, hawk, and gull (author's notes, original in private ownership). A hunting club was established on the north end in the early 1900s (Bullard, 2003).

Other Endeavors

Planned mercenary endeavors, which would have had enormous impacts on the island but which never came to fruition, include the development of a six-story hotel and strip mining for minerals. The hotel being considered in the early 1890s was to have an accompanying sanitarium or national health retreat, which would accommodate "upwards of 500 guests" and would be connected to the hotel by an electric railway (Fig. 10). The hotel "will be a palatial structure, on a scale of magnificence not inferior to the famous Ponce de Leon, or equally famous seaside hotels of California," so the prospectus read. Development was planned from river to ocean beach, encompassing Whitney Lake and the bluffs at Terrapin Point (Hunter Tract Prospectus). Fortunately, the developer, J. M. Hunter of Cincinnati, Ohio, ran out of funds before serious damage to the island could be done.

The only mining of heavy metals on the Georgia Coastal Plain took place in Folkston, Georgia, between 1965 and 1974, but in the 1950s the Glidden Company bid on the mining rights for Cumberland Island with an expected annual production of 125,000 tons of strip-mined material. The lease offer was denied but only as a result of litigation brought by a single Carnegie heir (GA Supreme Court: 213 GA 766 {1958} and 213 GA 493 {1957}), while the other members of the family supported it. Had the mining operation been successfully established, Cumberland Island would never have been selected as a national seashore because there would have been little of its natural integrity to save or enjoy.

Over the years, various cultures and interests have manipulated and exploited the island's natural systems, while natural ecological processes have also had an impact. The wide variety and ever-changing focus of pressures, coupled with the resilient nature of the ecosystem, have allowed wounds to heal and have made Cumberland Island what we see today. Far from a pristine natural system, the island, along with all the Georgia barrier islands, has weathered many storms, challenging an understanding of the ecosystems present today. Human manipulations and modifications are far from over. Designation as a national seashore within the National Park Service system was a protective measure against some ecosystem abuses, and inclusion in the National Wilderness Preservation System for part of the island supposedly gave further protection, but as we have seen, laws are easy to change and development difficult for managers to resist. Today's modifications fall more under the heading of abuses, such as supporting feral animals, bus tours, fire manipulation, and the introduction of exotic species.

Fire

All Cumberland Island communities are eligible for lightning strikes, but whether the powerful electrical charge dissipates without incident or ignites and perpetuates a fire depends upon the community and circumstances. Some habitats discourage fire by having a relatively open understory, fuels that do not readily burn, and by maintaining high humidity under a tight canopy. The maritime forest is such a community. During times of drought, ignition, even deliberate ignition using a drip torch, is sometimes not successful in a live-oak forest. Exceptions to this occur when the size of the area is not large enough for its natural protective mechanisms to function, such as on a linear ridge with fire on each side, or a thin strip of mixed oak community along a salt marsh with a highly flammable habitat (scrub) on the other side. In both cases, fire-generated wind may suck the heat and flames into the oak stand and override the natural protective measures. While light fires benefit live oaks, crowning, hot fires quickly kill them, and where trees are stunted and have an understory of thick palmetto, even cool fires may reach the crown. Creeping under oaks, "cool fire" often benefits live oak by damaging its major competitor, the thin-barked laurel oak. Slow-burning fires also reduce fuel, especially vines, which helps protect oaks during hot fires.

Old-timers knew the response of fire in live oak stands and usually constructed houses in that habitat, probably more for safety from wildfire than for aesthetics. During the big 1981 wildfire on Cumberland Island, a naive, young caretaker, frantic to survive the growing conflagration surrounding the residential compound for which he was responsible, was preparing to vacate the spot by going out in the marsh in his boat, when he noticed an older coworker leaning against a building, casually smoking a cigarette. "Aren't you worried about the fire?" he nervously asked his fellow worker, Jesse Bailey, who had been through many island fires. "It'll go out when it hits the oaks," Jesse calmly replied, and the fire obliged his prediction (author's personal field notes).

The ignition of fire from lightning strikes is usually predicated on drought or very dry conditions. Under those circumstances, two island communities are especially receptive to fire, the flatwood scrub and all the freshwater wetlands, both dynamic habitats that greatly benefit from fire. Without periodic, intense fires, the scrub community, known as a fire-adapted association, would change composition and structure, therefore it is not surprising that the area facilitates the ignition and spread of fire. Species there will resprout following even intense fires. The drier the fuels, the less likely the fire is to be extinguished and the more likely it is to burn to mineral soil, a condition which favors reestablishment of pines, the lightning rods of the community. Conflagrations seem to have occurred in roughly twenty-year periods (Turner, n.d.), allowing a substantial accumulation of fuel and assuring a hot, consuming burn. This is what the scrub needs to maintain itself and its integrity.

Soils in the scrub are low in organic material and nutrients are quickly leached away. Fire provides a pulse of nutrients of which the restricted suite of fire-adapted plants take advantage. These nutrients allow abundant fruiting in plants which otherwise produce minimal fruit. This cornucopia may last two years, and by then the regrowth, mainly from root sprouts, is again thick and shades the soil, with nutrients probably back to near minimal levels. The scrub is really a continuum of habitats from exposed mineral soil to thick, tangled, over head-high shrubs with a thinly scattered overstory of pine. Its intrinsic value to Cumberland Island diversity is multiplied by this dynamic aspect. To stabilize it is to change it, to kill it. Fortunately, the scrub covers such a large area on the island that elimination of all natural fire at this time is out of the question. The scrub will burn. From 1973 through 2014, the National Park Service attempted to extinguish every natural wildfire on the island. Another dire possibility is attempting to reduce fuel levels and thus discipline the community to a more manageable fire intensity when fire does occur. Despite the fact that most of the area is presently designated Wilderness by an Act of Congress, the National Park

Service plans to reduce fuel loads by manipulating fire in the area. Natural fire increases resistance and resilience characteristics of the vegetation, whereas exclusion reduces them. With manipulation, there may be changes in the availability of carbon and nutrients and a reduction in nitrogen-fixers, reducing the amount of already minimal nitrogen available. The timing of fires, seasonal and annual, also has long-term effects on stand structure and species composition. Short-term fire frequency promotes saw palmetto dominance (Schmalzer and Hinkle, 1992).

Freshwater wetlands are dependent upon fire also. Because Cumberland Island freshwater originates with rainfall, most, if not all, wetland systems are dry part of the time, which allows a wide range of vegetation types to become established. The longer an area is dry, the more upland forms take hold and choke out areas that would otherwise be open water. When enough water is available to refill the basins, and if it persists long enough, it may kill encroaching upland species, but their biomass will remain even in death and contribute to the slow filling of the wetland.

Palmettos advance into drying wetlands until rising water stops them. Then, as the water level creeps upward, they become as arboreal as possible to keep the growing bud dry, and at the same time expand their supporting roots above the bottom muck into the water for stability. As long as the water remains, they are safe, if not in their optimum habitat, but when the water level finally drops, they are extremely vulnerable to fire, with growing buds and sensitive roots well above ground. In this way, fire easily kills back invading individuals and reopens sloughs and ponds. Reduced standing vegetation means reduced transpiration (water loss through plants) and more available water. Fire also consumes the organic accumulation at the bottom of the system, recycling sequestered nutrients and providing more room for standing water, which will then be available for a longer period. Most large animals that use the wetlands are mobile and can flee approaching fire; alligators retreat deep in their dens and are there protected.

By maintaining open water in ponds and sloughs, fire also provides habitat for colonial wading birds such as wood storks, white ibis, herons, and egrets. On Cumberland Island, as elsewhere, those species forage in shallow, open water and nest in mixed-species groups in trees or shrubs growing in water. But it is more complicated than that. On Cumberland Island, when fire played a natural role, only two sites on the island met the requirements necessary for a nesting area and supported mixed-species wading-bird heronries, Heron or Nightingale Pond and one place in the Sweetwater slough complex. As the exclusion of fire permitted encroachment by surrounding vegetation, the nesting areas became indefensible against the bird's main predator, the raccoon. When the wetlands were kept open by fire, a foraging raccoon would have to wade or swim to the base of a nest tree or shrub to have access. The association of water with alligators is a basic survival tenet for raccoons, and they wisely forgo the temptation. The potential threat of an alligator lurking under water thus protects the nesting area. However, as soon as branches of vegetation on higher ground reach those of a nest tree, all safeguards are lost. After severe losses following receding water levels and/or invasion by surrounding vegetation, most colonies abandon the nesting site for several years or until conditions change. Heron Pond has not been used since 1989 and the Sweetwater site, an area with deeper water, since 2002, and it is unlikely they will be used again until fire changes the conditions and water returns.

All but a few stands of upland pine on Cumberland Island, where pine is the dominant species, are seral stages in old field recovery or were planted by the Carnegies. Those few natural stands, Yankee Paradise and some areas of pond pine along the edges of wetlands, will continue to attract lightning, and thus fire, but the composition of the others will likely alter to oak dominance and the attraction for lightning will be reduced although not eliminated. Continual manipulation of fire in all habitats results in great changes in community structure and nutrient cycling.

Being the largest barrier island along the Georgia coast, Cumberland has the greatest amount of scrub and fire-adapted habitat, close to 2,000 acres today. In the past it had more. In 1817, William Baldwin, medical doctor and botanist, described the island as having "but little good land: mostly pine barren and thin live oak hammocks" (Darlington, 1969). The early Timucuan name for Cumberland Island was Tacatacuru, which was the name used at the time of European arrivals in the late 1500s. A precise translation is not possible, but Dr. Julian Granberry, author of *A Grammar and Dictionary of the Timucua Language* (1993), suggested that one interpretation might be "the fire colored (island)" or perhaps simply "the hearth land, homeland." Knowing the tendency of Cumberland Island to burn and the vast acreage involved, it is not surprising that its early name referred to fire.

The National Park Service approved a fire management plan (February 2015), which authorizes the manipulation of fire throughout the island, despite the Wilderness designation.

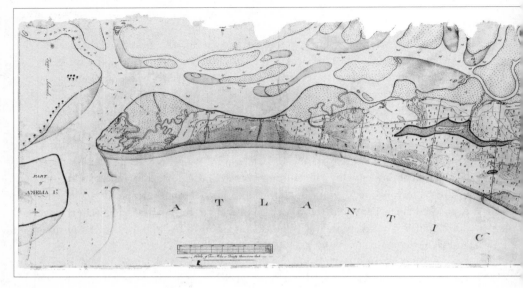

Figure 7

1802 map of Cumberland Island, Georgia, by John McKinnon. *(GDAH)*

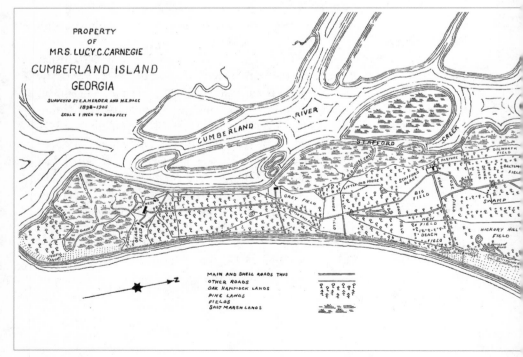

Figure 8

Carnegie property, Cumberland Island, 1898–1905.

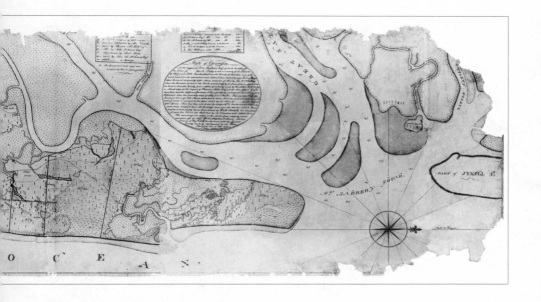

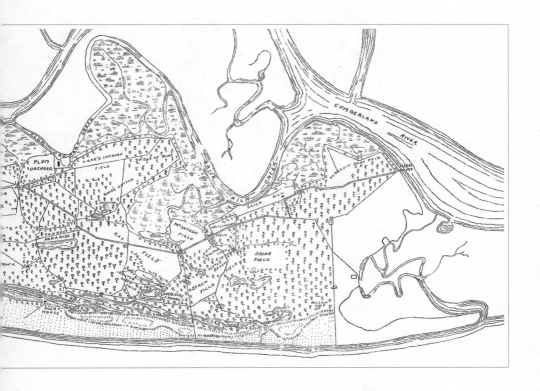

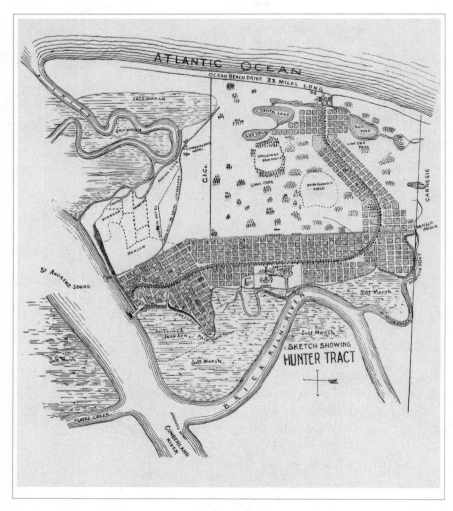

Figure 9
Proposed development on the north end of island.
(GDAH)

Figure 10
Cactus with Cochineal Insects, Dactylopiidae.

3

Communities

Talk of Georgia barrier island communities immediately conjures up images of an ocean beach, salt marsh, and maritime forest, all communities unto themselves but which may be further subdivided to provide a more detailed picture as shown by the vegetation map (Fig. 11). A community is generally defined as a group of organisms living together, sharing the environment. As might be expected, there is much overlap between designated communities. The division of island communities here is based first on abiotic conditions, such as topography, hydrology, soil, etc. and then on the biotic components that those conditions allow, such as vegetation and animals. Predominant plant and animal species are indicated. For more details on the vertebrates, check individual species accounts. A plant list is provided in Appendix I.

Beach/Dunes

Cumberland Island has 27 kilometers (17 miles) of uninterrupted ocean beach backed by dune habitat. The height of the area varies and is dynamic subject to wind and water, but the primary and secondary dune height averages about 3 meters (10 feet) and the rear dunes may reach 7.6 meters (25 feet). The vegetation is primarily herbaceous, with few woody species and no canopy. The beach/dune habitat is the most dynamic and harsh of island systems. Inhabitants must be adapted to intense high winds, shifting sand, and wildly fluctuating moisture and temperatures. Wind fills the air with salt spray that is quickly leached from beach soils but accumulates on aerial portions of plants. Special adaptations are necessary for plants to survive salt accumulation. For example, they may have glands that excrete excess salt, surfaces with heavy cutinization, (waterproofing), and leaves of reduced size. Plants may adapt to sands shifted by wave action and winds by developing elaborate, fast-growing root systems for stabilization. Few plants can tolerate the extreme conditions right at the ocean's edge, but the harsh circumstances ameliorate with distance inland and more complex communities become established. Beach/dune communities align in a linear pattern, and distance from the ocean and dune topography dictate their habitat conditions.

The general beach/dune habitat contains a mosaic of smaller, often linear but distinct areas composed of beach, primary and secondary dunes, interdune, and rear dune communities (Fig. 12). The beach community occupies the area of firm sand that is present from within the tidal zone up to the spring tide line or, the highest wrack line. Primary and secondary dune communities are found on the first lines of substantial dunes beyond the beach, as well as on older lines of somewhat less dynamic dunes that have built up to the west. Interdune communities are found in flat or low areas between and parallel the dunes. Rear dune communities inhabit the oldest active dunes that occur west of the interdune area and far enough away from the salt spray to support a wider variety of species. The transition from beach/dune to interior island communities is usually sharply defined. All are continually remodeled by natural forces and subject to reorganization.

Beach

Tidal cycles produce multiple wrack lines where flotsam and jetsam are deposited. Spring tides associated with the full and new moons occur every other week and push highest up the beach to determine the extent of the open beach habitat and, generally, the vegetation line. There is seasonal variation and tides are influenced by wind as well as the moon, so their height is not precisely predictable. No flowering vascular plants grow on the active beach at low tide, but hard rains sometimes ameliorate salinity levels, turning the damp sand dark green with algal growth. Runners of railroad vine may stretch from the central plant in the dunes as far as 23 meters (75 feet) to the summer high-tide line, and an occasional pioneering sea rocket may sometimes be washed by spring tides. Most of the larger, mobile island fauna visit the beach at one time or another.

Near the water's edge, shorebirds and gulls congregate to rest and feed. The vertebrate assemblage varies seasonally with many avian migrants, including peregrine falcons. Ospreys catch fish in the surf and usually carry their prey to an elevated point, sometimes a dune but more often a dead tree or branch, to consume it. Scavengers, such as crows and vultures, are common in the beach community to take advantage of an unpredictable resource. Other beach scavengers are raccoons and coyotes, which prowl the wrack line for forage. In the summer, Wilson's plovers, American oystercatchers, willets, laughing and herring gulls, royal terns, and least terns are commonly seen. During the winter, northern gannets may be seen feeding just beyond the surf, although they usually remain farther offshore. Common winter shorebirds include black-bellied plovers, semipalmated plovers, piping plovers, western sandpipers, and dunlins. Large groups of cormorants, laughing gulls, ring-billed gulls, and herring gulls are also common along with rafts of ducks just beyond the surf line. Deer occasionally frolic on the open beach, and a myopic armadillo or snake may become disoriented there.

The reptile most commonly seen on the beach in the summer is the loggerhead sea turtle. A few loggerheads, and fewer leatherbacks and greens, deposit their eggs in the primary dunes between May and August each year, and many, mostly juveniles, wash ashore dead or dying. Some alligators regularly venture into the ocean from wet interdune areas.

The beach is ever new and provides an exciting resource for a biologist. Regularly once a week, and sometimes daily since 1979, and opportunistically from 1973 to the present 2015, the beach has been surveyed for stranded or dead vertebrates. The list of species found dead on the beach (DOB) is surprisingly varied. Some insight into those species potentially eligible for island colonization may be gained from these data, and they serve as well for indirect monitoring of the health and security of neighboring marine species.

Primary and Secondary Dunes

The primary dunes are the first landward line of defense against storm surges. During such times, they absorb incessant pounding by high surf and scouring by gale-force winds. These dunes are sacrificial and thus ultimately dynamic. The vegetation in that community has special adaptations that increase the strength of the dunes by holding them together. Under normal conditions, the surf itself does not reach the dunes, and during that time, they are stabilized by vegetation. Sea oats thrive in the harsh conditions on the primary dunes where competition is drastically reduced because few other plants are as tolerant of high levels of salinity and strong winds. Rhizomes of this grass spread through the dunes and help hold them together. When blown sand encounters the aerial portion of the plant, it drops and accumulates at the base, increasing the height of the dune. As sea oats become buried in new sand, plant growth is stimulated and so the process of dune building continues (Wagner, 1964). Because they are so important to the formation and maintenance of the dune system, sea oats are protected by state law. Other grasses common on the primary dunes are seashore paspalum and seashore dropseed, which survive by sending out multiple rhizome branches, thus protecting patches of sand from the wind. Beach pennywort, beach croton, and, in the summer, railroad vine and beach morning glory are also common. The secondary dunes have had more time for vegetation to stabilize them and may support a wider variety of species including yucca and thistles.

Except for birds, most vertebrate activity, and perhaps invertebrate as well, in the primary dunes occurs at night. Rodents, especially the cotton rat and the cotton deermouse, forage in the dunes, probably for grass and seeds, as do rabbits and deer. Seasonally, and also nocturnally, loggerhead sea turtles lay clutches of eggs 50 to 60 centimeters (19 to >23 inches) deep in the dunes and leave them to incubate. Nests of the leatherback sea turtle and the green sea turtle have also been documented on Cumberland Island. Some eggs are found and eaten by the burrowing ghost crab, one of the most common residents of the dunes and beach. Shorebirds that nest in the dunes are, for the most part, rare or declining in numbers throughout their range. Loss of natural dune habitat is the main cause, but even on Cumberland Island the number of people, dogs, feral animals, and vehicles pose a significant threat. The distinctive American oystercatchers pick nesting sites usually in the low, soft sand just seaward of the primary dune line but safely above the spring tide line—precisely where beachcombers search for treasures. Wilson's plovers are more common and usually nest among the grasses higher on the dunes, which afford a little more protection from human influences. Species that feed on grass seeds, such as the red-winged blackbird, the mourning dove, and the ground dove, are principally associated with inland or terrestrial communities, but also frequent the primary dunes.

Interdune

Interdune communities develop in low areas between the primary and secondary dunes and the rear dunes, if they occur. They can include discrete single dunes but are usually flat, open areas that are dry the majority of the time. Because the area is so low, the slightest variance in elevation affects the hydrology and the availability of groundwater. Some species of vegetation signal proximity to the water table, the level of which is erratic, making the habitat harsh and unpredictable; sometimes xeric, sometimes waterlogged. Salt spray is still the overriding factor determining species composition in this area, but ground-water level is also significant. If the sea breaches primary dunes during severe storms, saltwater may funnel in to flood low areas and kill most vegetation. The most common scenario on Cumberland Island is for heavy rains associated with storms to fill the low area behind the primary dune line until an access to the sea is found, which is frequently a vehicle crossing or campground trail, but natural breaches also exist. Rivers of freshwater racing to the sea deepen the breach as they flow through the dunes and across the beach until high tide, when incoming saltwater backs up the flow and gains entry to the interdune. Salt water is lethal to most plants so the vegetation in the vicinity of the breach suffers more than normal stress. Standing water may occasionally remain weeks or months, after which revegetation begins.

Many of the same grasses found in the dune communities also occur in the drier sections of the interdune area. On the north end of the island, pink muhly grass covers acres of open interdune terrain, delicately coloring the area when it blooms in late September to early October. Another colorful addition to the flora is marsh pink or rose-of-Plymouth. These abundant small annuals may be up to 60 centimeters (about 20 inches) tall in the flat interdune area and produce numerous beautiful pink, quarter-sized flowers that belie the hostile nature of the environment. In damp areas, rushes, sedges, and capeweed are common, and wax myrtle usually becomes established in the areas closest to the water table. The tough, tolerant cabbage palm is a regular pioneer, as is live oak on slightly higher ground, while willows frequently join the wax myrtle in the low areas.

The remains of two invertebrates are commonly found in the open interdune area: the shell of the amber snail (*Succinea campestris*) and the exoskeleton of a large millipede, *Narceus americanus*. Amber snails (Fig. 13) were described by Thomas Say (1818) from specimens collected in Shaw's garden at Dungeness on Cumberland Island. Presumably, the millipedes are attracted to the area during wet periods or high humidity, then perish for lack of refuge from the intense sun. Another curious observation today is the number of pieces of ribbed mussel shells in small clusters about the area. Ribbed mussels are residents of the high salt marsh, not the interdune area, but were carried there as they passed through the gut of a feral hog.

Toads are surprisingly common in the interdune area and take advantage of the erratic, fish-free standing water to breed. Glass lizards, primarily burrowing forms that prefer loose, sandy soil, are regular members of this community. There was at least one active gopher tortoise burrow just behind the primary dunes for a year, but its burrow was ultimately eroded out by storm-associated high surf. Gopher tortoises are found mostly in inland areas on Cumberland Island, but on Amelia Island to the south, some are residents of the interdune community (P. Leary, pers. comm.) The interdune area is suited for cruising aerial predators such as harriers, kestrels, and merlins. Some avian species, most notably the least tern, nest on open ground in the interdune area. Colonies of usually fewer than fifty individuals have adapted to the potential hazards inherent in such a dynamic area. Although eggs occasionally get flooded and killed, nesting is more often successful. Foraging predators such as raccoons and snakes occur only infrequently, but the recently arrived coyote forages over a much larger area and may have a significant impact. Wilson's plover also frequently nests in open interdune areas and also sometimes loses clutches to heavy rains with standing water. The killdeer nests in this community as well as in more elevated areas, and black skimmers use similar open areas but have not nested on Cumberland Island since 1990. The open expanse is also used by the ground dove for foraging. Rabbits were common members of the interdune community in more vegetated areas prior to the National Park Service release of bobcats and the arrival of the coyote. Toads, small rodents, raccoons, and deer leave tracks at night, and mole tunnels are fairly common.

If beach accretion continues, over time the oldest or westernmost interdune areas develop into sloughs, and freshwater flora and fauna become established. The youngest interdune slough system on the island is the Big Slough area between Stafford Shoals and Willow Pond. Early in the twentieth century, when the Carnegies named the area "Big Slough," they said that no vegetation covered it except a few wax myrtles. Vegetation was able to become established after the cattle were removed, and today many areas there have an oak-cabbage palm canopy and would no longer be classified as "interdune."

Rear Dune

From Dungeness to Stafford, where the rear dune habitat has been protected by accretion to the east and abuts forest vegetation to the west, a continuous dune line occurs with stabilizing ground cover. Since this narrow, dynamic habitat encompasses relatively so little area, few animal species are regularly found in this community. One that does find it an exceptionally appropriate habitat is the six-lined racerunner lizard. This ground-dwelling lizard enjoys the hot, bright habitat and forages diurnally. In the more mature, canopied community, skinks are common. The present rear dunes from Willow Pond

Road north to Duckhouse Road are much younger and were treeless during World War II. A few palmetto clumps, myrtle, sand live oak, and tough bully are common but widely spaced. Herbaceous vegetation may be sparse but grasses include bluestem and sandspurs. Where the rear dune line has left oak skeletons, they are regularly used by birds of prey as roosts on which to feed and perhaps spy prey.

Encroachment of the rear dunes into the maritime forest was once facilitated by herds of cattle, which removed stabilizing vegetation. Even today, areas of mobile sand may be found well to the west of the interdune community. Prior to construction of the jetty, the beach/dune community sequence described here did not exist south of Willow Pond Road. Instead, severe erosion carried sand south to Amelia Island. See section on geology for details.

Maritime Forest

The maritime forest on Cumberland Island has endured much manipulation, from logging to agriculture to fire exclusion, through historic times to the present, producing a sometimes-confusing mosaic of vegetation associations. No areas are pristine. Overall, the community may cover 3,190 island hectares (7,882.6 acres). The forest is well canopied with an understory ranging from dense palmetto to thinly scattered shrubs and small trees (Fig. 15). There is little herbaceous ground cover due to reduced light.

Maritime forest differs from mainland coastal plain hardwood forests because of its proximity to the marine environment. The strongest natural forces imposed on the community are marine related and result in a biotic assemblage that reflects adaptations to these habitat conditions. Salt spray, strong winds, fire, and occasional drought conditions are the most stressful environmental factors affecting the biota. The community response is an altered species composition compared to mainland areas. Some zonal limits of vegetation occur at the edges of the forest, affecting calciphiles, for example, which seek calcium-rich soil on the western side, and from intense salt spray on the eastern, but the central portion varies primarily with elevation and soil type. While strong winds from hurricanes have the potential to drastically remodel all communities on the island, tornadoes have had a greater impact on Cumberland Island in the last few decades. The size of an area affected by a tornado varies greatly and is not necessarily linear; they may erratically touch down multiple times. Violent winds of both weather systems tear open the canopy and encourage diversity in an already complex system. Maritime forest covers most of the area on Cumberland Island. There is considerable variation in community structure within the hardwood forest, but such variation generally reflects different successional stages over time.

The plant species most characteristic of the maritime forest community is the Virginia live oak. Live oaks are found in all upland forests on Cumberland Island and thrive in wet areas as well, although are reduced in the scrub and areas of long leaf pine. Live oak is never dominant far inland from the sea (Bourdeau and Oosting, 1959), but in the marine-influenced environment they are able to successfully compete with other oak species due to their tolerance of marine influences, primarily salt spray, low-intensity fire, their ability to survive on nutrient-poor soils, and their longevity. The unusual sloping profile of the canopy of the eastern edge of the maritime forest is a result of direct contact with salt spray during high winds. A sand dune usually protects the base of the easternmost live oaks, but foliage and twigs above the dune intercept salt spray and become receptacles for salt deposition (Fig. 16). Abrasion of leaves and twigs by high winds carrying sand provide salt a lethal access to the plant. The effective pruning of twig tips stimulates lateral growth until the canopy becomes a nearly uniform surface, crowded with twigs. From the dune, the tightly closed canopy angles upward relative to the intensity of salt spray until the average island tree height in the area is attained. Salt-spray effects lessen with distance westward from the shore, and there the canopy becomes a bit more open.

The thick bark of the live oak offers moderate protection from cool fire, but the trees are sensitive to hot fire and even very large trees are sometimes killed by it. Underground buds on the roots or at the base of the trunk will sprout, allowing the tree to regenerate. Cool, frequent fires discourage competition of other oak species and tend to perpetuate the live-oak forest (Laessle and Monk, 1961). The maritime forest community has developed several characteristics to facilitate cool fires. The understory in a mature stand of oaks studied in northeast Florida was irregular, discontinuous, and averaged slightly over 50% cover (Laessle and Monk, 1961). Herbaceous growth is sparse in a mature stand, and fallen leaves (litter) lie flat, reducing susceptibility to fire. The most dramatic feature, and one that becomes evident during every forest fire on Cumberland Island, is the ability of the maritime forest to hold high humidity.

Under normal circumstances, raging fires come to an abrupt halt upon reaching a live oak stand. Each time, a few trees on the periphery may be maimed or lost, but the stand is otherwise unharmed. The more closed the canopy, the higher the humidity and the lower the chance for hot fires. Where there are gaps in the canopy allowing sunlight, Spanish moss thrives. The contribution provided by Spanish moss is significant, and it is considered possibly the second most important plant in the maritime oak forest (Johnson et al., 1974). By filling in the live-oak canopy, Spanish moss helps keep the humidity level high and limits growth in the understory by blocking sunlight. This also reduces the volume of the understory, which reduces the potential intensity of fire. Some associate species that are quite fire resistant, and are able to resprout if the leaves of the plant are destroyed, include the cabbage palm and saw palmetto. Sparkleberry, red bay, American holly, and wax myrtle may resprout if the entire aboveground portion is destroyed by fire. In contrast, in wet areas where the understory is usually tall and well developed, fire has killed very large live oaks on the island, especially on ridges separating the freshwater sloughs, where the canopy was limited by the sloughs and the height of the trees reduced (Ruckdeschel and Jordan, 1982). Fire scars that are found in most maritime forests of Cumberland Island testify to the importance of fire to this community.

The soils with which live oaks are generally associated on Cumberland Island have low natural fertility and are slightly to strongly acidic with low water availability, with the potential occurrence of a humate layer. They are designated Pottsburg sand, Cainhoy fine sand, and Mandarin fine sand, also known as Leon fine sand (Rigdon and Green, 1980). To survive on nutrient-poor soils, live oaks exhibit several adaptive features. Monk (1966) suggested that establishment of evergreen communities, such as the maritime forest community on Cumberland Island, may be the result of a need to conserve nutrients. Evergreens lose their leaves year-round rather than all in one season, and by distributing nutrients in shed leaves throughout the year, they presumably reduce loss. While live oaks are considered evergreens, they do lose their leaves synchronously in the spring, just in time for new growth to expand and reestablish a closed canopy. Perhaps the cover of newly fallen leaves helps hold moisture in the substrate and facilitates decomposition of older litter when the tree can make best use of released nutrients. It also would add some fire protection. The leaves are stiff and leathery to reduce water loss, and their small size and flat shape reduce the chance they will be blown or move far from under the tree. Dead leaves are persistent and decompose slowly, thus contributing to more efficient nutrient recycling. The wide-spreading and relatively shallow roots enable live oaks to quickly take advantage of nutrients released from the leaf litter.

Live oak is only moderately shade tolerant, which means that it prefers sunlight, and rarely are live-oak saplings found in a mature, well-canopied forest (Bourdeau and Oosting, 1959; Laessle and Monk, 1961). Seedlings have the interesting ability to survive if the top of the plant happens to be eaten or somehow destroyed. Buds near or below ground level will sprout in response to a major loss, and this resprouting process may be continued under dense canopies for fifty years or more. In this way, oaks, mostly of the white oak group, which includes live oaks, have the potential to accumulate seedlings with established root systems in well-canopied stands and await the opportunity for a canopy opening (Olson and Boyce, 1971). Live oak reproduction is largely by root sprouts, which are discouraged by fire and browsing and which rarely attain any size unless the main tree dies.

The normal life span for live oak has been estimated at 350 years (Porcher, 1995). A few very large live-oak trees may be found on Cumberland Island, usually around historic sites or on areas too steep, wet, or poor to clear for farmland. Their size is impressive and sparks curiosity about the original island forests. Live oaks do not attain great size in all forests, however, and rarely acquire the full, rounded canopy and spreading limbs of isolated individuals.

There are no sizeable stands of virgin live oak forest remaining on Cumberland Island, only uneven-aged forests. Second-growth forests have replaced old fields at various times, and live oaks were among the early colonizers. In 1947, a forester wrote of Cumberland Island, "Most of the former fields...have grown up to live oak jungle.... While live oaks are of high scenic value along drives and in dooryards, it can become a serious weed on Sea Islands such as Cumberland Island, starting to choke up fields soon after cultivation ceases" (Stoddard, 1947). In areas recently opened by fire or storm, such as some places along Duckhouse Road, the live-oak jungle Stoddard described is evident, with finger-sized live oaks in a competitive race for survival. Duncan (1982) suggested that remnants of original forest might be found at the margins of Sapelo Island, and the same may be true for Cumberland Island. Certainly, large individual live oaks occur along the western edge. Exceptionally large members of the Heath family are sometimes found on Cumberland Island along steep stream banks with large live oaks suggesting a history of reduced disturbance. Live oak was used for ship construction in the 1700s and 1800s, and some was cut on Cumberland Island. Due to its grain and growth form, it is not suitable for dimension lumber, so escaped logging thereafter.

Long-lived trees with large horizontal limbs and rough bark, such as the live oak, offer prime habitat for epiphytes, which are characteristic of the maritime forest. The larger and older the tree, the more likely it is to support large populations of multiple species. With their main source of nutrients available from the atmosphere, epiphytes can be of great value to host trees and the maritime community by increasing surface area to intercept and retain them. Bellis (1995) speculated that "tree inhabiting microflora may be as functionally important as those of the soil" in recycling minerals in the maritime forest. Epiphytes are not parasitic but use trees for support. The two most common epiphytes on Cumberland Island trees are Spanish moss and resurrection fern.

Spanish moss is not a true moss but a member of the flowering pineapple family. Roots serve only to anchor the species to the host plant while a layer of absorbing scales cover the plant and gather rainwater and windborne minerals, as do most epiphytes (Garth, 1964). Rainwater and sunlight are requirements, and growth is adversely affected by shade. Most inland live oaks on Cumberland Island wear a full complement of Spanish moss and would look out of place without it. As Archie Carr so eloquently put it, "A big old live oak tree without moss looks like a bishop in his underwear" (1994). Seldom is Spanish moss found growing on pine trees. Because rainwater is so important to epiphytes, Garth (1964) suggested that broad-leaved trees were better suited to meet the need. Rainwater is intercepted and distributed to run down the branches and stems of broad-leaved trees, as opposed to dripping off needles of pines directly to the ground. Pines also continually lose their lower branches, which would be a disadvantage to an epiphyte.

DeBrahm, observing virgin Southern forests in the mid-1700s, noted that Spanish moss grew on the trees of only "plantable lands" (DeVorsey, 1971), which included about half of the land on Cumberland Island. The species is certainly ubiquitous today in the regenerating forests. Bartram, also in the 1700s, commented on the abundance of Spanish moss, saying that it hung like streamers with "bulk and weight more than several men together could carry; and in some places, cart loads of it are lying on the ground, torn off by the violence of the wind" (Harper, 1958). Few places on Cumberland

Island could match that abundance today. Fresh Spanish moss does not remain on the ground very long on Cumberland Island due to feral livestock.

Might armfuls of it on the ground provide a distinct habitat for select invertebrates?

As a critical component of the maritime forest, Spanish moss also provides food for deer, nesting material for many species, and nesting habitat for several species of birds and a few bats, but, contrary to popular belief, it is not used by chiggers (Whitaker and Ruckdeschel, 2010). Green anoles are associated with Spanish moss high in trees. Historically, aboriginals used Spanish moss for garments and rope. Dried Spanish moss, termed "horsehair," resists insects and was used for stuffing mattresses, saddles, and horse collars, and was the basis for a commercial industry in the South. The Great Fire of Jacksonville in 1901 began in a Spanish moss factory (Foshee, 1988).

Two less common relatives of Spanish moss occur on Cumberland Island: southern needle leaf and ball moss. Southern needle-leaf, more common in Florida, is found in very few dispersed localities on Cumberland Island. Ball moss is more locally common and seems to prefer open areas adjacent to the salt marsh. It grows in a compact ball, firmly attached to a twig, and although able to remain secure in stronger winds than Spanish moss, it is frequently dislodged.

Only one species of fern is common as an epiphyte on Cumberland Island: resurrection fern. It is one of the most common ferns in South Georgia and ranges farther to the north along the coast to Virginia. The spores are wind borne, but once established, the creeping rhizomes form thick mats that cap the limb or support structure. To conserve water, dried fronds curl inward and lose their rich green color. Rain "resurrects" the plant and its lush green foliage again adorns the tree and contributes to the canopy.

Two other obligate epiphytic ferns and one non-epiphytic fern occur on Cumberland Island trees. The shoestring fern has only been reported in two counties in Georgia, Lincoln (near Augusta) and Camden (Cumberland Island; Bruce et al., 1979). It is a tropical fern commonly found on the trunks of saw palmetto in south Florida. On Cumberland it has been found on live-oak and sweet bay trees. Gold polypody is a large, showy fern found in only four Georgia counties and a few widely spaced localities on Cumberland Island. Island trees supporting shoestring and goldfoot ferns are mostly large and presumably quite old. Chain fern occasionally finds a suitable niche in a tree fork or hollow, as do several other unexpected plant species that are not epiphytes. Even tree species sometimes germinate and begin growing in crotches with suitable substrate.

The green-fly orchid is the only epiphytic orchid found on the island to date. The species is hardy and widespread from Florida to the Carolinas. On Cumberland Island it is found most commonly in proximity to wetlands and is locally common on bordering gums and oaks, where it has been recorded blooming from July through December.

Other very common epiphytes characteristic of the maritime forest are lichens, plants that are a synthesis of algae and fungus. Some species may contain nitrogen-fixing bacteria that ultimately aid the community as some nutrients are inevitably lost through leaching but replaced by atmospheric input (Art et al., 1974). Bryophyte populations, especially mosses, are also epiphytes of live oaks, and the variety of species and coverage increases considerably as the forest matures (Mackaness, 1942).

Live oaks may be dominant and the most characteristic plant species of the maritime forest, but a few other oak species and many other tree species occur and may be locally common, contributing to the canopy, especially in disturbed areas. The cabbage palm, also salt, wind, and fire tolerant, is found on all upland areas, including the active dune field, interdune area, in the maritime forest, especially along the western edge of the island, and in low inland areas. Palm forests, where that species dominates, occur in a few small areas on Cumberland Island. Lower cabbage palm fronds die as new ones appear and after drying, usually break off several inches to a foot from the base of the petiole. Petioles frequently remain attached to the trunk of the tree for a lengthy period, usually many years, and provide a unique habitat for some amphibians and reptiles and a host of invertebrates.

Most oak competition in the maritime forest is from laurel oak, which is fast growing and relatively short-lived. It has thinner bark than live oak and is less tolerant of fire. Other common forest associates are: pines (loblolly and slash on the south end, with longleaf included on the north end), Southern magnolia, American holly, red cedar, black cherry, and red bay. Saw palmetto, rusty lyonia, sparkleberry, and wax myrtle are common in the understory, and thinly scattered nutrush, spike grass, ruellia, and elephant's foot occur as ground cover. Red bay forms an important part of the understory of the maritime forest but began dying on Cumberland Island and elsewhere in 2005, victim of a fungus spread by an exotic ambrosia beetle native to India, Japan, Myanmar, and Taiwan. It was astonishing to see the volume of red bay that occurred in the forest when its death made it more obvious. Some island red bay plants continue to put out root sprouts, but there is no assurance the species will survive here. Another local species in the family Lauraceae that may also be affected is sassafras.

Saw palmetto is associated with most of the Cumberland Island communities and does well on impoverished soil and under a variety of environmental conditions but is not common in the dune area as it can tolerate only moderate deposits of sand. Much of the current distribution of saw palmetto on Cumberland Island indirectly reflects past land use. Remnants of a ditch may demarcate the edge of an old field with a solid wall of palmetto on the outside. In many instances, palmetto recolonization of old fields has been slow. Laessle (1942) observed that palmetto grew most vigorously where the soil was kept nearly saturated by seep water, and Hilmon (1968) found it most abundant on Leon fine sand. Palmetto is adapted to fire and its well-insulated stem is not often killed, though most leaves are usually consumed in a fire due to its low stature. Around the edges of temporary ponds, encroaching saw palmetto sometimes oversteps its bounds and is inundated by returning water. Persistent water causes it to vertically extend its usually prostrate trunk to keep the leaves above the water, but that response jeopardizes the aerial bud during the next drought/fire. In this way the temporary ponds are kept palmetto free. Where there is a high, fairly closed tree canopy in wet areas, palmetto may assume an arboreal form and reach 13 feet in height. This growth form is also susceptible to being killed by fire. In mature upland hardwood forests, frequency of palmetto is reduced and reproduction is rare or absent. Persistence of the species in those situations has been suggested as due to age since disturbance. Palmetto fruit is important in the diet of deer and raccoons and is used commercially as a basis for a medication to reduce enlargement of the human prostate gland. Botanist William Baldwin, in 1843, proclaimed saw palmetto shoots (the growing bud) "more sweet and tender than" the heart of the cabbage palm, and gave Catherine Miller of Dungeness credit for his information (Darlington, 1969).

The many diverse niches in the maritime forest make it habitable for many animal species lacking special requirements for food or shelter. The most highly visible resident mammals include armadillos, squirrels, raccoons, and deer. Pileated woodpeckers and wild turkeys are birds commonly seen, and, in season, the forest is alive with nesting and migrating passerines (small song birds). Amphibians and reptiles are rarely obvious, but three lizards, the ground skink and two species of lined skinks, and one amphibian, the eastern spadefoot, are good candidates to be seen if conditions are right.

Pine

While live oaks are the most characteristic tree species of the maritime forest, on Cumberland, at this time, pines have gained disproportionate numbers and wide distribution. Only the longleaf is a dominant member of a natural fire-maintained community on the mainland in the Southeast. The other pines are all members or components of various communities and, depending upon circumstances, are more or less abundant.

The typical longleaf pine community supports several species, floral and faunal, that are intimately associated with it, and all are adapted to the rigors of fire. Such adaptations require time to develop and indicate a long association. Most of the species characteristic of the typical longleaf community, however, are absent from Cumberland Island. Longleaf pine itself is found on only a few Southern barrier islands. Whether this reflects soils, original distribution relative to suitable habitat, anthropogenic influences, or other inclement circumstances is not clear.

Five species of pine occur on Cumberland Island: slash pine, loblolly pine, longleaf pine, pond pine, and spruce pine. Some species have been aided and others hindered by human activities. For example, abandoned fields provide excellent habitat for loblolly reproduction, which, along with plantings and disruption of the natural fire regime, may have served to augment the amount of that species on Cumberland Island. A natural island fire regime facilitates the establishment and persistence of longleaf and pond pine, whereas manipulation of the fire regime may have the opposite effect on those species and favor others. Slash, spruce, and loblolly are not adapted to frequent fires. With no disturbance and with frequent fires, loblolly pine reproduction is slight, even though they grow rapidly and can tolerate a wide range of habitats. Loblolly is thought to have been a minor component in the mixed-hardwood forest prior to European modifications of the landscape. Slash pine is the species most often planted commercially. Although it may have more tolerance to the marine environment than the other species, it too is fast growing and relatively sensitive to fire, especially frequent fire. Spruce pine differs from the other species in being quite shade tolerant and highly sensitive to fire. Spruce pine is usually found scattered in mixed hardwoods and rarely in a pure stand. It is not common on Cumberland Island; only isolated individuals occur. Pond pine is quite compatible with and dependent on the natural island fire regime. Its cones do not open easily unless heated, and seedling survival is increased with the intensity of fire (Fowells, 1965). Pond pine is unique among island pines in its ability to sprout new growth following injury, especially from fire. It does well in poorly drained areas, such as the scrub, and is sparsely associated with most upland areas. Because of adaptations to fire, the trees are frequently stunted or misshapen and not of prime timber quality. In 1947, Stoddard said that the island pond pine had "no great value as saw timber due to its roughness and crook, though it is saleable either as saw timber or pulpwood."

One of the earliest descriptions of Cumberland Island, in 1736, reported the bluff at the north end "covered with tall pine trees" (Moore, 1983). A supporting account of Fort St. Andrews at Terrapin Point, written in 1742, described the eminence as having "a dense girdle of lofty and large pines" and a nearby "open pine grove" (Torres, 1977). In 1785, General Nathanael Greene noted there was some "good pine timber" toward the north end of the island, which could have easily included the Yankee Paradise area since Greene's perspective was from Dungeness (Torres, 1977). These early descriptions of Cumberland Island were probably of longleaf pine.

Longleaf pines require frequent fire or catastrophic events to open the canopy for continued reproduction, as they are shade intolerant. These long-lived, 450-plus years, pines are flexible in their soil and moisture requirements and highly adapted to fire. The growing bud of every young seedling is protected at ground level by a dense collar of evergreen needles, and growth in height is delayed for several years while a substantial taproot develops that serves for nutrient storage. The tree then shoots up several feet in one year, minimizing the time it is vulnerable to fire. Resinous needles encourage fire, and the seeds germinate best on mineral soil. The canopy in a mature longleaf pine stand is loose and open, a characteristic that facilitates fire.

Generally, fire control and feral livestock have hindered longleaf pine. Hog relish the bark of pine roots and have a significant impact on seedlings, and thus regeneration. The species of wiregrass that are the most notable components of the typical mainland longleaf community—*Aristida stricta* and *A. beyrichiana*—are absent from Cumberland and the other Georgia barrier islands, although other *Aristida* spp. occur (Sharpe, 1977). Indigo snakes are also absent from the Georgia barrier islands. The Cumberland Island pocket gopher would have been a member of the longleaf community as long as the community retained its integrity through natural ecological processes, such as fire. As the area changed from an inland sand ridge to a maritime forest, it became untenable habitat for many of the usual members of the community. Gopher tortoises (possibly introduced) and rattlesnakes occur on the island and are considered members of a typical longleaf community. Another is the elusive red-tailed skink. One species of woodpecker historically found on Cumberland Island, the red-cockaded woodpecker, is an important longleaf resident. It specializes in forging nest cavities in live pines afflicted with red-heart disease, caused by the fungus *Phellinus pini*. Since the red-heart fungus usually attacks older trees, the woodpeckers prefer stands of older timber. As older stands were exploited for lumber, woodpecker populations everywhere declined, and the red-cockaded woodpecker is presently on the endangered species list. If enough of the critical components are present when and if natural processes are allowed to regain control on Cumberland Island, we might expect a colony of red-cockaded woodpeckers to become established in longleaf stands. For other less mobile species, colonization may be too ambitious.

One invertebrate common under the bark of living island pines, an arachnid, is thought to have been described from a specimen from Cumberland Island. In 1821, Thomas Say described a new scorpion he found in his travels to the "sea islands" of Georgia, but the specimens were lost. Since Say spent the most time on Cumberland Island, it is thought that he collected the specimens here. Subsequently there was a taxonomic mix-up, and the name of Say's specimen was conveyed to a Texas specimen. R. M. Shelley with the North Carolina State Museum of Natural Science verified that Say's original description of *Centruroides hentzi* fits the present Cumberland Island specimens (Shelley and Sissom, 1995).

Older stands of pine also have snags, standing but dead trees, which provide habitat for many species. Some woodpeckers utilize dead pines for nest cavities as well as foraging areas, and bats, especially the *Lasiurus* species and evening bats, sometimes roost beneath loose bark. Reptiles, too, such as the scarlet kingsnake, seem to preferentially occupy pine snags, perhaps because lizards, one of their main food items, also favor them. Many insects, from reduviids (assassin bugs) to roaches, are regularly found in rotting pines.

In the late 1930s, an area of virgin longleaf pine on Cumberland Island that had escaped fire for at least seventy-five years had a dense understory of nearly 100% hardwoods and consequently no pine reproduction (Heyward,

1939). In 1947, an area of approximately 2,000 acres, possibly some of the same area observed by Heyward, "occupying the higher central portion of the island," was examined, and increment borings of the pines revealed ages that ran from 100 to 200 years (Stoddard, 1947). The area was probably the vicinity of Yankee Paradise.

We may never know the full extent of pine distribution on Cumberland Island prior to early agricultural pursuits, but insight into the distribution may be found in a 1954 letter to the Carnegies from Hercules Powder Company in Brunswick, Georgia. Resin-laden pine stumps were utilized as raw material by that company, and there was interest in the stumps on the island. The letter referred to Carnegie logging operations in 1939 and 1946, stating, "Some of the 15 year cut stumps have developed into ones suitable for our purposes; however they are rather sparse and located in pockets throughout the pine timber stands" (GDAH). The stumps of original-growth timber would contain the most resin, and the letter suggested that those trees were in small scattered stands and logged during World War II. Each time, following the "catastrophe" of logging, the Yankee Paradise area and others were apparently naturally replaced by pine forest, although there is a sprinkling of mature oaks and cabbage palms in the forest today. There was a lightning-ignited fire in the Yankee Paradise vicinity in 1986, but due to the National Park Service's policy of total suppression at the time, it was extinguished before it could be of much aid. Individuals and small groups of pines are scattered over the north end, and several old fields there have been colonized by longleaf pine.

Along with longleaf pine, two other species of pine were also logged on the island: loblolly and slash. Loblolly is a large, commercially valuable tree, but no sizeable stands were identified in 1947 (Stoddard, 1947). Slash pine is the only species besides longleaf that provides naval stores, but it is suscep-tible to fire damage. It was described in 1947 as being in "scattered patch-es...that in general occupy the wetter ground" (Stoddard, 1947).

By the 1950s, Carnegie heirs were again searching for a way to finan-cially exploit their Cumberland Island property to pay the bills and were probably influenced by a letter in 1953 from G. DeLoach, director of the Georgia Forestry Commission. Mr. DeLoach informed the Carnegie heirs that he had made increment borings of twenty-five to thirty trees, ranging in diameter from 14 to 24 inches, and that the majority of the pine timber was the same age. Mr. DeLoach determined the trees to have had a "slow growth rate in the last 40 to 50 years," and he estimated their age at over 100 years. He advised that the majority of timber was overmature and that "the only young growth noticed was in a very few small spots where the under-growth and hardwood had been removed. On the majority of the island," he continued, "it is almost impossible for sufficient sunlight to reach the seedlings due to the shade caused by oak and other hardwoods." His admonishment was familiar:

> The value of the island from the standpoint of forest productivity is decreasing each year. Unless some action is taken this situation will continue until the timber resources of the island will be valueless; in other words, to sum the situation up, the death rate will continue to be greater than the annual growth of the existing mature timber and with no young growth or reproduction to offset this loss, the timber volume that is in the existing trees will decrease due to death until no remaining pine timber will be left on the island. (GDAH)

The northernmost Carnegie property was logged at that time.

Records show the Carnegie estate procured 150,000 seedlings of slash pine and an equal number of loblolly in 1953, at least 50,000 slash pine seedlings in 1954, and at least 100,000 slash pine seedlings in 1955. On the latter date, they were being planted mostly in or near the logged-over timber, the old burned area near Plum Orchard, the burn near Whitney Lake, and Hickory Hill skeet field (GDAH). Many old fields have nearly pure stands of pine, but except for the recalcitrant, highly flammable scrub, few areas have experienced intense fire or catastrophic events to open a sizeable rent in the canopy and thus promote pine regeneration. Attempts at fire suppression of some areas have probably been the island policy for 200 years, perhaps since the mission era, and it will be some time before the effects of past human manipulation are neutralized by natural processes and the distribution of pine on Cumberland Island is again ecologically controlled. Presently, the pine species composition probably still reflects the introduction of the slash and loblolly seedlings, recovering old fields, and the ever-more-efficient drastic manipulation of natural fire.

Scrub

The open scrub is a fire-adapted community in various seral stages depending upon time since the last fire. This resilient community is found on the deep, poorly drained fine sands of Leon or Mandarin soils underlain by a layer or two of hardpan (humate). Pines are loosely scattered throughout, but there is no canopy (Fig. 17). In some areas, saw palmetto and shrubs are thick, while other areas are fairly open. The largest contiguous area of scrub covers the center of the north end of the island, with smaller communities scattered elsewhere. The areas occur on Pleistocene core sediments, the older portion of the island, and are fairly level.

J. B. Peeples (1911–1987), long-time island associate, woodsman, farmer, and knowledgeable Camden County resident, referred to this large area of tangled, thick vegetation on the north end of the island as the "badlands." Whether his descriptive term referred to the unwelcome fire-prone adaptations of the community, the difficulty of traversing it on foot, the uselessness of the land for farming, or some other reason is unknown, but those characteristics well distinguish the habitat. The designation "scrub" has been applied to several different habitats in the Southeast, and while they may not all contain the same species, the areas usually share the characteristics of low soil fertility and well-drained, xeric conditions. Descriptions of "flatwoods" (Laessle, 1942; Davis, 1943) may more closely mirror the community that is called scrub on Cumberland Island. Roland Harper (1914) suggested that the flatwoods on Amelia Island were "something like those of the mainland, but without longleaf pine." Much of the area is poorly drained, punctuated with shallow, temporary ponds, has impoverished soil, and is intimately associated with fire. Adaptations of the vegetation to these conditions include small stature, slow growth, evergreenness, heavily cutinized leaves, and the ability to sprout from rootstocks, often resulting in multistemmed trees. Of all the communities on the island, the scrub has probably suffered the least abuse by man.

Plants characteristic of the Cumberland Island scrub association are pond pine, slash pine, live oak, Chapman's oak, myrtle oak, staggerbush, fetterbush, saw palmetto, and inkberry. Species composition is dictated primarily by the frequency of fire and is sometimes used as the criterion for subdividing the classification into several groups, namely oak-palmetto forest, oak scrub, and open-pine scrub. The longer time a scrub community goes without fire, the less receptive it is to fire and the more its composition will be altered from communities that experience a natural fire regime. Stands of scrub representing at least three different fire regimes are found on the island and support very different habitats with different dominant species. Whether these differences would have occurred without human intervention is unknown, but the National Park Service aggressively suppressed fire from the 1970s to 2015. Designations of the three resulting stages of the scrub community are oak-palmetto, open-pine scrub, and oak scrub. The large, nearly homogeneous stand of oak-palmetto on the south end from Dungeness north to and beyond Greyfield is thought to have been scrub forest on moderately drained soils freed from fire for 75 to 100 years (Bozeman, 1975). On the 1802 map, much of this area is designated what is interpreted to be treeless "scrub." It may not be coincidental that this area has long endured neighboring human residences and activities and is also on the narrowest portion of the island, where fire might more easily be contained. With probable logging of scattered pines and the exclusion of fire, oaks became dominant with a dense palmetto understory, and species diversity was reduced. Once an oak canopy formed, reception to fire was greatly reduced and the "scrub" is now categorized as "oak-palmetto" forest (Bozeman, 1975). The palmetto understory is thick, and the humidity afforded by the oak canopy makes the area attractive to some amphibians and reptiles, such as tree frogs, toads, snakes, lizards, and many passerine birds.

Besides the several characteristics mentioned, the lack of a canopy also results in seasonal temperature extremes. The area is much hotter in the summer and much colder in the winter than adjacent canopied communities. Species diversity is greater in scrub areas with frequent fire and includes some species found nowhere else on the island, that is, small butterwort, Savannah milkweed, and deer's tongue. Animals that regularly use the open scrub include nesting ospreys, woodpeckers, ground doves, and roosting vultures, many of which use pine snags resulting from fires. Rabbits were common prior to the National Park Service release of thirty-two bobcats. Racerunner lizards are commonly seen along the roads and open areas during warm months, and snake tracks crisscross the road. Except for new growth following a fire, pine flatwoods of northern Florida are considered "suboptimal" habitat for deer due to the poor nutritional quality of forage (Kilgo and Labisky, 1995), but the scattered pond/grasslands within the scrub provide additional resources.

Many temporary ponds occur in the open scrub habitat on the north end and augment the complexity of the scrub community structure. A detailed discussion of the ponds themselves will be found under "Freshwater Communities," but here follows an explanation of the intimate role the ponds play in the ecology of the scrub. The elevation of the scrubland is roughly between 3.5 and 7.5 meters (12 to 25 feet), and the water level in the scattered ponds more or less reflects that of the groundwater table. Because the water table fluctuates so frequently, most of the ponds are only damp or dry much of the time and able to support a luxuriant growth of grasses, that is, bluestem, cordgrass, maidencane, and in wetter areas, sawgrass. Good stands of grass occur even around the edges of deeper ponds such as Whitney Lake. During drought conditions, grasses are the ultimate tinder for lightning fires, and most of the natural fires on the north end of Cumberland Island can trace their origin to the edge of a grass pond or slough. Likewise, fire-scarred snags border most all the ponds.

The last major fires recorded in the open scrub on the north end were in the summers of 1954, 1981, and 2008. The majority of fires on the island occur during summer lightning storms. While there may not seem to be any good time for fire, summer is the most natural time. Cool winter fires may alter regeneration patterns and have a negative impact on cold-blooded species hibernating or hiding under bark. Fires in spring and fall may affect nesting and migrating avian species. When there is a single point of ignition for a fire, the method of burning is an advancing line. High winds may carry sparks and burning debris ahead of the line and ignite other areas, which then begin advancing also. Such a situation has the potential to trap animals and may have accounted for some of the deaths associated with the 1981 fire, which was aided by winds gusting to 40 mph (Ruckdeschel and Jordan, 1982).

Presumably, mobile species that reside in the scrub either avoid lethal temperatures and smoke during a fire by retreating underground or out of the area, and are able to recolonize it following a burn. There is much competition for the remains of animals killed by fire. Carcasses disappear within a day, greatly limiting an assessment of mortality. Species that survive well within burned areas include skinks, six-lined racerunner lizards, alligators, and the eastern mole, all of which had to have endured the fire underground.

With the release of nutrients following a fire, saw palmetto and ericaceous shrubs, such as blueberries and huckleberries, bloom and fruit prodigiously, providing much food for wildlife. Tender new plant shoots attract browsers and grazers, and some species rarely found on the island become common, that is, the moss *Funaria hygrometrica* and the fungus *Pyronema* sp. The most dramatic recovery after the 1981 fire was demonstrated by a pawpaw, which grew over 60 centimeters (2 feet), flowered, and was heavy in fruit within two months following the fire (Ruckdeschel and Jordan, 1982).

Freshwater Communities

The biological aspects of water (as opposed to the hydrology addressed in the geology section) deserve separate attention here. Freshwater is at a premium on barrier islands and influences vegetation patterns and animal distributions. Periodic drought conditions when all but a few of the deepest areas, such as Whitney Lake, are dry emphasize the importance of the resource. All wetlands on the island are relatively shallow with constantly fluctuating water levels, which, directly or indirectly, reflect the groundwater table. Adaptations to fluctuating water levels or absence of surface water must be made by island biota and are critically tested. Reproductive cycles dependent upon water may have to skip years, and the potential for desiccation is great for many species. Fire frequency accompanies drought and presents more hazards. The oscillating, unreliable nature of available freshwater contributes greatly to the overall dynamic nature of island populations. Recycling of nutrients is facilitated by fluctuating water levels. As biota is killed by either rising or falling water, organic material accumulates and nutrients are released through decomposition.

The Cumberland Island freshwater resources have been divided into the following categories to simplify discussion: a) more or less lentic or still-water habitats, which include lakes, ponds, sloughs, interdune myrtle sloughs, and wet savannas, and b) more or less lotic or flowing-water systems, including hardwood swamp forests with associated streams and seeps. There is some ambiguity and considerable overlap among the categories. The different slough designations may reflect different stages in the development of those systems.

Sloughs

"Slough" is a word in common use in the South and designates a linear body of sluggish, shallow water. Other definitions range from "any minor drainage clogged with vegetation" (Clewel, 1985) to "a hollow full of soft, deep mud" (*Webster's New World Dictionary*, 1970). Inland island sloughs, interdune myrtle sloughs, and savannas all occur on Fripp-Duckston soils of Holocene origin. The Fripp-Duckston soil complex is characterized by rapid permeability and low available water capacity. Sloughs differ in distance from the ocean and thus influence of salt spray.

Wet Savanna

Savanna-like conditions occur on the Fripp-Duckston Holocene sands of the peninsula extending north from Whitney Lake, known locally as the Cedar Dock area. This is an early stage of the interdune Myrtle Slough community and ultimately the inland slough system. There are no united dune ridges to clearly delineate a slough, as there are further south, but the wet area does lie in an irregular band west of the active beach dune complex. Parallel dune ridges are forming in the expanded, fairly large interdune area. During wet periods there is much standing water up to knee deep, but the area is usually only damp or dry. In a survey of the island done in the 1970s (Hillestad et al., 1975), the wet-savanna area was designated "unstabilized dunes," a condition either caused and/or maintained by feral animals. This area was a favorite for large herds of cattle and has changed complexion greatly since their removal. The amount of herbaceous vegetation has increased significantly and all but a few random dunes have been stabilized.

The vegetation most indicative of the wet savanna is rushes. Much of the wet area was free of tall herbaceous species during its initial development. Wax myrtle is common, as is an occasional pioneering willow. This developing habitat is still in a transitional stage with willows increasing in abundance.

Standing water is much too temporary and infrequent to support a fish population, but this area is the haunt of the island glass lizard. While more widely distributed congeneric relatives may also be found in the wet-savanna community, this species is most frequently found in that habitat. Other species that commonly frequent the area are the little grass frog, the southern leopard frog, tree frogs, and mud turtles. Alligators in the area are usually small ones due to the limited protection offered by the ephemeral shallow water. Rabbits were abundant in the area two decades ago, and signs of raccoons and deer are always prevalent.

The wet savannas are adjoined by higher, drier ground that extends the savanna-like condition. Meadows of pink muhly grass and extensive areas of bluestem stretch between scattered pines and live oaks. This large amount of open area invites avian predators, which are common, many seasonally. Turkeys enjoy the sometimes-abundant crop of dew berries on the higher ground, and mourning doves are usually seen.

Interdune Myrtle Slough

Somewhat freed from restrictions imposed by being immediately adjacent to the ocean and salt spray, and with a more stable hydrologic regime, vegetation patterns in the interdune area change, with more species able to survive. Interdune areas may undergo several floristic changes as their distance from the ocean increases and as more species become established and stabilized, ultimately maturing to an inland slough. Slough systems in many seral stages may be found on Cumberland Island. The first woody colonizer in interdune areas slightly removed from the salt influence is wax myrtle, which forms dense, nearly monospecific stands due to its clonal form of reproduction (Fig. 18), relatively fast growth, and the allelopathic properties of the leaf litter. The litter suppresses growth of other species by the release of toxins. Because wax myrtle is a nitrogen-fixing species—it has a symbiotic association with the actinomycte (bacterium-fungi) *Frankia* sp., which produces an enzyme to fix nitrogen—it can outcompete other shrubs in the nitrogen-poor soils, and thus it forms a special island habitat. Studies show that the availability of nitrogen is greater in and around a myrtle thicket, which facilitates succession, although one contradictory study showed that leaching removed the nitrogen before it could be of use. This habitat, common to most of the Georgia barrier islands, is still subject to the influence of salt spray during severe weather, at which times large areas of myrtle may be killed. Following the nearly sovereign reign of myrtle, other species infiltrate and composition slowly diversifies. If the beach continues to accrete, separating the area even further from the sea, tree species, beginning with cabbage palm and sand live oak, appear at the fringe, and soon some of these areas mature into inland slough systems.

Harriers, merlins, and kestrels are common seasonally and hunt in the interdune myrtle community area, as do owls. Most large island mammals such as deer and armadillo are common inhabitants.

With the establishment of myrtle and the protective cover it affords, select amphibians and reptiles become more abundant and reproduce in the fish-free water of the interdunes. Eastern spadefoots are especially adapted to take advantage of such temporary water for reproduction, and their tadpoles are carnivorous, finding an abundant resource in mosquito larvae.

The dense band of wax myrtle in the interdune area from south of Dungeness to Stafford is a recent and particularly valuable reestablished resource to migrating birds such as tree swallows. Flocks of thousands of swallows feed on myrtle berries during their autumn (October and November) and spring (February into March) migrations. The wax, which coats the fruit of the plant, is composed of mono- and diglycerides and has a high melting point. Most animals cannot easily assimilate such lipids, yet yellow-rumped warblers and tree swallows are able to efficiently utilize those fatty acids. One swallow, a vehicle fatality on the beach, contained 67 myrtle berries in its gut—a weight load that may well have contributed to its demise. Until the feral cattle were removed from the island, the interdune myrtle habitat was so heavily browsed the shrubs never grew over one foot high, and development or succession of the system was stalled.

Inland Slough

Inland sloughs are farthest removed from the sea and have the additional protection of forest vegetation on intervening ridges. The main area on Cumberland Island referred to as inland sloughs ("Sweetwater Lake" on USGS topographic maps) occurs as swales between a series of broken relict dune ridges inland from and running parallel to the beach-dune complex, extending from Willow Pond north to Whitney Lake (Fig. 19). Another younger slough system lies east of the Duckhouse ridge, roughly between Stafford Shoals and Duckhouse. In general, and except for occasional alligator holes, the sloughs are shallow and frequently dry. Fluctuating water level and fire are two factors important in maintaining their character. The unpredictable and sometimes rapidly changing water level discourages many species. Coupled with occasional fire at times of drought, this slows or stalls the succession of vegetation and maintains areas of open water and herbaceous vegetation. As an example, people frequently canoed the sloughs from Duckhouse Road to Whitney Lake prior to the mid-1970s, but such a trip would be impractical, if not impossible, today due to the thick, brushy vegetation. The 1981 fire was extinguished before it went far south in the sloughs, which allowed shrubs, especially the swamp loosestrife, to proliferate. Swamp loosestrife or water willow is a colonial shrub that establishes tight colonies by rooting from the tips of branches as well as by seeds and is able to withstand considerable submergence and drought. Without drought coupled with fire, the anticipated succession of the sloughs would be from open water to submergent and emergent vegetation, and finally to shrubs and wooded swamp (Johnson et al., 1974). Some sections of the sloughs have stands of deciduous bottomland hardwoods.

Three smaller, pond-like sloughs occur on South Point. Only one is isolated enough to be protected from saltwater intrusion during spring tides. The other two receive varying amounts of saltwater and support a brackish water flora and fauna (Kozel, 1991).

Aquatic vegetation characteristic of the Cumberland Island slough community includes floating species, such as the fast-growing duckweeds, watermeal, and two other aquatic species that have special mechanisms to compensate for low nitrogen availability. The mosquito or water fern, tiniest of ferns, is so abundant at times that it blankets the surface of the water. Maturing plants turn a beautiful deep red color. Pores in the fronds contain the efficient nitrogen-fixing blue-green algae *Anabaena*, and the fern has been used for centuries in China and Vietnam as a natural fertilizer for rice paddies. When mature, a blanket of water fern is approximately two centimeters (<1 inch) thick and contains about 110 pounds of nitrogen per hectare (Brill, 1979). When the plants die and decompose, they release nitrogen into the system.

The bladderwort, also common in the sloughs, is a carnivorous plant that captures prey to fulfill its mineral requirements. The most obvious species on Cumberland Island is floating bladderwort, with its inflated "spokes" radiating out from a central hub, resembling a floating miniature wagon wheel. Attractive yellow flowers are borne on stalks arising from the hub and add a welcome touch of color to the ponds and sloughs beginning in February. Beneath the floating wheel hang stems upon which many bladder-like traps occur. A negative pressure develops inside these hollow structures with a trapdoor sealing them tight. When trigger hairs around the trapdoor are brushed by minute crustaceans, the door springs open (in), sucks in everything within its reach, closes, and the prey is digested. Some microscopic animals, such as rotifers, apparently live inside the bladders and may also contribute nutrients.

Spike rushes and peat moss are common along shallow edges, and most of the sloughs are shallow enough for emergent vegetation to cover the water. Pickerelweed, arrowheads, and water lilies are common. Several shrub species in the mallow family are abundant and provide a spectacular display when they bloom in late summer. The young shoots of these robust perennials are heavily browsed by vertebrates and the velvet leaves eaten by insects as well. The Carolina willow is a prominent colonizing and invading tree species on all intermittently wet areas. The easily broken twigs quickly take root in damp situations, forming discrete, tight, nearly monospecific groves of leaning trunks, branches, and matted roots. These tangles offer a protected habitat to several vertebrate species, primarily reptiles, especially during low water when there are few moist refuges available. Willows are sensitive to fire, which usually keeps them from choking the wetlands. Two other woody species common to the open sloughs are buttonbush and dahoon holly.

As wildlife habitat, the width, depth, acreage, and adjacent terrestrial communities contribute to make the inland slough community perhaps the most popular on the island. Most vertebrate species probably occupy the community. The sloughs support the most regularly used nesting area for colonial wading birds on Cumberland Island, which, from 1985 to 1998, included the endangered wood stork. Interestingly, only one area in the entire slough system has been used by colonial nesting wading birds for the past two decades, although many other avian species nest in association with the sloughs. Starting in 1885, the open sloughs were used extensively enough by ducks during migration to warrant construction of a comfortable overnight retreat for hunters, the Duckhouse. Deer regularly forage in the area, wading to feed on the floating and emergent aquatic vegetation and browsing and grazing the lush herbaceous vegetation during low water. The most visible vertebrates in the area are mosquitofish, tree frogs, the little grass frog, the southern leopard frog, alligators, yellow and red-bellied turtles, Florida softshell turtles, ribbon snakes, cottonmouths, green anoles, ducks in season, including nesting wood ducks, coots, common moorhens, all the wading birds, and otters. Common animals present but not usually seen include the giant salamander called "Congo eel," the beautiful mud snake, and two species of crayfishes.

Ponds

Ponds on Cumberland Island are more shallow than areas designated "lake," slightly more shallow than most of the sloughs, and differ further from the sloughs in their shape and hydrologic connection with other water systems (Fig. 14). The majority of ponds are isolated. Most are found on poorly drained Leon or Mandarin soils and have only indirect connections with each other and other surface-water systems. Size averages between less than .5 to 6 hectares (1 to 15 acres). Pines have been logged adjacent to some ponds and a few attempts at drainage have been made. Only one large pond appears to have been drained with productive results as farmland, Swamp Field pond. In 1802, it was an undeveloped sawgrass pond. The canal drainage system installed after that time still exists and modifies the hydrologic regime of the area and the recolonizing vegetation.

Beyond anthropogenic pursuits, fluctuating water level and fire are the two most important factors to the maintenance of temporary ponds. Most of the natural ponds on the island are temporary and thus wear two hats, that of pond and, alternately, when dry, grassland. The area of scrub on the north end of the island is dotted with temporary ponds ranging in depth from ankle-deep to almost waist-deep, and supporting zones of vegetation appropriate to the various water levels. The deepest areas are usually free of emergent vegetation, a condition enhanced by alligator activity, and in times of drought support ground cover such as spike rushes, knotweeds, and various species of seedbox.

Sawgrass is a frequent component of the high salt-marsh vegetation adjoining bluffs, which provide freshwater seeps, and is able to grow in either fresh or slightly brackish water. It is the common grass of the Everglades and, sometimes in association with chain fern, forms impenetrable colonies in a few of the freshwater ponds on Cumberland Island. Areas that support sawgrass are low relative to the water table and wet most of the time, which helps protect grass roots from fire. The crowded growth form of the tall, tough grass and root mat offers several vertebrate species significant protection from avian and mammalian predators. At times of low water, aquatic species in particular benefit from the refuge.

Regardless of water level, the most common island pond vegetation is grass, maidencane and bunch cordgrass, their separate niches determined by average water level. Areas a little drier than those supporting sawgrass support abundant stands of maidencane, which can adapt to water over 2 meters (6 feet; Godfrey and Wooten, 1979) and is much more abundant than sawgrass. Thick stands of maidencane are threaded with alligator runs, which are used as trails by many species during low water. Besides the alligator, no native island species significantly disturbs the sensitive roots of maidencane (Kushlan, 1972) although many feed on the young shoots. (See impact of feral animals.) Small feeding patches, where repeated grazing encourages new growth, are maintained by deer, and maidencane is also a food resource for rabbits, rodents, and invertebrates.

The next step up in elevation in the ponds supports sand or bunch cordgrass, the latter common name being much more appropriate as a descriptive term. The tough, long, narrow leaf blades fountain out of a central clump, which is so dense it cannot be walked through. Basal clumps are usually spaced and allow circumnavigation but will support the weight of an average person. The leaves often form a canopy excluding sunlight and understory species, but in times of low water, the area beneath that canopy shows much activity and is riddled with trails of all sizes from alligator to snake. Recently, fire ants have made use of the elevated basal clumps of cordgrass during rising water levels, precluding use by island vertebrates. Rabbits, snakes, and turtles have been observed using cordgrass "platforms" in the past.

The highest and driest areas of the ponds support various herbaceous species but are characterized by bluestem. Being the first areas to dry with a falling water level, both bunch cordgrass and bluestem are likely to burn in every fire covering the area but usually resprout quickly. The lack of understory beneath the cordgrass may help protect the basal clump from hot fire while the fountain of leaves above is quickly consumed. Vegetation in the bluestem zone is low, fairly sparse, and fire usually passes quickly.

Other aquatic plants common in the temporary ponds are duckweed, watermeal, lizard's tail, arrowhead, bladderwort, rushes and sedges, spike rushes, and peat moss. In season, with the edges of a pond damp or free of standing water, seedbox, marsh fleabane, and smartweed are common. Willows, buttonbush, wax myrtle, and persimmon tend to invade damp or dry ponds in some areas. Without major fluctuations of the water level to facilitate periodic fire, the composition of the ponds slowly changes to hardwood swamp. There are several isolated ponds with stands of gum trees and a few, such as Oyster Pond, with nearly pure stands of red maple.

If the ponds have water through the winter and spring, they bustle with activity from February through April. The water teems with invertebrates such as clam shrimp (Order Conchostraca) and fairy shrimp (Order Anostraca). Crayfish are abundant with *Procambarus paeninsulanus* occupying the wetter sites and *P. talpoides* the drier ones and out into the surrounding scrub. Mosquitofish that have been secretive all winter become visible and prolific. The only other species of fish documented in ponds not influenced by saltwater is the American eel. Following several years of drought, it may take fish populations many months to recover enough to repopulate an entire pond. During this time, mosquitoes proliferate. Mole salamanders use select ponds for breeding, and by spring their larva and those of newts and anurans (frogs and toads) contribute to enlarging vertebrate populations in the ponds. Few of the natural ponds support full-time turtle populations, but occasional individuals of the chicken turtle and the eastern mud turtle might be expected. Snakes are scarce and rarely seen around or in the water, but likely ones to be seen are the ribbon snake and the banded water snake. Green anoles are common on vegetation surrounding the ponds, especially saw palmetto, and alligators become active with warmer temperatures. Alligators are one of the most regular components of the pond fauna and maintain vegetation-free areas and dens or holes that hold water long after a pond has dried. One adult alligator per moderate-sized pond seems to be the rule on Cumberland Island, but young animals up to three years old may accompany their mothers, and males visit the females in season.

All the wading bird species in the area use the ponds at some time, and kingfishers are common. Red-winged blackbirds nest in surrounding tall grasses and shrubs as well as in many other places on the island. Mammals that obviously use the pond resources are deer, raccoons, and, during the cold months, otters and mink. The grass habitat provided at times of low water is heavily used by rabbits and rodents. All species, floral and faunal, reliant upon the pond community suffer disaster from feral swine on Cumberland Island, especially during times of drought, at which time the pond bottoms are completely uprooted. Feral horses, grazers with little grass from which to choose on the island, wade the ponds to crop maidencane when it appears, and, in the process, greatly disturb the substrate.

Whitney Lake

Island lakes, ponds, and sloughs share similar biota and water regimes. Only two areas are designated "lake" on Cumberland Island, Whitney Lake and Retta Lake. Both are integral parts of the Holocene slough system, with greater depth and expanse of open water than adjoining areas. The sloughs of which they are a part parallel the beach inland on the east side of the island. Whitney Lake is the largest natural body of open freshwater on any of the Georgia barrier islands (Fig. 20) and was historically much larger than it is today. Grazing by feral animals, especially cattle, prevented vegetation from stabilizing the dunes to the east of the lake. Wind-blown sand was constantly deposited at the edge of the water, shrinking the lake and leaving a flat, plain-like, sparsely vegetated meadow east of it. With the removal of the cattle, pressure on vegetation was relieved and it slowly got ahead of the blowing sand. Wax myrtle quickly became established along the eastern edge of the open water and effectively blocked the wind-blown sand. The fringe of myrtle also changed the limnology of the lake by protecting the open water from strong wind. Wind moves water, and in a relatively shallow area can cause mixing of the various thermal layers. Earlier, Stoneburner and Smock (1979) observed that there was no thermal stratification, which has returned today. Although drying allows oxidation and probably some reduction of organic matter (Odum and Harvey, 1988), the ultimate stability of the lake depends upon the frequency and intensity of fire to remove accumulated organic material and halt the encroachment of shrubs and trees.

The open water of Whitney Lake in the 1970s was about 1.2 to 1.5 meters (4 to 5 feet) deep, and the deepest area, which was on the east side, was 3.7 to 4.6 meters (12 to 15 feet) deep. From there, the bottom sloped up to a shallow, marshy border on the west. Mats of floating vegetation consisting of frog's-bit, alligatorweed, bladderwort, and waterspider orchid cover large areas of open water. They are sensitive to low temperatures and killed by hard freezes, after which they sink. With no hard freeze, the extensive mats continue to enlarge annually and are pushed around by the wind. Bordering open water, emergent vegetation reflects the average water depth with cordgrass on the drier sites and sawgrass and rushes in wetter areas. Surrounding palmetto indicates the average high water line. American lotus was common around the margin of the lake during the 1970s and 1980s but has become less abundant. The fruit of the lotus is delicious, as well as the fleshy rhizomes, and actively foraged by feral hogs. Water lilies are common.

Some species of fish found in the lake were introduced for sport fishing, as they were in Lake Retta in 1907. Largemouth bass and "bream" (sunfish) were introduced at that time. Hillestad et al. (1975) found bluegills, warmouth, bass, yellow bullheads, and mosquito fish in Whitney Lake in 1974. All but the yellow bullhead have been recently documented, and it may have disappeared. The presence of this species on Sapelo has been suggested as an introduction (Dahlberg and Scott, 1971). Whitney Lake has been a popular fishing spot for over a century and recurring introductions would not be surprising. Inadvertent introductions associated with freshwater fishing activities have also occurred. Fishermen using "spring lizards" (salamanders) for bait, purchased on the mainland, have released the animals on Cumberland Island at the end of a fishing trip. It is unlikely that these animals could find the proper habitat in which to survive but may account for unusual records.

Amphibians and reptiles are the most populous vertebrates in and around the lake. Alligators are the most visible and sometimes, in the spring, also audible. Another common summer call is the wonderful, explosive, double bass grunt of the pig frog, seldom repeated more than a couple times in quick succession, and an excellent representation of its namesake. In season, and more often nocturnally, choruses of green tree frogs, leopard frogs, and southeren cricket frogs may be heard. Amphibians stick to the shallow margins of the lake and the floating mats of vegetation, while the heads of turtles, such as the yellow-bellied slider, Florida red-bellied cooter, and the Florida softshell, may be seen in deeper water. Wading birds fish along the shallow edges, and migratory flocks of tree swallows take advantage of the open water to drink. Green herons and red-winged blackbirds nest in appropriate adjacent areas, and black vultures sometimes roost in dead trees south of the open water. Gallinules are common summer inhabitants, and for over a century migrating ducks have been hunted on and around the lake during autumn and winter. Otters are common residents during the winter but forsake the lake for areas more alligator-free during warm months.

Feral livestock continue to have a great impact on the lake. In the past, cattle and horses reduced the size of the open water by facilitating sand movement, and pressure on stabilizing vegetation from horses persists. Feral swine root the periphery in search of food and thereby keep vegetation churned. Feral horses wade out, sometimes belly or shoulder deep in the lake, grazing on floating and emergent vegetation to supplement their inadequate island diet.

Hardwood Swamp

The hardwood swamp forest is the only community on the island where deciduous trees predominate (Fig. 21). Gums and red maple are the two most common species, with water ash and the evergreens loblolly bay, sweet bay, and red bay usually present. If the canopy is tight enough and the standing water frequent and deep enough, there is little understory. In shallow areas or at the headwaters of a swamp, a tight, barely penetrable understory of tall fetterbush, augmented by staggerbush and wax myrtle, is common on slightly higher terrain. The whole is often tightly surrounded by thick palmetto, making access difficult at a point other than the low end of the associated stream. The water level fluctuates as in other systems, and streams are sometimes dry. Lizard's tail frequently borders the streams where they are shallow and there is enough sunlight, and an occasional stand of switchcane may also be found. The sizes of the stands of hardwood swamp vary but some are fairly large and somewhat protected from fire by moisture, species composition, and amount of understory. In only a few circumstances is there a noticeable gradient in the topography or relief of the main body of an island swamp. Drainage is slow and there are no well-defined channels until the main stream is reached. Nearly all streams ultimately drain directly into salt marsh, and all but three flow to the western edge of the island. Three short streams with thinly wooded swamps drain to the northeast into the Christmas Creek salt marsh. The streams usually have clean, hard sand bottoms where there is noticeable flow.

As the gradient decreases upstream, the flow ceases to be obvious, organic material accumulates, and bottom sediments are soft.

The high borders of some swamps were included in fields where drainage was practical, but most of the wooded swamps were avoided in agricultural pursuits and now support some large trees. One enormous sweetbay discovered by R. Murlless measured 582 centimeters (19 feet 1 inch) in circumference at breast height in 1992, and was registered a national champion tree in 2004.

Water steeped in a swamp is dark with tannic acid and the only fish in appreciable numbers are mosquitofish. Closer to the edge of the island and the influence of the marine environment, fish species composition may be augmented by the sailfin molly, mummichog, or the sheephead minnow. Description of the brackish water habitat is under "Salt Marsh."

Cricket frogs and tree frogs are in their element with the shallow water of the wooded swamps, and reptiles frequently seen include cottonmouths, mud turtles, and, of course, the alligator. Alligators often take advantage of stream banks in which to construct dens. The open, usually shallow water of the interior of the swamps is advertised to birds in winter through loss of the canopy and is used by migrating birds, including ducks.

Otters make use of stream banks for dens also, often tunneling between tree roots that limit the entrance size and add strength to the accommodations. Raccoon tracks are common along streams, and, in times of low water, armadillos are common both along streams and in the swamps as well. The thick, brushy vegetation of headwaters usually has deer trails and offers a good refuge for large animals. A beaver once constructed a den in a wooded swamp on the island, but it was short-lived, probably due to alligator intervention.

One usual component of wooded freshwater wetlands in south Georgia is noticeably absent from Cumberland Island: cypress trees. Fewer than half a dozen individuals are widely distributed around the island. Cypress is reported to have been abundant during the Pleistocene Epoch (Berry, 1916) and presumably would have occupied appropriate habitat on and around what was to become Cumberland Island. Viable seeds continue to arrive at the island as flotsam (S. Hendricks, pers. comm.), so why is that species not a component of the island wetland forests today? A comprehensive list of Georgia barrier island plants (Sharpe, 1977) shows cypress occurs only on Cumberland and Sapelo islands. Drainage of the swamps on Sapelo has been given as the reason for the low number of trees found there (Teal and Teal, 1964). Cypress is valued for its rot-resistant lumber, and large island stands would have been relatively easily accessible and may have been logged. Persistent stumps should be evident if that were the case but none have been found. Regeneration of cypress requires a dry site, although seeds may remain in water as long as 30 months and still germinate. Seedlings are sensitive to submergence and even plants as tall as 30 centimeters may be killed by too much standing water. The fluctuating hydroperiods on Cumberland Island would seem to suit the species, but perhaps the limited size of the wetlands and the water regime combine to render it too vulnerable to fire. Mature cypress trees resist fire as long as the soil remains wet and the roots are protected. The high incidence of fire and few areas with continuously saturated soil would naturally restrict cypress stands on Cumberland Island but can hardly account for the scarceness of the species. Cypress seeds are resinous, which deters birds and rodents from eating them, but rabbits and deer are known to eat seedlings. Seedlings will resprout, so only during years of high herbivore populations might grazers hinder regeneration. The impact of feral animals on regeneration has likely been severe. Pressure from native herbivore populations augmented by herds of feral cattle, feral horses, and feral swine may have prevented regeneration. Feral swine would uproot and consume seedlings and have been incriminated in studies elsewhere as a major deterrent to cypress regeneration (Wood and Roark, 1980). Since cypress trees are long-lived, with virgin timber estimated at 800 to 900 years old (Williston and Shropshire, 1980), possibly they could become more numerous when feral livestock are removed.

Seep

Rainfall recharging the island groundwater is confined and supported by the surrounding heavier saltwater-saturated sands. In a generalized cross section of the island, groundwater tends to follow the contour of the high ground, forming a lens or band within the porous sand. This places much of the freshwater well above sea level and allows freshwater seeps at the edge of the island, especially where relief is steep. Underlying layers of humate may influence groundwater flow. Rarely does water flow from the seeps in more than a trickle, but it is fairly reliable and is the last widespread source of freshwater during times of drought (Fig. 22). It provides for a distinct community at the periphery of the high salt marsh. Occasional spring and storm tides may inundate the area but the freshwater provided by seeps is of significant value to wildlife since it is so widely, albeit irregularly, distributed. Presence of a seep is usually advertised by rushes and perhaps sawgrass at the high edge of the salt marsh. Brackish water plants include waterhysop, arrowgrass, and grasswort. During wet years, leopard frogs are common around seep areas, and alligators frequently modify them and construct dens in the adjacent banks. If there is enough freshwater for the hatchlings, alligators may nest in this habitat.

Salt Marsh

Barrier islands along the Georgia coast are not separated from the mainland by saltwater alone, but by saltwater and grasses in an intimate association with marine sediments that form the basis for the extensive salt-marsh ecosystem. Tidal creeks weave their way through soft, velvet mud, cutting channels that drain adjacent areas at low tide (Fig. 23), but it is the salt marsh ecosystem as a whole that truly isolates the barrier islands from the mainland. There is one point, known as the dividings, behind (west of) every Georgia barrier island where the incoming tides meet. As the water slows, suspended sediments drop, so the site is continually acquiring silt. The size and stability of these areas may have an influence on the species composition of the mobile island fauna.

The appearance of the salt marsh is deceptive. From a distance it looks impeccably neat and clean and level as a wheat field, while in reality the surface is channeled and potholed and covered with a sometimes deep layer of tenacious clay loam (pluff mud), underlain by clays of various colors and covered with a stand of cordgrass of varying height but all reaching a uniform height. At ebb tide in low wind conditions, the marsh has a distinctive odor, a mixture of gasses produced by anaerobic decay of dead organic material near the surface. Chemicals dissolved in saltwater and exposed on the drying surfaces of plants and muck add to the fragrance. In 1775, Bernard Romans (1961) described the smell as "a most horrid, and to me a suffocating stench," but he went on to say that he had never heard anything contrary to the prevailing opinion of great salubrity in dwelling near the sea "even among the thickest of these marshes." Although difficult to describe, anyone who has pushed a boat or stick into the rich marsh mud will recognize the strong, sulfurous odors released.

Gently sloping terrain and tides twice daily provide an ideal setting for the vast salt-marsh community of Georgia. Saltwater tolerance is a prerequisite for plants living in the soft, shifting mud, and the degree of their tolerance results in distinctive vegetation zones based upon elevation and thus proximity to saltwater. The majority of low marsh that is at least partially inundated twice daily supports a monospecific stand of smooth cordgrass, which has different growth forms depending upon its location in the marsh. The grass grows tall beside tidal creeks so that the tops of those plants are equal in height or slightly above the shorter version growing on adjacent higher ground. The resulting stand is of such a uniform height that people unfamiliar with the area and the salt marsh community have questioned whether it was mowed. Poet Sidney Lanier described the beautiful marsh at Brunswick as "A league and a league of marsh-grass, waist-high, broad in blade, / Green and all of a height, and unflecked with a light or a shade, / stretch leisurely off, in a pleasant plain, / To the terminal blue of the main" (Ginn, 1987).

Plants and animals must maintain specified concentrations of salts within their bodies (osmoregulation), and their external environment influences the method of maintenance. Saltwater is lethal to plants adapted only to terrestrial or freshwater life. To be a dominant species over such a large area and inimitable ecosystem indicates a distinct competitive advantage. Smooth cordgrass has evolved many special adaptations which allow it sole occupancy of this dynamic environment. The roots of the grass effectively reduce the amount of salt taken in, and glands in leaves excrete excess salt to maintain essential water balance. It has overcome the problem of having its rhizomes and roots in an anaerobic environment by having the stems transport oxygen to the roots, and is able to function with the rhythm of the tides. Smooth cordgrass is perennial with an extremely well-developed root system that stabilizes loose sediments and is able to utilize iron sulfides available in the mud to meet its high iron requirement. Flower stalks are sent up in September and October, after which the upper part of the plant begins to die. New growth develops during the usually mild Georgia winter but is obscured until spring by the tall dead grass of the previous season. High tides during the spring and autumn remove the dead grass stalks and make way for new growth. Shocks of dead grass stalks form giant mats which float out the rivers on high tides to be deposited on the ocean beach. These trap sand and form the basis of new or expanded sand dunes and help stabilize the beleaguered winter beach.

The clearly defined bands of vegetation adjacent to the monospecific cordgrass marsh may be characterized as first a) high marsh, including salt flats or pans; next b) shrub border thicket; and, occasionally, c) shell mounds. The ground of the high marsh is firm and inundated only with spring (new or full moon) or storm tides and is sparsely vegetated. Salts accumulate through evaporation, restricting vegetation to those species adapted to a hypersaline environment. Glasswort and saltwort are two common components, along with very short cordgrass and sea lavender. Fiddler crabs are common here.

The shrub border thicket may be head high and is composed mainly of marsh elder and groundsel, with sea ox-eye and knee- to over waist-high needle rush as an outside border. Rarely is this band of vegetation very wide on Cumberland Island, and it is sometimes no more than one shrub deep.

Shell mounds may be natural accumulations of oyster shell or be of Native American origin, and they sometimes occur out in the high marsh (rising sea level), along the border shrub thicket, or as calcareous hammocks adjacent to the border thicket under the forest canopy. Several fairly rare plant species are found only on these mounds due to the calcium available from decaying shells. Calciphytes or calcium-loving plant species found on Cumberland Island include Florida privet, buckthorn, soapberry, and Christmasberry.

Some authors include the distinctive freshwater habitat that borders parts of the western side of the island in with a description of the salt marsh because of its proximity, but here seeps are included with freshwater communities. It is, however, a fairly constant, if irregularly occurring, feature in the marsh-to-upland sequence.

Familiar insects of particular interest that breed in the salt marsh include some midges, sand gnats or no-see-ums (*Culicoides* spp.), deer (*Chrysops* spp.) and horse flies (*Tabanus* spp.), and mosquitoes, especially *Aedes sollicitans*, the salt marsh mosquito. Females of these groups require a blood meal for reproduction and are known carriers of several, some possibly introduced, disease organisms. Tiny, annoying sand gnats of three species have been found to harbor encephalitis viruses in Georgia, and elsewhere malaria parasites, and also to be intermediate hosts of filarial worms. Deer and horse flies may transmit anthrax and trypanosomes, causing livestock diseases, and the salt marsh mosquito carries the filarial worm producing "heartworms" in dogs. Neither malaria parasites nor the yellow fever or encephalitis viruses have yet been associated with this species of mosquito, which is one reason the early planters considered the Georgia coast, with its mainly offshore breezes, to be a healthy retreat. Larvae of sand gnats and deer and horse flies mature in the mud of the low marsh, while mosquito eggs are laid on the damp mud of the high marsh and have the ability to withstand lengthy drought and avoid desiccation. When heavy rains or spring tides leave temporary pools, the eggs hatch and larvae flourish. Hoof imprints left by feral horses provide fine mosquito nurseries.

Some familiar mollusks are characteristic of the low salt marsh, such as oysters and clams, and some prefer the higher marsh: periwinkles (*Littorina irrorata* Say) and ribbed mussels (*Geukensia demissa* Dillwyn). The rosy glandina (*Euglandina rosea* Férussac) is a terrestrial mollusk-eating snail and is a common denizen of the highest shrub border thicket, probably avoiding spring tides.

The alligator is the reptile most likely to be seen in brackish water, with diamond-backed terrapins second. Small, green, Kemp's ridley and loggerhead sea turtles may frequent the larger tidal creeks, and mud turtles occasionally venture out freshwater creeks into brackish water in the high marsh. No snakes or lizards are commonly associated with the salt marsh in Georgia, nor are any amphibians, but the Southern leopard frog may reside in freshwater habitats adjacent to the high marsh and utilize it on occasion. No doubt, alligators used to be much more numerous in this habitat than they are today, despite the fact that they must move to freshwater frequently to avoid dehydration. In the open salt marsh they are easily visible and accessible by boat and thereby easily killed, a fact that has probably contributed to their present low numbers in this habitat. Alligator population density in the salt marsh environment may have been an important factor in the nesting success and thus status (population numbers) of the diamondback-terrapin. Were the sandy shores adjacent to tidal creeks covered with basking alligators, as they were a couple of centuries ago, raccoons and other egg-eating vertebrates would not depredate terrapin eggs with the impunity they do today. Diamondback-terrapin numbers never recovered from the impact of the culinary trade, and coupled with loss of habitat and mortality sustained in commercial crab traps, Georgia terrapin numbers remain low.

Relatively few vertebrates make the salt marsh their permanent home. Anyone who has spent time around a marsh has heard the taunting "laugh" of one of them, the clapper rail. By spending most all their time in the salt marsh, clapper rails avoid much human contact and maintain low visibility. The saying "thin as a rail" refers to the way these medium-sized birds skillfully maneuver through the tight vertical stems of the cordgrass. Rails are common to abundant where the habitat is not degraded, and there is a legal hunting season for them. Hundreds have been shot in a season in the Christmas Creek marsh alone. Other avian species commonly found in the salt marsh are the long-billed marsh wren, red-winged blackbird, sparrows, grackles, egrets, herons, ibis, and wood storks. Seasonally, marsh hawks may be seen gliding and circling over the grass in search of prey.

Native herbivorous mammals that graze smooth cordgrass on the island include white-tailed deer, marsh oryzomys, and, in the water, manatees, but feral horses far overshadow any impact the native species have on the high-marsh ecosystem. Green sea turtles and manatees may compete for the limited food resources in the marshes around Cumberland, but at this time it is unlikely that the impact of either is great. Most native grazers of the marsh grass are invertebrates.

Invertebrates and fishes of the salt marsh attract raccoons, otters, and minks, and, of course, the ubiquitous feral hog. Raccoons and otters prudently change their feeding habits in summer and winter and are frequently seen in the high salt marsh during the warmer months. During the winter, when alligator activity is reduced, these small omnivore-carnivores may return to the inland freshwater ponds and sloughs and again hunt with impunity. Crabs, especially fiddler crabs, provide a fairly reliable food supply in the salt marsh, while turtle and bird eggs are seasonal. Ribbed mussels are eaten also, especially by feral hogs. These thin-shelled marine bivalves cluster in the intermediate to high salt marsh with the upper quarter of their shells exposed, and they are easily collected. Hogs swim the tidal creeks at an intermediate tide, or one that will allow them access to the opposite bank above the fringe of sharp oyster shells, and forage all the marsh that will support their weight, being sure to return before the tide drops and again exposes the oyster banks. The impact of feral horses on the salt marsh ecosystem is enormous. The state has a Marshland Protection Act ostensibly to protect that important environment from human abuse for all Georgia citizens. Its enforcement has been criticized on many issues, and it has been rendered impotent on Cumberland Island with regard to charismatic livestock. Island shellfish beds are sometimes closed to public harvest because of pollution from livestock, but no one will take responsibility for allowing the impact to continue.

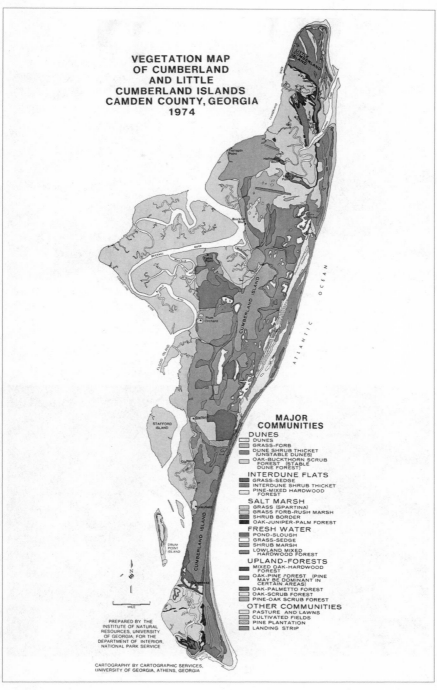

Figure 11

Vegetation map.

(National Park Service)

Figure 12

Beach dunes.

Figure 13

Amber snail.

(M. Minno)

Figure 14
Temporary pond in scrub.

Figure 15
Maritime forest on Cumberland Island.

Figure 16

Terminal twigs killed by sand and salt.

Figure 17

Scrub habitat, Cumberland Island.

Figure 18
Parallel dunes and sloughs of Holocene origin.

Figure 19
Whitney Lake, on Cumberland Island, 1997.

Figure 20
Linear wax myrtle thicket.

Figure 21
Hardwood swamp, Cumberland Island.

Figure 22
Seep, Cumberland Island.

Figure 23
Salt marsh tidal creek..

4

Species Accounts

Introduction

Bearing in mind the geologic events that created Cumberland Island, its size, and distance from the mainland, a species reduction from that on the mainland is to be expected. The smaller an island, the less diverse habitats it has to offer, and, consequently, the fewer species it can support. Sea-level rise, which isolated Cumberland from the mainland, proceeded over a long period and thus provided warning of a gradually changing environment. Rather than total extinction of species which found the changing habitat hostile, there was probably a slow westward emigration of those species following their preferred habitats, and a time for resident species to begin adjusting to the new conditions. After complete isolation of the island, chances for colonization were greatly reduced, if not eliminated, for smaller species. At that time, extinction, perhaps facilitated by catastrophic events or the extremes of harsh environmental conditions on the island, is likely to have been the main change to the resident species composition. Large mobile animals, which used the island seasonally or part-time, could continue doing so by swimming or perhaps crossing over at low tide. Vertebrate colonization has continued both on the island and the mainland with the armadillo, beaver, and coyote.

Factors that affect species composition on the island begin with available habitat. Can the basic requirements of a species be met by existing conditions? How much latitude is there in a particular species' ecological tolerance? For example, if a freshwater species cannot tolerate even moderate drought conditions, where it may have to endure strange bedfellows for some time until water returns, it may not make it. If, on the other hand, it has adaptations to aestivate during dry, hot times and can rebound from low population numbers caused by the harsh island conditions, survival is likely. Whether a species is short- or long-lived is also a factor. Short-lived species may not be able to withstand the vagaries of environmental conditions for long enough to survive. Cumberland Island is large enough to have a variety of habitats, which tends to ameliorate extreme situations by offering options and so reduce the potential for extinctions. Competition is another factor that affects species composition everywhere, but especially on islands. Competition is so great from exotic feral livestock (horses and hogs) on Cumberland Island that other competitive relationships pale or are obscured. Livestock compete for food and drastically modify the habitat, creating a stressed ecosystem for all native island species.

The most important single factor facing most island vertebrates is the availability of freshwater. The larger the island, the more available water is, but climatic extremes, which influence water availability, punctuate normal rhythms in an unstable, cyclic way. An example is the predicted twenty- to thirty-year fire cycle of the scrub community on the north end of the island. During catastrophic climatic events, such as hurricanes, the elevation of the island, becomes as important as the diversity/complexity of habitats, as all can quickly change with rising water.

Distribution of vertebrates on the Georgia barrier islands may be influenced by several factors. The geologic age of the islands varies and, consequently, so does the vegetation and available habitats. Islands with upland Pleistocene components may have supported vertebrates through the period of rising sea level and ultimate isolation, whereas those islands of Holocene origin were presumably colonized after the uplands developed.

Several of the islands have bridges to the mainland—Tybee, St. Simons, and Jekyll islands in Georgia, and Amelia Island, Florida—and are developed. Bridges allow access by mobile vertebrates, such as opossums, and also facilitate transport of smaller, less mobile ones, such as lizards, frogs, and snakes, especially in association with landscaping activities.

This Presentation

Specific Cumberland Island data should be clearly identified in this book. Island information is taken from field notes from the 1960s into 2014. Diet information is based on stomach and/or fecal contents of island animals. Parasites sometimes offer insight into vertebrate distributions, and they are an equally legitimate component of the island fauna. The majority of data reported is from opportunistically collected dead or dying animals. Roadkills and the beach provide productive places to find such animals. Animals found stranded on the beach are sometimes designated DOB, dead on the beach. Those found as roadkills may be DOR.

Many people associated with Cumberland Island were interviewed for historical information. They are identified in the references.

Fish

Only four species of fish recorded on Cumberland Island are considered strictly freshwater species, they are all game species, and all may have been introduced. Nine species have been recorded that may be associated with the sea or brackish water in some way, and all have broad ecological tolerances.

Nomenclature follows "American Fisheries Society Special Publication Number 12, 1980, A List of Common and Scientific Names of Fishes from the United States and Canada."

Species Accounts

ORDER SILURIFORMES. Family Ictaluridae. **Yellow Bullhead**. *Ictalurus natalis* (LeSueur, 1819). A typical freshwater catfish, this species is locally common in the St. Marys and Suwanee rivers. The two Cumberland Island localities reported are Whitney Lake and Swamp Field drain (Hillestad et al., 1975), but the water at that drain is now mostly brackish and an unlikely place for a freshwater fish.

ORDER ANGUILLIFORMES. Family Anguillidae. **American Eel**. *Anguilla rostrata* (LeSueur, 1817). The American eel seen around Cumberland Island is greenish brown on the dorsal surface and light yellowish to white below. It has a typical snake-like shape but with an uninterrupted dorsal fin that continues around the animal and serves as a tail and anal fin as well. It also has pectoral fins but lacks pelvic fins. Females are typically 300 to 914 millimeters (12 to 36 inches) in length, while males are smaller, usually less than 508 millimeters (20 inches). The average size on and around Cumberland Island is 432 millimeters total length (17 inches), range 200 to >600 millimeters. Small animals have been found in March and April.

On Cumberland Island American eels have been found at the outlets on the ocean and western side of the island, dead on the beach, and in freshwater ponds. Live animals, including invertebrates, fishes, amphibians, and even carrion are eaten. One island animal had consumed a mosquitofish.

ORDER CYPRINODONTIFORMES. Family Cyprinodontidae. **Sheeps-head Minnow**. *Cyprinodon variegatus* (Lacepède, 1803). A stocky-bodied topminnow to 75 millimeters (3 inches) in length, the sheepshead has irregular vertical bands on the lower sides. Females have a dark spot near the rear of the dorsal fin, while males have a dark border along the tip of the tail. Males are colorful during breeding, adding blue and orange to their usually rather dull color scheme.

This species has a broad ecological tolerance and can survive in a wide temperature range.

Along the Georgia coast it prefers areas of high salt marsh and low salinity water. On Cumberland Island specific localities include the south end ponds, the Big Slough beach outlet, Red Bridge Creek, and seeps along the western edge of the island.

_____. Family Cyprinodontidae. **Marsh Killifish**. *Fundulus confluentus* Goode and Bean, 1879. The marsh killifish is a small, to 75 millimeters (3 inches), brownish-yellow, brackish water species, in which the male and female have different side patterns. The male has many narrow white vertical bars running the length of the body. The female has narrow black vertical bars and a black spot in the dorsal fin. On Cumberland Island, these killifish have been reported from Red Bridge Creek and Swamp Field drain. Low salinity creeks and pools are their preference, but they can also use freshwater.

_____. Family Cyprinodontidae. **Mummichog**. *Fundulus heteroclitus* (Linnaeus, 1766). Mummichogs are a little larger than some of the other island cyprinodonts and may reach 125 millimeters (five inches) in length, with alternating silver and dark vertical bars on the sides. They can survive a wide range of ecological conditions, including salinity and temperature extremes, spend limited time in freshwater, and spawn in the intertidal zone.

Mummichogs prefer high salt marsh habitat. Specific Cumberland Island localities include Brickhill Creek, Red Bridge Creek, and other creeks that drain on the west side of the island. Blue crabs, *Callinectes sapidus*, are probably major predators, but on Cumberland Island they have also been fed to nestling wood storks and great egrets, indicating pressure from wading birds.

_____. Family Poeciliidae. **Mosquitofish**. *Gambusia affinis* (Baird and Girard, 1853). This small, hardy fish, rarely over four centimeters (1.5 inches) total length, is the most common fish on Cumberland Island. It is typically grayish or dark above, with a white belly with a transparent spot through which the black peritoneum of the body cavity is often visible. Females are usually larger than males.

It is viviparous (bears living young) and adaptable to a wide range of environmental conditions. Activity is visible on Cumberland Island in all months, but during cool weather, at a water temperature of 64.4 °F at about five inches depth, they disappear from sight. Food consists of aquatic insects, small crustaceans, and some plant material. They, in turn, reluctantly feed many island vertebrates.

_____. Family Poeciliidae. **Sailfin Molly**. *Poecilia latipinna* (LeSueur, 1821). The sailfin molly is a small fish that may reach 125 millimeters (5 inches) in length, and the male has an exceptionally high and long dorsal fin, the basis for the common name. The female is not colorful, but the male may have orange and blue on the edge of the dorsal and caudal fins, and blue on the body. They are livebearers and feed on plant material.

Both salt and freshwater are used by this species, but in salinities below four parts per thousand they do poorly. High salt marshes and brackish tidal creeks are their preferred habitat. All freshwater streams or seeps from the island are commonly used.

ORDER PERCIFORMES. Family Centrarchidae. Warmouth. *Lepomis gulosus* (Cuvier, 1829). This freshwater sunfish has a large mouth, and dark lines radiate out from behind the eye. It is a greenish-brown color with irregular darker blotches on the back and sides, and a yellowish belly.

The length may reach 25.4 to 279 millimeters (10 to 11 inches), but most are 127 to 178 millimeters (5 to 7 inches).

The warmouth has been reported in Whitney Lake, Sweetwater, and Whitney outlet on the island. This is a freshwater sport fish and may have been introduced on Cumberland Island with the other sport fish. A local common name is "warmouth perch."

_____. Family Centrarchidae. **Bluegill**. *Lepomis macrochirus* Rafinesque, 1819. Freshwater bluegills can exceed 356 millimeters (14 inches) in length, but most are 177 to 229 millimeters (7 to 9 inches). Breeding males are very colorful, with orange to red on the breast and blue on the sides, but typically they are dark greenish with a metallic sheen on the back and upper sides, and have dark vertical bars along the side, with a light yellowish belly. The flexible large lobe that forms the gill cover is solid black, and along with the vertical bars on the side, quickly distinguishes a bluegill from a warmouth.

Bluegills have been noted in Whitney Lake, Sweetwater, and Plum Pond on Cumberland Island. This species is likely the "bream" introduced to Lake Retta in the Sweetwater complex in 1905, as it is a popular game fish.

_____. Family Centrarchidae. **Black Crappie**. *Pomoxis nigro-maculatus* (LeSueur, 1829). One of the several local common names for the crappie is speckled or white perch, and people who have fished in Whitney Lake have mentioned catching an occasional "perch." Other than that, there are no Cumberland Island records of this species.

The crappie has more than three anal spines, which distinguish it from the bluegill and warmouth. They are common in the St. Marys River. The species is popular as a game fish, so could have been introduced.

_____. Family Centrarchidae. **Largemouth Bass**. *Micropterus salmoides* (Lacepède, 1802). A premier freshwater sport fish, the largemouth bass may reach 711 millimeters (28 inches) in total length, but most adults are smaller, 177 to 381 millimeters (7 to 15 inches). The back and upper sides are dark green, and the lower sides and belly whitish. An irregular dark band runs lengthwise along the lateral midline but may fade in older fish. They eat smaller fish, amphibians, crayfish, and nearly anything that moves.

Introductions, because of its ranking as a game fish, have spread the largemouth bass across most of the US. It was introduced on Cumberland Island in 1905 in Retta Lake in the Sweetwater complex, whose wetland terminates in Whitney Lake to the north and Willow Pond to the south (J. Greenway, pers. comm.). Whitney Lake was commonly fished in the 1970s and bass were caught, and they were still there in 1984. Reported Cumberland Island localities include the Whitney outlet and Plum Pond (Hillestad et al., 1975) and possibly Whitney Lake (J. Greenway, pers. comm.).

_____. Family Gerridae. **Mojarras**. *Eucinostomus* sp. This is a schooling species of saltwater fish, one of which was collected in the Whitney outlet (Hillestad et al., 1975), but the conditions at the time are unknown. Extremely high tides may flood that area, making it a temporary saltwater pond.

_____. Family Eleotridae. **Fat Sleeper.** *Dormitator maculatus* (Bloch, 1792). Fat sleepers found around Cumberland Island have been minnow-sized. In life, it is a dark fish with a striking blue shoulder spot.

Fat sleepers may be found in the streams draining Cumberland Island and in contiguous freshwater areas. During an extreme high-water event, one was found eaten by a two-toed amphiuma in the Whitney outlet.

_____. Family Mugillidae. **Striped Mullet.** *Mugil cephalus* Linnaeus, 1758. Typically less than 500 millimeters (20 inches) in total length, the striped mullet is dark on the dorsal surface, silver with dark stripes on the sides, and has a white belly. There is a small four-spined dorsal fin anterior to and separate from the soft dorsal fin, and there are eight anal rays. The small mouth is shaped like an inverted "V," and the animal feeds primarily on detritus.

Mullet are reported to commonly enter freshwater, but the animals reported from Whitney Lake (Hillestad et al., 1975) may have been introduced, since access from the ocean is possible but complicated and unlikely. These mullet also spawn only offshore, so no inland population could survive for long. Around Cumberland Island, they are sometimes found in beach outlets.

Amphibians and Reptiles

Introduction. When rising sea levels in the Holocene Era isolated Cumberland Island from the mainland, ecological habitats and communities changed in response to new environmental pressures. Freshwater wetlands shrank as saltwater encroached and environmental extremes became more prevalent. Fewer species succeeded on Cumberland Island than on the adjacent mainland (Table 3). Most amphibians are particularly intolerant of saltwater, which restricted their later colonization of the island. During environmental extremes, such as times of drought, species using wetlands usually emigrate from drying ponds and sloughs to take refuge in or under rotten logs or in burrows in the surrounding thick vegetation in order to reduce water loss. They may survive without reproducing for multiple years. Some turtle hatchlings may delay emergence from their nest chambers if environmental conditions are too harsh, spending the winter underground, emerging the following spring. Currently on Cumberland Island, with nonindigenous feral swine, amphibian and reptile losses must be exorbitant during times of drought, when foraging swine churn every centimeter of dry pond bottom, as well as peripheral areas. They also root under, into, and disperse rotten logs, leaving few safe refuges for amphibians and reptiles.

Human-induced changes have also affected amphibians and reptiles. In the past, draining wetlands for agriculture occurred, and more recently the control of natural fire in wetlands has been particularly devastating. Fire is an important part of the ecology of Cumberland Island wetlands and of amphibians and reptiles. Although some individuals may be killed by fire, the long-term benefits to the wetland community are enormous.

The first formal list of amphibians and reptiles on Cumberland Island was provided by Hillestad et al. (1975), and Shoop and Ruckdeschel (1986) presented several additions and corrections, and (2003) comments on biogeography. The following species on the original list lacked vouchers and their occurrence on the island is unsubstantiated:

Oak Toad	*Anaxyrus quercicus*
Five-lined Skink	*Plestiodon fasciatus*
Florida Pine Snake	*Pituophis melanoleucus*

(Nomenclature follows "The Society for the Study of Amphibians and Reptiles," web edition 6.1.)

Amphibians

Species Accounts.

ORDER ANURA. Family Bufonidae. **Southern Toad.** *Anaxyrus terrestris* (Bonnaterre, 1789). Synonym: *Bufo terrestris*. This medium-sized toad, with a body length from 41 to 75 millimeters (1.6 to 2.9 inches), may be larger on islands. The skin is warty, dry, and variable in color from brown through gray, blackish, and red. The belly is light. Cranial ridges are prominent in adults and have large, knobby posterior ends, a diagnostic characteristic for the species.

This species is found on most Georgia barrier islands, preferring sandy soils in hardwood hammocks, open scrub, and pine woods. Breeding is in ponds and temporary water rather than flowing streams. On the island, they occur in the upland maritime forest and may venture into open interdune regions at night.

Their call is a prolonged trill, a chorus of which can be deafening. They hop rather than walk and can negotiate steps up to a porch surprisingly well.

Activity on the island has been noted in all months except December and January and is highest in spring and summer.

Southern Toads will eat almost anything that moves that they can swallow, but insects are their most common food. On the island, lepidopteran larvae and adult beetles of families Scarabaeidae, Derondontidae, and Haliplidae have been identified in stomach contents.

Breeding, as judged by calling and amplexus, has been recorded on the island from February into September, with a peak in April and minor peaks in March, June, and August. The eggs hatch in two to four days, and the tadpoles develop in one to two months into tiny dark toadlets or metamorphs, seven to ten millimeters long. These have been recorded on the island April through November, with a clear peak in May.

Mortality factors on the island include garter snakes, which go into shallow toad burrows and forcefully remove the occupant. Ribbon snakes feed on small and newly metamorphosed toads. Some die in island wildfires and many are killed by vehicles on wet roads.

_____. Family Hylidae. **Southern Cricket Frog**. *Acris gryllus* (LeConte, 1825). This very small frog, 1.6 to 3.2 centimeters (.62 to 1.25 inches), has a triangle between and behind its eyes, and a single dark stripe on the thigh between two light stripes. The color is highly variable and can be yellowish green, dark green, reddish or brown and gray with patterns and often a middorsal stripe.

They have been reported from Sapelo, Little Cumberland, and Cumberland islands, and Amelia Island, Florida. Habitat requirements for this species are broad, and cricket frogs make use of river bottom swamps and edges of most bodies of water. On the island they are found along the Sweetwater sloughs and around most all wet areas.

The call is reminiscent of that of a cricket, but also of a metal clicker. Single separated calls, gick-gick-gick, usually precede a rapid burst of them. Calling on the island has been heard from February into September, with a peak in March and April, and can begin before breeding season. Island activity occurs throughout the year.

_____. Family Hylidae. **Green Treefrog**. *Hyla cinerea* (Schneider, 1799). This is a fairly large, 3.2 to 5.7 millimeters (1.25 to 2.25 inches), but svelte tree frog. The tips of the toes are expanded to facilitate climbing and maintain a reliable grasp on smooth, wet surfaces. These frogs are able to change color due to temperature, light condition, or stress and may be dull gray or brown in the winter, which would aid in camouflage. During warm months, they are usually various shades of green, as their name implies, often with a few tiny black-bordered flecks of gold or yellow scattered about. The best diagnostic character is an unbroken silvery yellow to white line between the upper lip and the groin, although in a few individuals it stops short or is completely absent. The tadpole is medium-sized, greenish to yellowish, and has a long tail.

Green tree frogs occur on most of the Georgia barrier islands and on Amelia Island, Florida. Permanent freshwater habitats are preferred over temporary wetlands. Since such habitats are scarce on Cumberland Island, this species is generally found only in the wettest areas, such as Whitney Lake and the Sweetwater system. Because they are usually found above or beside water on emergent vegetation or shrubs, they are considered arboreal and not aquatic. They spend winters on the island in or under rotten logs or anything that offers protection from the elements.

The call is a nonmelodious "quonk," which when heard singly is quite different from a large chorus producing thirty to sixty calls a minute. High humidity is more important than temperature to initiate calling, and for that reason this species, along with the squirrel treefrog, is sometimes called the rain frog. They may call day or night on the island between March and August, with a peak from April through June. Activity on Cumberland Island has been observed in all months except February, September, October, and December. In nearby Florida, however, they are active year-round.

Breeding season on the island, as judged by calling, begins in March and continues through August, with a peak in April through June. Metamorphs have been recorded on the island in June and July.

On the island, recorded vertebrate predators include ribbon snakes and raccoons. Some of these frogs have been killed in island wildfires, and during heavy summer rains, green tree frogs are frequently killed by vehicles as they sit on or cross warm, wet roads.

_____. Family Hylidae. **Pine Woods Treefrog**. *Hyla femoralis* Bosc, 1800. This small tree frog, about 40 millimeters (1.5 inches) snout-vent length, can be almost any shade from light brown through gray to dark brown, colors which can change depending on light, temperature, humidity, and background. Dark blotches with no regular pattern are frequently observed on the dorsal surface. The belly is cream to white. The most obvious identifying characters are the yellow or orange spots on the rear of the thighs that are normally observed only when jumping or taking a long step.

Pine woods treefrogs are found on Ossabaw, St. Catherines, Sapelo, and Cumberland islands in Georgia. Preferred habitats include pine flatwoods and sand hills where temporary water for breeding occurs. They are not usually found around dwellings. On Cumberland Island they inhabit the maritime forest and most wetlands.

Their call is very distinctive and similar to a telegraph communication in Morse code, although no particular sequence is discernible. Choruses resemble an imitation of machine-gun bursts, da-da-dada-da-da repeated rapidly in pulses of ten or twenty or more.

Based on calls, breeding on Cumberland peaks in March and continues through June. Calls may be heard outside the breeding season, but the function of these calls is unknown.

_____. Family Hylidae. **Barking Treefrog**. *Hyla gratiosa* Le-Conte, 1856. This is our largest native tree frog, about 51 millimeters (2 inches) or more in total length. It generally has rounded irregular spots on a background color ranging from shades of bright green, brown, and gray. A few individuals may lack spots, however, and appear uniform in color, but color and pattern are subject to change. The legs are banded in variable colors, and the belly is white. The skin on the back is evenly granular, and the belly skin is rough. The head is broad and the short digits terminate in conspicuous disks.

They have been reported from Ossabaw and Cumberland islands in Georgia and Amelia Island, Florida. On Cumberland Island they occur around most wetlands and throughout the scrub/flatwoods community. Their general habitat preferences are pine-hardwood uplands, pine flatwoods, deciduous lowland forests, and high hammocks.

The call, a single note, is distinctive and sounds resonating and hollow, as if amplified. Calling and activity have been recorded on the island from April through August, with most encounters occurring in June and July.

_____. Family Hylidae. **Squirrel Treefrog**. *Hyla squirella* Bosc, 1800. This relatively small, smooth-skinned tree frog, with a maximum snout-vent length of 45 millimeters (1.7 inches), is one of the most common on the island. The toes terminate in expanded discs. This species changes color rapidly (metachrosis), making an all-inclusive description difficult. There is no distinctive pattern, with color ranging from yellow-green through shades of green and brown to dark brown; dorsal patterns and markings also may change rapidly. The belly is white. Most squirrel tree frogs are green, but they lack the conspicuous white dorso-lateral stripe of the green treefrog.

Squirrel treefrogs are found on most of the Georgia barrier islands and tolerate any habitat that provides moisture, which on Cumberland includes freshwater wetlands, maritime forest, scrub, and around human habitation.

They may call anytime during the summer in conjunction with high humidity prior to rain, and for this reason they are also called "rain frogs." The call produced at that time is very squirrel-like, that is, scolding, raspy, and croaking. The mating call is a raucous, duck-like, nonmelodious "waa-a-a." On Cumberland Island they call from March through September, with a peak in June and July. Activity on Cumberland occurs from February through November. Tiny metamorphs have been observed on Cumberland in May, June, and October.

On the island, a source of mortality is wildfire. Animals around temporary ponds try to retreat downwards into moist, peaty muck, and if they are lucky, there they will survive the hurried pass of fire through the grass above. Freezing temperatures kill some on the island.

_____. Family Hylidae. **Cope's Gray Treefrog**. *Hyla chrysoscelis* Cope, 1880. This moderately large tree frog reaches nearly 50 millimeters (2 inches) in length. Adults are generally gray, as the common name suggests, but they have the ability to change color between shades of gray, brown, and light to olive green. Irregularly shaped darker gray blotches, sometimes outlined in black, are scattered over the coarsely granulated upper surfaces, and there is a characteristic light area below the eye. The under surfaces may be tinged with light yellow, and the inside of the hind legs are spotted in a striking deep yellow. A lichen-like color pattern aids in camouflage, and the bright yellow spots on the legs serve as "flash colors" and may serve an anti-predator function.

On Cumberland Island, temporary ponds in the scrub support this species (National Park Service). They are especially noisy after summer rains, easily recognized by their melodic trill.

_____. Family Hylidae. **Spring Peeper**. *Pseudacris crucifer* (Wied-Neuwied, 1838). This small brown, tan, or olive-green frog (19 to 32 millimeters, .75 to 1.25 inches) has a relatively reliable and distinguishing dark "X" across its back. There may be a dark line between the eyes, and the belly is light. The snout is pointed, and toe pads are conspicuous.

The species occurs on Sapelo and Cumberland islands, Georgia, and on adjacent Amelia Island, Florida. Spring peepers are found in a broad range of habitats, from open lowland marshes to riparian areas along wooded streams, and even in disturbed forest.

Their call differs from that of all the other treefrogs on Cumberland Island (but not the mainland) and can be compared to a short, clear, high-pitched whistle. Activity has been recorded on Cumberland Island in all months except April and July through October, but this species is likely active year-round under favorable environmental conditions.

Calls have been heard on Cumberland from November through March, with a prominent peak in January and about half as much activity in February and March. Newly transformed metamorphs have been recorded on Cumberland in May and June.

_____. Family Hylidae. **Little Grass Frog**. *Pseudacris ocularis* (Bosc and Daudin, 1801). This tiny, 11- to 16-millimeter (.44- to .62-inch) frog is the smallest anuran in North America. The general coloration is bronze or brown or even reddish, with a dark line extending through the eye and onto the side of the body. There may be a middorsal stripe and narrow dark stripes separating colors of the back and sides. The skin of the back is covered with fine warts, and the belly skin is finely granulated. The toes are slightly webbed and the tips are expanded into small pads. Its eyes are large; the tympanum is inconspicuous.

Little grass frogs are found on the barrier islands of Ossabaw, St. Catherines, Sapelo, and Cumberland, Georgia, and on Amelia Island, Florida. Preferred habitats are low pine flatwoods and grassy areas surrounding open wetlands. On Cumberland Island they occupy all wetlands, both interdune and upland, and have been recorded on cordgrass at the edge of a brackish salt marsh. Ideal breeding sites are fish-free shallow water.

The call is high-pitched, insect-like, and inaudible to some people. Calls may be heard on Cumberland in every month, with a peak from January to March; March is the most common month in which they breed.

_____. Family Hylidae. **Southern Chorus Frog**. *Pseudacris nigrita* (LeConte, 1825). This small frog, about 32 millimeters (about 1.2 inches) snout-vent length, is similar in size to a cricket frog but with a white upper lip and long hind legs. The background color is grayish brown, and there is a wide darker band from the snout along the side of the body, over the front limbs, and angling to the white belly. The skin is coarsely granular with irregular dark blotches.

The southern chorus frog is found on Sapelo and Cumberland islands (National Park Service) in moist upland areas, permanent water, and around temporary ponds.

Heavy rains stimulate calling, and calls sound as if someone is running their fingers over the tines of a plastic comb. December through early spring is breeding season, after which they spend most of their time in leaf litter or underground (Jensen et al., 2008).

_____. Family Microhylidae. **Eastern Narrow-mouthed Toad.** *Gastrophryne carolinensis* (Holbrook, 1836). This very distinctive, small frog, 2.2 to 3.2 centimeters (.87 to 1.25 inches) in length, has a noticeably point-ed, tiny head and a fold of skin across the neck behind the eyes. Its general shape is plump and pear-like. The color ranges through shades of brown, gray, and reddish, and there is often a light or contrasting-colored wide stripe along the sides from eye to groin. The belly is darkly mottled, and in males there are fine dark spots on the throat, whereas females usually lack throat and pectoral markings. There is no visible tympanum, the eye pupil is circular, and the skin is relatively smooth. The toes have no webbing, but there is a spade for digging on each hind foot.

These small frogs have been recorded from Ossabaw, St. Catherines, Sapelo, Little Cumberland, and Cumberland islands, Georgia, and Amelia Island, Florida. Eastern narrow-mouthed frogs require loose, friable, and moist soils, and they spend days under or in rotten logs or some form of cov-er, usually in shallow burrows. Edges of wetlands surrounded by maritime forests, even in proximity to the salt marsh, are habitats used on Cumberland Island. They have been reported from under boards in a salt marsh and even breeding in "water too salty to drink" (Neill, 1958).

The male usually calls from the edge of the water with a most distinc-tive call resembling the nasal bleat of a lamb. The duration of the buzzing call is 0.5 to 4 seconds. Calls may be heard on Cumberland Island from April through September, with the highest activity from June through Sep-tember. General activity has been recorded in March. Gravid females have been found on the island in July and August.

On Cumberland Island, their diet includes spider mites, beetles, uni-dentified flies, and ants but is also subsidized by introduced amphipods.

_____. Family Pelobatitdae. **Eastern Spadefoot.** *Scaphiopus holbrookii* (Harlan, 1835). The Eastern Spadefoot is a medium-sized, 4.4 to 5.7 centimeters (1.75 to 2.25 inches), plump anuran with a short, broad head and protuberant eyes, which recess when closed. Unlike all other frogs on

Cumberland, the pupil of the eye is vertical rather than horizontal. There are no cranial crests, the conspicuous parotoid glands are more round than oblong, and the tympanum is smaller than the eye. The characteristic for which the species is named, the "spade," is a relatively large, dark horny process on the inner surface of each hind foot and used for digging. The toes are completely webbed. The general background color is a shade of brown or gray, which may be almost black. Two light-yellowish to olive-colored lines run down backwards from the eye and meet near the rump, frequently resulting in the shape of an hourglass. The throat and belly are light to white, and the skin has tiny tubercles.

They occur on the Georgia barrier islands of Tybee, Ossabaw, St. Catherines, Sapelo, Little Cumberland, and Cumberland. Spadefoots are found in most upland, wooded island habitats. For breeding they require fish-free water, which means truly temporary and ephemeral; they can breed in even small puddles as long as sufficient water allows for development.

Once heard, their call cannot be mistaken for that of another species. It is an extremely loud, low-pitched, explosive single grunt repeated periodically. The head rears up during the call and the entire body contributes to the effort. Heavy rain initiates calling and breeding, and although usually nocturnal, calls may be heard during the day. Calling on Cumberland has been recorded from February through October, with general activity January through November. A 17 February record involved about a dozen individuals in the upland forest and about six in the scrub at 0200 hours. It followed three inches of rain the day before and rain all that night, for a total of seven inches in two days. The high temperature on 17 February was 66°F, and the low that night was 50°F. Spadefoot eggs hatch within two days and the quickly developing tadpoles may metamorphose in two to eight weeks, depending upon temperature.

The negative impact of foraging livestock, now limited to feral hogs and horses, on island eastern spadefoots is unknown but has the potential to be greater than on other, more mobile species.

_____. Family Ranidae. **Pig Frog**. *Lithobates grylio* (Stejneger, 1901). Synonym: *Rana grylio*. The pig frog is a large (80 to 162 millimeters; 3.1 to 6.4 inches) heavy frog with shades of green or brown, often with irregular dark blotches toward the rear. There may be crossbars on the thighs and feet, and the belly is light, usually with some mottling. It has no dorso-lateral ridges, and the tympanum is larger than the eye. The hind feet are completely webbed to the tips of the toes. Adults are similar in appearance to bullfrogs.

The species has been reported from the barrier islands of Ossabaw, Sapelo, and Cumberland, where it is found at all permanent to semipermanent water, such as Whitney Lake, Willow Pond, and the Sweetwater sloughs. Being an aquatic species, it prefers open permanent water with floating and emergent vegetation.

Activity has been observed on Cumberland Island from January through October. This is the most aquatic of our island frogs, and it spends most of its time in water. The call is a forceful deep bass grunt usually repeated three or four times in succession, with a timbre that cannot be imitated. As the common name implies, the call sounds like the grunt of a pig.

Calls may be heard on Cumberland from March through September, with a peak in May and June. Tadpoles first appear in March and April, and young have been seen on Cumberland from February through May.

_____. Family Ranidae. **Southern Leopard Frog.** *Lithobates spheno-cephalus* (Cope, 1886). Synonyms: *Rana utricularia, Rana sphenocephala.* The leopard frog is medium-sized, 51 to 127 millimeters (2 to 5 inches), a trim frog with a pointed snout. Its general color is brown or green or a mixture thereof, and it usually has dark unpaired spots on the back between light dorso-lateral ridges. There may be less pronounced ridges that are not accentuated by color in between the flanking lateral ridges. There are usually dark bars on the hind legs, and the belly is plain white or light. The fairly constant white spot in the center of the tympanum gives the appearance of a second eye. The hind toes are webbed.

The southern leopard frog is found on most of the Georgia barrier islands and Amelia Island, Florida. This adaptable frog uses any freshwater or brackish water habitats along the coast. On Cumberland Island it is abundant around all the freshwater habitats and at freshwater seeps along the high salt marsh.

This species has been called an "enterprising hunter," and that it is. In warm weather, after spending the day in proximity to a body of water, they synchronously disperse to forage at dusk, well away from the security of the water. After three or four hops, they sit motionless for a minute or two, then hop again. When surprised on the edge of a pond, they may or may not take refuge in the water. It has been my observation that when they avoid the water, there is likely to be a small alligator or other threat lurking nearby. Activity has been observed throughout the year on Cumberland Island.

Their repertoire of calls is quite diverse, including a series of low-pitched chuckles, a drawn-out guttural croak similar to the sound made by rubbing an inflated balloon, and a high-pitched call for help, which is made repeatedly when the frog is seized by a snake or other predator. This call may sound almost bird-like. Calls have been heard in all months on Cumberland Island, but least activity has been recorded during the summer, May through August. There is a definite spike in calling from January through March, with February being the busiest month. Tadpoles have been observed on Cumberland in almost every month, with a peak in June.

Their size allows leopard frogs to consume crayfish and, in brackish areas of the island, fiddler crabs. They will patiently wait near a pile of scat or rotting fruit for flies. The following prey have been recorded in their island diet: earthworms, amphipods, spiders, terrestrial gastropods, crickets, beetles, and unidentified Lepidoptera—larvae and adults, crane fly larvae, unidentified adult flies, and ants.

Some island leopard frogs are infested with a chigger. See Appendix VI A. Black racers stalk and capture adult southern leopard frogs.

ORDER CAUDATA. Family Ambystomatidae. **Mole Salamander.** *Ambystoma talpoideum* (Holbrook, 1838). The mole salamander is a short, chunky salamander, 81 to 122 millimeters (3.25 to 4.75 inches) in length, with a large, broad head. The color is gray, brown, or almost black, often with light bluish-gray flecks, and a bluish-gray belly. In large larvae and transformed juveniles, there is a dark midventral stripe. The front feet have four toes, with five on the rear.

So far, the only Georgia barrier island where this species has been reported is Cumberland, and here it occurs in the scrub, where it uses temporary ponds for breeding in November and December. It is also on Amelia Island, Florida. Larvae and metamorphs have been recorded on the island from March through August. Feral swine have the potential to seriously impact this terrestrial species.

_____. Family Amphiumidae. **Two-toed Amphiuma.** *Amphiuma means* Garden, 1821. Other common names for this species are more generally descriptive, such as "Congo eel" or "lamper eel," which immediately convey the long, linear appearance of this very large and hefty aquatic salamander. The largest measured on the island so far has been 935 millimeters (30 inches) in total length. Although they have four limbs, the limbs are so tiny as to be easily overlooked and are considered nonfunctional. The small eyes are flush on top of the head, and the sloping, wide snout projects beyond the lower jaw. External gills are lacking except briefly during the larval stage. The dorsal color is a uniform brown or gray, which lightens on the lower sides and more so on the belly. The skin is smooth and protected by a slippery coat of mucous that makes the animal extremely difficult to hold.

They tend to avoid flowing water and prefer even temporary aquatic habitats where they can burrow in organic muck. The Georgia barrier islands of St. Catherines, Sapelo, and Cumberland have populations, and also Amelia Island, Florida. On Cumberland Island they use most of the established temporary ponds and the sloughs.

Island activity has been recorded in every month except February and December but under normal conditions is highest from April through August. With extreme high water, activity increases in September and October. High-water extremes were noted in 1984, 1988, 1989, 1991, and 1995. When wetlands dry, amphiumas are able to form a cocoon to protect themselves from water loss and remain underground for long periods. They burrow and use crayfish burrows, which provide a moist environment and protection from predators.

Sharp teeth serve the amphiuma well in capturing prey on the island. The three most important foods here are crayfish (*Procambarus paeninsulanus*), insects, and amphibians (Whitaker and Ruckdeschel, 2009). Insect groups represented were Coleoptera, Hemiptera, Diptera, Lepidoptera, Orthoptera, Gryllidae, Odonata, along with Mollusca (*Physa heterostropha*.) and a few other invertebrates. Vertebrates made up 16.6% of the volume in our food study and items varied seasonally, with crayfish being high in spring and summer and insects high in autumn. Smaller individuals ate more insects and fish.

The nematodes *Hedruris siredonis* and larvae of *Ascaridia* sp. and a cestode have been found in Cumberland Island amphiuma (Bursey, pers. comm.).

One aquatic snake, the mud snake, specializes in feeding upon amphiumas. Rear teeth in the upper jaw are enlarged and facilitate holding the slippery prey (Mitchell, 1994). On the island, alligators and raccoons have been documented as predators. Several individuals have been observed to have been killed by wildfire, which usually occurs at times of drought, when two-toed amphiumas are the most vulnerable. Foraging feral swine, no doubt, also have an impact at those times.

During times of drought, breaches in the dune system which allow drainage become filled with blowing sand, which in turn raises the water level in the slough system. Substantial rain causes another breach to open, and what was a lentic situation suddenly becomes a fast-moving stream, the outlet of which is the ocean. Whether amphiuma are involuntarily carried with the flow or are exploring for new habitats is unknown, but on occasion many have died as a result of encountering saltwater.

_____. Family Plethodontidae. **Southern Dusky Salamander.** *Desmognathus auriculatus* (Holbrook, 1838). This medium-sized salamander, 80 to 150 millimeters (3 to 6 inches) in length, is brown or almost black with light spots along the sides. There is always a light line between the eye and jaw, although it may be faded. The belly is dark. Naso-labial grooves are present, eyes are bulging and conspicuous, and the front legs are much smaller than the rear. The tail is laterally compressed near the tip and keeled.

Cumberland is the only Georgia barrier island on which this species has been documented, but it is also on Amelia Island, Florida. Specific Cumberland Island localities are Stafford and the Yankee Paradise Creek into Swamp Field.

During drought conditions, these salamanders retreat vertically with the water table. They have been noted on Cumberland Island in March and August.

_____. Family Plethodontidae. **Dwarf Salamander.** *Eurycea quadridigitata* (Holbrook, 1842). This small, slim salamander is between 54 and 90 millimeters (2 to 3.5 inches) long, with the tail being 50% to 60% of the total length. The dorsal surface is brownish yellow, tan, or bronze and may have small dark spots; the sides have a dark stripe below which is lighter and fades into a light or yellow belly. A key identifying character is the number of toes on the hind foot, four as opposed to the usual five. Mature males have cirri, small projections from the nostrils, which aid in odor detection, and both sexes have naso-labial grooves.

They are on the Georgia barrier islands of Ossabaw, St. Catherines, and Cumberland. Any damp or wet place is suitable habitat for this salamander, including pond edges, low flatwoods, swamps, and bottomlands. They occur in uplands adjacent to water during summer and autumn and migrate to the breeding sites from January through April. Although usually in proximity to freshwater, dwarf salamanders are terrestrial. On Cumberland Island, specific localities include the Sweetwater sloughs, Ashley Pond, and Brickhill Pond.

_____. Family Salamandridae. **Eastern Newt.** *Notophthalmus viridescens* (Rafinesque, 1820). Aquatic adults are dull olive green to brownish, with many small dark spots and variable larger red spots, more or less ringed with black. The belly is light yellow and has a sprinkling of dark spots. The skin is granular and they have a noticeable odor. There are no costal grooves. This is a medium-sized salamander with a total length of between 58 and 140 millimeters (2.3 to 5.5 inches). No efts have been found on Cumberland Island. The larvae metamorphose directly to adults, but do not disperse far from wetlands.

The species is found throughout Georgia and on the barrier islands of Ossabaw, St. Catherines, Sapelo, and Cumberland. Local island habitats include the Sweetwater slough complex and temporary ponds in the scrub.

Gravid females have been found on Cumberland in November, and larvae have been documented in April, May, and July. Animals in breeding condition have been noted in April, November, and January.

Skin secretions of all stages of newts are toxic and discourage toad and raccoon predators. In aquatic situations, newts are prey of the two-toed amphiuma on the island. Feral swine eliminate rotten logs and obvious places of refuge for salamanders on Cumberland Island, and probably greatly limit the newt's terrestrial distribution.

Reptiles

Species Accounts.

ORDER CROCODYLIA. Family Alligatoridae. **American Alligator.** *Alligator mississippiensis* (Daudin, 1801). The American alligator is a solidly built, medium- to large-sized reptile with four short legs, a tail more than half the length of the body, and an intimidating disposition. The skin and several longitudinal rows of ridges containing osteoderms (separate small bones embedded in the skin) follow the dorsal surface of the body onto the tail (Fig. 25) and effectively provide dorsal protection. The external nares are near the tip of the snout, and the nose and eyes are elevated on the skull so as to allow breathing and vision while most of the animal is submerged. Only dead alligators can be measured precisely, and the largest measured on Cumberland Island (10.4 feet) was found dead on the beach and may not have been an island resident. Hatchlings are about 20 centimeters (8 inches) total length and grow about a foot a year with adequate food. Adults are black on the dorsal surface with a creamy white belly. Young are black with transverse bands of bright yellow and are very colorful. Adult females are smaller than adult males.

Alligators are on all of the barrier islands. Freshwater sloughs, including Whitney Lake, isolated temporary ponds, freshwater drains, and seeps along the edge of the island, all provide habitat. For protection from environmental conditions, alligators may excavate dens in and around any wetland, including streams, temporary ponds, or even salt marsh. Most temporary ponds in the scrub have alligator holes or dens.

Alligators are opportunistic feeders and will take whatever prey they can overpower. Small alligators consume small prey, such as crustaceans and insects, whereas large ones fill a very different niche and take mammals, including raccoons, deer, feral hogs, and even feral horses on Cumberland Island. They have also been documented eating marsh rabbits, armadillos, otters, and rice rats on the island (Shoop and Ruckdeschel, 1990) and also carrion. If resources are not available, adults can go years without feeding because of their low metabolic rate.

On Cumberland Island, small temporary ponds in the scrub frequently support individual females, which are courted by males paying each a visit at their home pond. Bellowing is a part of courtship performed by both males and females. The site of a nest is in proximity to water but must not be inundated. Heavy rains during the end of the incubation period (1988) once killed several clutches of eggs on the island, presumably by preventing oxygen exchange. I verified that alligators survived in dens in dry temporary ponds in the scrub following a two-year drought and the great 1981 wildfire, even though there was no sign of surface activity or standing water at the time.

Nest construction on Cumberland Island begins the end of June; hatching begins the first part of September. Females produce one clutch of eggs per year, usually between thirty and fifty eggs. Sexual maturity is attained at a total length of about five to six feet. The number of eggs in a clutch is correlated with the body size of the female, so that the smallest females produce the smallest clutches. A female on Little Cumberland Island five-feet long oviposited only five eggs in a small (about 1- to 2-feet high) nest adjacent to a yard pond. Three of the five eggs were viable.

At the time of hatching, the female frequently opens the nest to help the young escape. She may carry them to the water in her mouth, making several trips. One nest I checked after the female had opened it surprised me with the grunting sound of a hatchling. One whole egg was left in the nest and the female was with her young in the water. I took the unhatched egg back to the lab and allowed it to hatch. The hatchling inside had a congenital defect, permanently coiling its tail like a rope on the deck of a ship.

The nematode *Ortleppascaris anatipini* was found in an alligator found dead on the Cumberland Island beach (C. Bursey, pers. comm.).

Alligators were abundant in the Southeast in the 1700s, when decimation of the populations began. None of the early literature (Bartram, 1791 [in Harper, 1958]; Holbrook, 1842 [1976]; Hallock, 1876) contradicted reports of high densities of large alligators throughout most of the range. Alligator leather became popular in the mid-1800s, and seeing so many large predators along the waterways activated early "sportsmen." Passengers on steamboats gathered near the bow to wantonly shoot the animals, and this "sport" continued for many years, vastly depleting the population. At least 2,500,000 alligators were killed in Florida from 1880 to 1893 (Chabreck, 1968).

Alligators continued to be persecuted into the 1900s. In the late 1930s, farmer and naturalist M. N. Hopkins recalled how nearly every island in a south Georgia river was stinky with rotting gator carcasses. It has been estimated that 10 million animals were killed for hides from 1870 through about 1970 (Fogarty and Campbell, 1978), and many prior to that, further reducing their populations. The US Fish and Wildlife Service described the alligator as "threatened with extinction" in 1967 and included it under provisions of the Endangered Species Act of 1973. Because alligator populations were already drastically reduced by the end of the 1900s, when scientific studies of the alligator were just beginning, little is known about the original extent of the ecological role of the alligator in the South.

Alligator nests, trails, and dens affect local ecology in marshlands. When alligators construct nest mounds in low-lying terrain, the accumulation of the organic material over time elevates the immediate area. As upland vegetation takes hold, small hammocks are produced. These islands increase community diversity and are beneficial to many species. Even during times of drought, alligator dens provide refuge for many species. Dens normally are excavated down to the water table, sustaining fish, amphibian, and reptiles to repopulate those areas when water returns.

Discussion

Historically, alligators populated estuarine as well as freshwater, where they hauled out on all available "beaches" along the tidal creeks and hammocks. Their presence, out of and in the water, incidentally offered protection to diamondback terrapin nests. Currently, such protection is lacking, leaving turtle eggs more vulnerable to predators. The same holds true with open areas along our freshwater rivers and ponds with regard to the vulnerability of freshwater turtle eggs. Alligators no doubt played an important role in turtle ecology in the past, even for sea turtles, and particularly on nesting beaches such as Cape Canaveral, where a thin strip of beach is separated from the mainland by a body of water. An occasional black bear might find its way out to the beach, but raccoons and mink would be vulnerable crossing open water with a full complement of alligators. Freshwater flows from behind the primary dunes across the ocean beach on Cumberland Island during wet weather, and the presence of alligators could protect nearby sea turtle nests by discouraging predators.

Colonial nesting wading birds also depend upon alligators. Great egrets, snowy egrets, wood storks, glossy ibis, and night herons all rely on the presence of an alligator in the water beneath their nest trees to discourage predators (Ruckdeschel and Shoop, 1987; Fig. 26). During times of drought, the birds refrain from initiating nesting. If nesting is underway when the water level drops far enough to allow shallow water access to the base of a nest tree, raccoons take advantage of the alligator-free route to consume eggs and/or chicks.

Alligators also have an intimate relationship with black vultures, which regularly fly over to check alligator holes for carcasses. As a carcass decomposes and the alligator is able to pull it apart, fragments become more accessible to vultures. Vultures seem comfortable in the presence of an alligator with enough food to share, although they are extremely careful about how close they get. Adults may feed on the opposite side of a large carcass from an alligator. Adult vultures do not allow their young in proximity of an alligator near a carcass. When there were millions of large alligators in the Southeast, they may have helped provide a substantial part of the vulture's diet. And the alligator-vulture relationship may not end there. On Cumberland, a black vulture laid eggs about ten feet from the water hole of a large alligator that had been confined in a 15- by 20-foot area for several years.

The surrounding undeveloped land had natural vegetation, so the choice was deliberate. I have observed vultures, surprised by my presence, fly up from near other alligator holes where they were not immediately next to the water as if drinking. Because vultures already have a feeding relationship with alligators and are used to being around them, they may be taking advantage of the potential protection an alligator would provide their nest. Vultures nest on the ground or in cavities near the ground, so their eggs and young are vulnerable to predation.

We usually think of the "food pyramid" with predators at the top being far fewer in number than their prey at the base. This graphic representation works for mammals but not reptiles, such as alligators. In the classic food pyramid, avian and mammalian predators compose the highest trophic levels, but because of high metabolic expenditures (food requirements) they are unable to maintain high population numbers. The alligator's low metabolic rate and its ability to fast for extended periods, modifying its growth rate commensurate with food intake, allows for enormous populations at the top of the trophic scale. Because of this, large alligators likely played major roles as predators on mammals in some Southeast ecosystems. This would influence mammal distribution, seasonal behavior, and terrestrial community structure. For example, the spread of the armadillo across the South corresponded with the extermination of alligators in that region. The presettlement population of alligators in Florida was in the millions, while the number of panthers in Florida at the same time has been estimated at only 1,400 animals (Simberloff and Cox, 1987). Despite the lower metabolic rates of large alligators that resulted in a lower predation rate per animal, the enormous number of large alligators made them the most significant predator at the time.

Most of this discussion on ecology relates to large alligators because individual size dictates ecological role. Small animals, up to four feet, are more likely to be mammalian prey than predators. Diets and ecological impacts differ with size. Although the American alligator was declared an endangered species, the designation was ultimately changed to "threatened due to similarity of appearance to other protected crocodilians" (Federal Register, 10 January 1977). Today, Georgia and other states have quota-based alligator hunting seasons. The legal size limit is a total length of four feet or more, with no upper limit, which means that the size structure of the population is unnaturally skewed, as large animals are preferentially eliminated. This also means that proportionally larger, prime breeding males are killed. While numbers of moderate-sized adult animals can perpetuate the species, much of the ecological influence of the alligator has been sacrificed. Humans are loath to tolerate a large predator once its location is known, and coupled with a cash value for its hide and eminently edible flesh, it is to be expected that large alligators will continue to be killed by the general public. During the years 1973 to 2009, I found thirty-seven dead alligators in this national park, none of which died of natural causes.

ORDER SQUAMATA. Family Anguidae. **Eastern Glass Lizard.** *Ophisaurus ventralis* (Linnaeus, 1766). Two distinguishing characteristics of this species are that none of the labial scales reach the eye orbit and there is no middorsal stripe. Above the lateral groove, which runs the length of the body, a dark brown stripe occurs from the head onto and along the upper side of the tail. There are no markings below the groove. The dorsum in young animals is light brown or tan, but the pattern may be lost with age and become greenish with small dark checkering. Some scales frequently have white markings. The belly is light to yellowish and sometimes pinkish. Regenerated tails are of a different color, usually uniform brown. Two-thirds of the length of this animal is tail. The largest specimen recorded from Cumberland Island was 650 millimeters (25.5 inches) total length. Legs are lacking, contributing to an earlier name, "glass snake." Unlike snakes, it has eyelids and external ear openings and does not have the feel of a supple, fluid snake. Scales on the lizard are ridged and supported by osteoderms (embedded tiny bones), so while shiny and protective, they reduce flexibility and make the animal firm or stiff to the touch.

These lizards have been reported on most of the Georgia barrier islands. They prefer open areas and on Cumberland Island make use of the vegetated interdunes, habitats around wetlands, the north end scrub, and disturbed areas, such as yards.

These are primarily fossorial, burrowing animals, but they spend much time actively foraging on the surface, preferably in thick litter or under partial cover, infrequently climbing. I watched an adult-sized animal forage four feet off the ground in a trellis covered with blooming flamelilies and swarming with insects in September. Activity on Cumberland Island has been recorded from February through November. Defenses besides tail autotomy include camouflage and a unique immobility behavior. An animal seen foraging on firm ground with—little or no litter but quite a few sticks near it—straightened out at my approach and held its arrow-straight posture until

III

well after the threat had passed. That lizard would have easily been overlooked had I not seen it before it froze in that stick-like position.

Stomach contents of twelve eastern glass lizards on Cumberland Island were examined for food items. The most important by volume was in the family Gryllidae, crickets, mostly *Nemobius* sp., with caterpillars and spiders second (Whitaker et al., 2012b).

Ticks frequently attach in the lateral groove or around the eyes, and a trombiculid mite has been collected on island eastern glass lizards. See Appendix VI. A.

Verified predators on Cumberland Island are the black racer, eastern coachwhip, and armadillo. Several eastern glass lizards have been killed on island roads by vehicles, and a few, including a female containing six eggs, have been killed in wildfire.

_____. Family Anguidae. **Island Glass Lizard.** *Ophisaurus compressus* Cope, 1900. This small, maximum 61 centimeters (23.8 inches), relative of the eastern glass lizard is identified by the presence of one or more labial scales that reach the eye orbit and a dark middorsal stripe, which may be broken. A dark brown stripe on each side above the lateral groove begins with several vertical light bars behind the eye. There are no markings below the groove. The overall body color is a light tan and the underside is pale. Legs are lacking, and the tail is two and one quarter to three times the length of the body. The tail lacks fracture planes so is less likely to break than the tail of the eastern glass lizard. The scales are shiny but very stiff with osteoderms (tiny embedded bones) incorporated in them. Although snake-like in appearance, island glass lizards have eyelids and lateral ear openings, unlike snakes.

Island glass lizards have been reported on the Georgia islands of Sapelo and Cumberland and Amelia Island, Florida. On Cumberland (Shoop and Ruckdeschel, 1997), the species uses interdune areas, including wet savannas and myrtle-sedge habitat. It has not been found on the beach proper. Activity on Cumberland Island has been recorded in February, July through September, and in November. They have been recorded in bobcat feces and as road mortalities on the island.

_____. Family Polychrotidae. **Green Anole.** *Anolis carolinensis* (Voight, 1832). This small to medium-sized lizard has the ability to change color from an unmarked brown or grayish color to several shades of green. The belly is light. The largest recorded specimen from Cumberland Island had a total length of 181 millimeters (about seven inches). Chromatic variation is related to body temperature, stress, and behavior, as well as camouflage.

They are found throughout Georgia except in the northeast corner of the state, and they occur on most of the barrier islands. Habitat tolerance is wide, but dense woody vegetation in open areas, such as the edges of the many temporary ponds on the island, and forested areas are preferred.

These diurnal animals are primarily arboreal, spending much time in Spanish moss high in trees, although they are frequently seen scurrying across island roads. Activity on the island has been recorded in every month, with a peak from March through May. They do not become dormant and are active throughout the winter on warm days. Their choices of winter refuges are sometimes poor, resulting in several animals found killed by freezes on the island.

Lepidopteran larvae were the most important food items by volume in eleven anoles checked on Cumberland Island (Whitaker et al., 2012b). Crickets, spiders, true bugs (Hemiptera), various flies, and ants were also represented in their diet. Surprisingly large insects may be taken by this species, including moths, beetles, and other small arthropods.

On the island, courting and mating have been observed in April and May, and general activity peaks in May. Females with eggs have been encountered here in April and June, and hatchlings occur from July through September.

Mites have been collected on green anoles on Cumberland Island. Two species of parasitic protozoa were found in the blood of Cumberland Island anoles between 1967 and 1970 (Jordan and Friend, 1971). See Appendix VI. A.

Adults on the island have been prey of chicken snakes and opossums. Lizard eggs are eaten by armadillos. Wildfires kill some, as do freezes. Cold temperatures also slow movement, causing some to fall from trees or become vehicle fatalities. One cold February day, four fresh adults were found run over on a short stretch of road on the south end of the island.

_____. Family Phrynosomatidae. **Eastern Fence Lizard.** *Sceloporus undulatus* (Latreille, 1801). This medium-sized lizard, 100 to 185 millimeters (3.9 to 7.2 in.) total length, cannot be confused with any other Cumberland Island lizard. Its rough body scales are matte, keeled, and each has a point overlapping the following scale. Color differs somewhat geographically and with sex but is usually brown or gray and sometimes rusty.

Females are more likely than males to have an irregular pattern of crossbars on the back, and their bellies are usually pale. Males have outstanding lateral patches of iridescent blue or greenish blue bordered by black on the belly and a splash of that color on the dark throat.

Dry upland forests with open canopies allowing plenty of sun are preferred by this species. Pine woods and scrub, especially edges, are used. On the barrier islands they have been reported from Cumberland, Sapelo, and Jekyll islands. Cumberland Island habitats most used are at Hickory Hill and the hammock ridges east of Roller Coaster Road. Activity on Cumberland Island occurs throughout the year.

Ants were the most important dietary item by volume in stomachs of five eastern fence lizards from Cumberland Island. Caterpillars ranked second, with a few spiders (Whitaker et al., 2012b).

Mating on Cumberland Island was observed by H. B. Jordan on 4 April, and elongate oval, leathery eggs were found the first week of July. On Cumberland, clutches of four and six have been recorded, and two clutches a season may be oviposited. No parental care is provided.

Ticks have been collected on fence lizards on Cumberland Island, and larval trombiculid mites have been found between and beneath the scales. Protozoan parasites were found in the blood of Cumberland Island eastern fence lizards between 1968 and 1970 (Jordan and Friend, 1971). See Appendix VI. A.

On Cumberland Island, introduced opossums have been verified as predators.

_____. Family Scincidae. **Mole Skink.** *Plestiodon egregius* (Baird, 1859). Synonym: *Eumeces egregius.* This small, 90 to 152 millimeters (3.5 to 5.9 inch) total length, lizard has a thick, heavy tail and tiny limbs. The dorsal body color is brown, tan, or gray, with a wide dorsolateral dark-brown stripe that is bordered on both sides by a light stripe. There is no middorsal stripe, but there are two rows of enlarged scales down the center of the back. The belly is light or pale and the tail bright reddish orange to sometimes pinkish. Scales are smooth and overlapping, giving the animal a glossy appearance.

The only Georgia barrier island supporting a population of mole skinks is Cumberland, where they have been observed only at the north end, but not in beach interdune habitats.

While they spend most of their time underground, on the island they have been recorded active on the surface or under objects, as well as underground, in all months except November through January.

A female containing eight eggs was found dead on the island on 29 April.

_____. Family Scincidae. **Southeastern Five-lined Skink**. *Plestiodon inexpectatus* Taylor, 1932. Synonym: *Eumeces inexpectatus*. This medium-sized, glossy lizard may reach 216 millimeters (8.5 inches) total length and can be confused with a young broad-headed skink. Both have parallel light stripes on the dorsal surface, on a brown to black background. An easy distinguishing characteristic is the scale arrangement on the underside of the tail. This species has scales of uniform size, whereas those of the broad-headed skink are wide in the central row. The dorsal stripes of juveniles may be orange to reddish on the head, light on the body, with a tail of bright blue. The stripes fade with age, more so in the male than the female, and the blue of the tail changes to a gray brown at sexual maturity. During breeding season, the heads of males enlarge and the brownish color becomes reddish orange.

They occur on many of the Georgia barrier islands, including some of Holocene origin, preferring dry, wooded areas. On Cumberland they are found in the scrub and on the wooded Holocene ridges in the Sweetwater complex, as well as in upland forests.

Activity on Cumberland Island has been observed in March, April, and June through August. This is among the first lizard species to disappear at the onset of cool autumn temperatures.

The stomachs of two island southeastern five-lined skinks were examined for food items revealing a wasp and spiders in equal amounts. Ticks have been collected on this lizard on the island. See Appendix VI. A. Some of these lizards have been killed in island wildfires.

_____. Family Scincidae. **Broad-headed Skink**. *Plestiodon laticeps* (Schneider, 1801). Synonym: *Eumeces laticeps*. This largest of the Cumberland Island lizards may reach 324 millimeters (12.8 inches) total length with robust proportions. Cumberland Island specimens have been recorded at 310 and 311 millimeters (slightly more than 12 inches), with an average total length of 236 millimeters (9.3 inches). Their smooth overlapping scales are glossy and include osteoderms in most vulnerable places, providing a firm, protective armor. Five narrow, light stripes run the length of the black body of the juvenile and disappear behind the hind legs; the tail of the young is an eye-catching blue. Pattern and color change with sexual maturity, when stripes usually disappear and the overall color becomes brown, tan, or bronze, with an orange head. Males are larger than females, and during the mating season, hormones cause the large, jowly head of the male to further enlarge and its orange color to intensify. The naturalist Archie Carr (Carr and Goin, 1959) described this lizard as having an "undeservedly sinister look," and many rural people say it is poisonous. It is not. The belly is light and unmarked. Juveniles of this species may be differentiated from southeastern five-lined skinks by scale patterns. Broad-heads have a central row of enlarged scales on the underside of the tail, whereas the scales are of uniform size in the southeastern five-lined skink.

They are found throughout Georgia although are not common in the mountains, and they have been reported from the barrier islands of Wassaw, Ossabaw, St. Catherines, Sapelo, Little St. Simons, Jekyll, Little Cumberland, and Cumberland. Being semiarboreal, they are associated with oaks and prefer large trees, which usually have holes for refuge, but they also use disturbed areas. One lives in my chicken house. On Cumberland Island, any moist, forested area serves them, such as Yankee Paradise Hills, the ridge hammocks in the Sweetwater complex, and the scrub. Activity on Cumberland Island has been recorded from March through September, with a peak in May.

The stomachs of four Cumberland Island broad-headed skinks contained a wide variety of species. Spiders topped the list by volume, with caterpillars, click beetles, and chrysomelid beetles following (Whitaker et al., 2012b). I witnessed an adult broad-headed skink follow the buzzing, slow flight of a carpenter bee, *Xylocopa* sp., with his eye and snatch it out of the air. After a brief tussle, the skink subdued and swallowed the bee.

Mating has been observed on Cumberland Island in May, and females with eggs are seen in June and July; hatchlings occur primarily from July to August. Tick larvae and nymphs have been collected from this skink on Cumberland Island, as have trombiculid mites. See Appendix VI A.

Unusually hard freezes have claimed several of these lizards on the island. Mortality is occasionally observed after natural wildfires, and a few of these lizards are killed by vehicles.

_____. Family Scincidae. **Ground Skink.** *Scincella lateralis* (Say, 1823). A small, 76 to 130 millimeters (3 to 5.13 inches) total length, fast, long-tailed lizard, the ground skink has shiny, smooth, overlapping scales and a long tail. The dorsal color is tan to brown, frequently peppered with small dark spots, with a little reddish rust color around the head and neck of adults. A dorsolateral dark stripe, beginning behind the eye, runs the length of the body and onto the tail on each side. Below that, a light brown fades into the white to yellowish belly, which becomes bright yellow in males during the breeding season. A distinguishing characteristic, which no other island lizard has, is a transparent oval window on its lower eyelid.

They are found on most of the Georgia barrier islands, including Ossabaw, St. Catherines, Sapelo, Little Cumberland, and Cumberland. On Cumberland the species is found in most maritime forest habitats, the north end scrub, the Holocene Sweetwater ridges, and particularly the wooded areas surrounding wetlands.

Activity has been recorded on Cumberland Island in every month but December, with peaks in June. During cold weather, they are found under logs, a habit which may lead to predation by armadillos and feral hogs.

The most important foods in five Cumberland Island ground skinks by volume were spiders, then crickets, followed by caterpillars. Spiders occurred in all stomachs (Whitaker et al., 2012b).

Hatchlings have been seen on Cumberland in August and September. Males with bright yellow undersides have been observed in November. These lizards are relatively short-lived, and complete population turnover occurs in about three years.

On Cumberland Island, a ground skink was found inside a cottonmouth, and four, or parts of four, skinks were observed in armadillo stomachs. Interestingly, two animals found in stomachs in February were whole and thus could have been dormant when captured, whereas two from warmer months were represented by only a tail each. One ground skink has been found dead on the road.

_____. Family Teiidae. **Six-lined Racerunner**. *Aspidoscelis sexlineatus* (Linnaeus, 1766). Synonym: *Cnemidophorus sexlineatus*. This attractive, medium-sized lizard, 152 to 241 millimeters (5.9 to 9.4 inches) total length, has a long whip-like tail, which is very thin and narrow at the tip. The largest Cumberland Island specimens measured were 236 and 240 millimeters (9.3 to 9.4 inches) total length. The background color of the dorsum is dark brown, with six narrow, yellowish longitudinal stripes (lines) running from the eye to behind the rear legs. Scales on the back are minute and nonoverlapping, giving the animal a velvety appearance.

They may be found throughout Georgia in open, well-drained, sunny, sandy areas and on most of the barrier islands. On Cumberland Island, they are found in the scrub on the north end, interdune areas, wooded Holocene ridges, and open, disturbed places. Activity on Cumberland Island occurs from March through October, with a peak from April through August.

The most important food of twenty-four racerunners from Cumberland Island was spiders, followed by caterpillars, little brown crickets, *Nemobius* sp., froghoppers (spittlebugs), and beetles (Whitaker et al., 2012b). Nematodes have been found in the gut of Cumberland Island racerunners.

Mating has been observed on Cumberland Island at the end of April and in June. Females with eggs are seen in June and July, and hatchlings from June through September, with a peak in July and August. On Cumberland Island, coachwhips have been observed eating racerunners, and vehicles cause great mortality.

_____. Family Colubridae. **Scarlet Snake.** *Cemophora coccinea* (Blumenbach, 1738). This snake is small, usually not more than 550 millimeters (21.5 inches) total length and averages 383 millimeters (14.9 inches). On Cumberland Island, the largest individual recorded was 513 millimeters (about 20 inches). It is slim and brightly colored with a repetitive pattern of scarlet, black, and white bands across the dorsum; the scarlet bands are the most prominent. The underside is unmarked and white to yellowish. The snout, which is scarlet and pointed, projects beyond the lower jaw. Young have the same markings as adults, with hatchlings as small as 113 millimeters (4.4 inches). The enlarged rostral scale on the snout is an adaptation for burrowing, and the enlarged posterior teeth in the rear of the upper jaw facilitate consumption of reptile eggs by slicing them open in order to swallow the contents. The alternate red, black, and light bands cause some confusion with the coral snake on the mainland, but coral snakes have not been documented on Cumberland Island.

The scarlet snake has been reported on the Georgia islands of Wassaw, Ossabaw, St. Catherines, Sapelo, and Cumberland. Its preferred habitat is open forests, such as pine flatwoods and mixed-pine hardwoods, with friable soils and much organic litter for burrowing, which on Cumberland Island includes the north end scrub community, edge of the forest, and disturbed sites around structures.

Activity on Cumberland Island has been recorded from May through November, with a peak in June and July. Even though scarlet snakes are adapted for burrowing in sandy, loose soil, they are considered only semifossorial because they also spend time above ground, usually at night.

Raccoons have been verified as predators on Cumberland Island, but the most significant island mortality occurs as a result of vehicles. Almost 30% of the island observations have been roadkills.

_____. Family Colubridae. **Southern Black Racer.** *Coluber constrictor* Linnaeus, 1758. The black racer is a long, streamlined, extremely supple, unpatterned black snake averaging 906 millimeters (36 inches) in total length on Cumberland Island. The longest racer measured on Cumberland Island was 1,475 millimeters (58 inches) total length. The scales are smooth and satiny with a luster, although not glossy. Dorsal color is uniform black to charcoal gray, whereas the underside is several shades lighter but still a slate gray; the chin and throat are white. The young have a different pattern from the adults, with brown to reddish blotches across the center of the back on a light-gray background. This juvenile pattern fades by the end of the second year.

Racers occur on most of the Georgia barrier islands and Amelia Island, Florida, in nearly all terrestrial habitats, especially dry open woods, as well as in pine flatwoods and along streams and swamps. Racers may be observed throughout Cumberland Island but are not frequently seen in the open interdune area. Activity on Cumberland has been recorded in every month of the year but mostly from March through September with a peak in May.

Undetected for about 20 minutes, I once watched an interesting neck-waving behavior in what appeared to be a foraging racer (about 1 meter, 3 feet long). The snake would stop forward motion with the head and anterior third of the body held off the ground about one and a quarter to one and a half inches, then with its head and lower two-thirds of the body held motionless, the neck region sinuously waved laterally with ripples running forward in a repeated motion. After a few seconds, it resumed foraging and repeated the behavior several times. I saw no other snakes in the vicinity. Fitch (1963) described "spasmodic rippling movements" of the male as he lay in contact with the female, and my observations occurred in mid-April as snakes might be seeking mates, so perhaps this was some form of precourtship behavior.

Stomachs from island racers have contained tree frogs, a caterpillar, and small, unidentified snakes. Internal parasites of island racers include three nematodes, *Physaloptera abjecta*, *Ophidascaris ashi*, and *Kalicephalus costatus*, and a lung fluke, *Renifer ellipticus* (Bursey, pers. comm.), which is a digenetic trematode, likely using an aquatic snail and the southern leopard frog as intermediate hosts, with the racer as the definitive host. These flukes have been collected in island racers from March through June and in September and October. A tick has also been recorded on island racers. See Appendix VI A.

Mating on Cumberland Island has been observed from March through May. One large (4 foot) Cumberland Island racer was found mauled and mortally wounded by an introduced bobcat, although most recorded mortality on the island has been from vehicles. On two occasions, racers were found lethally caught in cast nets, which had been left piled outside.

_____. Family Colubridae. **Southern Ringneck Snake.** *Diadophis punctatus* (Linnaeus, 1766). The southern ringneck snake is small and slim with an adult average total length of about 300 millimeters (12 inches). The dorsal surface is a uniformly dark gray to slate gray, interrupted only by a narrow, light-yellowish to pale ring around the neck; this ring may be incomplete. The belly is yellow with a midventral row of dark spots, one on each scale. The head is small, scales are smooth, and the anal scale is divided. Young have the same pattern as adults. A hatchling was recorded on Cumberland Island on 6 October.

Ringnecks have not been reported on any of the other Georgia barrier islands, only Cumberland and Amelia Island, Florida. The species prefers low, wet, or very moist wooded areas, such as pine flatwoods and habitats around wetlands. On Cumberland they are known from Swamp Field, the Sweetwater sloughs, around Whitney Lake, and in the north end scrub.

While they become dormant during cold weather, sometimes in groups, ringnecks may be active throughout a warm winter. Activity on Cumberland Island has been recorded from April through October.

Other snakes have been suggested as the most important predators of this small snake, but on Cumberland Island, feral hogs probably have a greater impact on the population. All of the moist habitats used by the southern ringneck are also favorite haunts of the many feral hogs. The introduced Virginia opossum has been verified as an island predator of the ringneck, and armadillos are potential predators. A few of these snakes have been found killed on Cumberland Island in natural wildfires.

_____. Family Colubridae. **Cornsnake.** *Pantherophis guttatus* (Linnaeus, 1766). Synonym: *Elaphe guttata*. This is a colorful, slender, medium-sized snake that may reach 1,830 millimeters (almost 72 inches) but averages 887 millimeters (34.9 inches) total length on Cumberland Island; the largest measured thus far was 1,600 millimeters (62.9 inches). The blotches or saddles of rusty brown across the back vary in color from orange red to deep, rich rusty brown and are bordered by a thin black line. There may be similarly colored spots low on the side. Between and below the markings, the background color ranges from a golden orange tan to brown. There is usually an arrow-shaped pattern on the top of the head pointing forward and a rusty stripe from the eye to the gape and on to the neck. The underside is porcelain white with blocky black markings in an irregular pattern. In cross section, the body is not round but is flattened on the ventral surface and round on top like a loaf of bread.

They occur on the Georgia barrier islands of Wassaw, Ossabaw, St. Catherines, Sapelo, and Cumberland and on Amelia Island, Florida. Open hardwood forests are their preferred habitats, but habitat edges (ecotones) suit them, as do flatwoods and disturbed areas. They can occupy any area that supports small vertebrates, especially mammals.

Activity has been recorded in every month on Cumberland Island, with a peak from April through May; least activity occurs in January and February. They take refuge from cold underground or in rotten logs; one was found frozen to death under a piece of tin in 1983.

Breeding occurs in April and May throughout its range, and peak activity is recorded on Cumberland Island during these months.

Environmental extremes, such as hard freezes and natural wildfires, kill a few individuals, but most documented mortality on Cumberland Island has been the result of malicious destruction by people and vehicular traffic.

_____. Family Colubridae. **Yellow Rat snake or Chicken Snake.** *Pantherophis obsoletus* (Say, 1823). Synonym: *Elaphe obsoleta.* Four well-defined brown longitudinal stripes on a uniformly yellow-tan background quickly identify this fairly large snake. It is long and usually relatively slim, with Cumberland Island lengths averaging around 1,571 millimeters (62 inches) total length. The largest individual recorded from the island was 1,980 millimeters (more than 6 feet.). The underside is a pale yellow tan to off-white. Young have a pattern of blotches.

The yellow rat snake is found on most of the Georgia barrier islands and Amelia Island, Florida, in the upland maritime forest. Observations of habitat use on Cumberland Island may be somewhat biased by human development and chicken houses. This may be the most commonly observed snake living in close association with humans.

Activity on Cumberland Island has been recorded in every month, with a peak in May and June.

Their predilection for eggs no doubt gained them the common name "chicken snake," for everyone keeping chickens on Cumberland Island runs into them sooner or later. The greatest depredations in my chicken house occur in July and August. In 1996, depredations on my chicken eggs were so numerous that C. R. Shoop and I began marking captured snakes before releasing them away from the house. One individual was caught several times after returning from relocation sites a little more than half a mile away, then about three-quarters of a mile distant, then a little less than a mile in a different direction, and finally about two miles with the scrub-flatwoods community intervening, from which location it did not return. Usually only eggs were eaten, but occasionally young chickens were taken, and once an adult rooster was strangled to death in the chicken house.

On Cumberland Island, eastern gray squirrels, a treefrog, and the green anole have been recorded in their diet. Larval trombiculid mites are frequently found between the scales of the head and neck region of this species on Cumberland Island.

Mating on Cumberland Island has been recorded in June. The number of eggs usually averages about fifteen, and clutches are oviposited in summer in rotten logs or under cover.

I have found yellow rat snakes dead with puncture wounds suggesting avian capture. A few are killed by vehicles on Cumberland and a few die in wildfires, but the majority of my records confirm deliberate killing by chicken housekeepers or malicious destruction by people afraid of snakes.

_____. Family Colubridae. **Mud Snake.** *Farancia abacura* (Holbrook, 1836). The mud snake is a large, relatively thick-bodied, glossy snake with a bright, colorful belly and lower sides of the body. The scales are smooth, the anal scale is frequently divided, the eyes are small, and the tail terminates in a sharp point. The dorsal coloration is black, and the belly has irregular red or pink crossbars that extend a short way onto the lower sides; this coloration is visible when the snake is in an upright position. The chin may be colored yellow or orange yellow. The young are colored like adults, but the red may reach higher on the sides. Although they can get much larger, the average length is about 1,219 millimeters (4 feet) total length.

They have been reported from the barrier islands of Sapelo and Cumberland. The lentic, sometimes stagnant, nonflowing freshwater of the island sloughs and ponds suits them perfectly, and they may be found in and around all of the more permanent wetlands when water is present.

Island specimens have been recorded only from April through June. A hatchling was found on Cumberland Island in May about 100 feet from water on dry, elevated ground. The only reported Cumberland Island mortality resulted from direct human contact.

_____. Family Colubridae. **Kingsnake**. *Lampropeltis getula* (Linnaeus, 1766). Although the pattern of this snake is variable, it is distinctive enough to be easily recognized. The smooth scales are shiny and black with narrow white to off-white crossbars, fairly widely spaced across the back. Each bar usually forks on the lower end, and the belly is black with some irregular white checkering. The largest Cumberland Island specimen measured was 1,626 millimeters (64 inches).

It has been reported on most of the local barrier islands. Kingsnakes like to be near water, such as the edge of wetlands, but will use a wide variety of habitats, avoiding xeric, very dry situations. The Sweetwater sloughs, just inside the tree line behind the interdune area, and the scrub are good Cumberland locations for it.

Their activity is typically crepuscular but may be nocturnal during the heat of summer. Activity has been recorded on Cumberland Island in every month except January, with a peak in May.

Trombiculid mites occur on this species on Cumberland Island.

The kingsnake is easily caught and killed, and both capture for pets and malicious killing have been noted on the island. Several animals have been found as roadkills, but no significant source of mortality has been identified. As in many other areas on the mainland, observations of the species have declined significantly in the last few decades. I recorded only two sightings from 1990 to 2010 (twenty years), whereas there were eighteen between 1974 and 1990 (sixteen years).

_____. Family Colubridae. **Scarlet Kingsnake**. *Lampropeltis elapsoides* (Holbrook, 1838). This brightly colored, eye-catching snake always demands a close look. The repeated pattern of red-black-yellow-black-red bands completely around the body immediately suggests the venomous coral snake, but in the coral snake the colors are in a different order. Remember, "red and yellow will kill a fellow, but red and black, friend of Jack." Red and yellow are always separated by black in the scarlet kingsnake. The coral snake also has a black snout, whereas the scarlet kingsnake has a red snout. The largest recorded individual from Cumberland Island was 581 millimeters (22.8 inches) total length.

They have been reported from the Georgia barrier islands of Sapelo and Cumberland and from Amelia Island, Florida. This is typically a snake of open pine woods or flatwoods. On Cumberland Island, specific records are available from Yankee Paradise, Stafford Place, and the Brickhill area.

Activity on Cumberland has been noted from February through November, with peaks in March and May. One animal was found inactive from cold in March. It is adept at climbing and worming its way under the bark of standing dead pine trees, where it forages using both cruising and ambush strategies.

One animal was observed entering the nest of a diamondback-terrapin, but it was not determined if eggs had been consumed. All island specimens examined have had empty guts.

The only island mortality recorded has been from vehicles; road mortality comprised about 30% of all scarlet kingsnake observations on the island.

_____. Family Colubridae. **Coachwhip**. *Masticophis flagellum* Shaw, 1802. This extremely long, lithe snake averages more than 1,524 millimeters (60 inches) total length on Cumberland Island, with the longest recorded individual measuring 2,060 millimeters (81.1 inches). The coloration is unlike any other local snake. The long, large head and anterior part of the body are black, which color changes gradually to dark brown and finally to a light tan on the posterior end. The proportion of dark to light tan is variable. The belly is similarly colored, perhaps a few shades lighter. Juvenile coloration differs markedly; a pattern of brown marks across the back is visible on a lighter brown background. The snake has the appearance of a braided whip, hence the common name.

They occur on the Georgia barrier islands of Sapelo, Little Cumberland, and Cumberland and on Amelia Island, Florida. Dry uplands with open understories are their preferred habitat, but they may be found in almost any Cumberland Island habitat, including the interdune area and beach. Specific localities include the Stafford area, Yankee Paradise, and the ridges of the Sweetwater sloughs.

Activity on Cumberland Island has been noted from March to November, with a spike in May. I have no winter (December to February) records.

Diurnal activity is usually during the warmest times of the day; at night they retreat to a protected refuge, usually underground. Speed is their greatest asset. As the fastest of the North American snakes, they use speed both to escape threats and to catch prey. It seems appropriate that this fastest of snakes prefers to dine on the fastest of lizards, the racerunner. The other lizard recorded in their Cumberland Island diet is the glass lizard.

Mating on Cumberland Island has been reported in May; fourteen eggs were found in an island specimen on 15 May, and a hatchling was observed on the island in late August.

Chiggers have been collected on island specimens, and another mite is frequent around the eyes. See Appendix VI A.

Coachwhips have been deliberately killed by people on the island, and several have been killed by vehicles. One animal was found caught in a cast net left on the ground, and a few individuals have been found with wounds that suggest avian predation attempts.

_____. Family Colubridae. **Rough Green Snake**. *Opheodrys aestivus* (Linnaeus, 1766). Extremely long, thin, and supple, this attractive snake averages 566 millimeters (22 inches) total length on Cumberland Island, with the longest specimen measured at 808 millimeters (about 32 inches). The color is a bright uniform green, which perfectly matches new spring vegetation. The belly is pale yellow to off-white. Young are colored similarly to adults. In death, the color turns blue gray. Scales are keeled, thus the name "rough green snake," but they do not produce a rough feeling except in large animals. A hatchling was found on Cumberland Island on 8 August.

This species has been reported from the Georgia barrier islands of Ossabaw, Sapelo, Little Cumberland, and Cumberland and also from Amelia Island, Florida. Specific Cumberland localities for this snake include Whitney Lake and the Sweetwater complex, the Willow Pond area, around Dungeness, and in the north end scrub.

Activity on Cumberland Island occurs from March into December, with no outstanding peaks. Cold weather causes a retreat to the warmth of the ground in a protected area. One cold early April, an individual was found inactive under a board.

The greatest mortality documented on Cumberland Island is due to vehicles; 40% of the observations of this species have resulted from road fatalities. A grackle was seen carrying one specimen, but it could not be determined if the snake had been scavenged as a roadkill or if the grackle actually caught the snake. Roadkills have been recorded from April through November with no particular peaks. A few animals have been deliberately killed by humans and a few by wildfire.

_____. Family Colubridae. **Pine Woods Littersnake.** *Rhadinaea flavilata* (Cope, 1871). This elusive, small snake averages about 300 millimeters (12 inches) total length. The dorsal coloration is a golden to reddish brown with no pattern. The belly is pale to yellowish, also without pattern. The head is a shade or two darker than the body with a narrow dark line from the eye to the angle of the jaw. Smooth scales give the animal a glossy appearance. It has enlarged rear upper teeth and mild venom, which it uses to subdue prey. It is not harmful to humans.

Specimens have been found on Little Cumberland (one) and on Cumberland (one; Ruckdeschel, 2012) islands, and the species has been collected on Amelia Island, Florida, but none have been verified on the other Georgia islands. Low, poorly drained pine woods are their preferred habitat, but they also use rotten logs and loose bark in hardwood hammocks.

It has been suggested that arrival of the pine woods snake on islands may have been via rotten logs during times of high water, but it is also likely this species was on Cumberland Island at the time of isolation from the mainland.

_____. Family Colubridae. **Southern Banded Watersnake.** *Nerodia fasciata* (Linnaeus, 1766). The average total length on Cumberland Island is 634 millimeters (almost 25 inches), and the largest animal measured 1,193 millimeters (47 inches) total length. There is much variation in color and pattern of this species, but the background color is usually brown and there are usually dark crossbars along the back and onto the tail. As the animals mature, the crossbars frequently become obscured as the overall color darkens. Many times the only bright color visible is in patches along the lower sides. The belly is cream to light yellow with irregular reddish markings on each scale. There is often a dark stripe from the eye to the angle of the jaw.

This species is found on most of the Georgia barrier islands and Amelia Island, Florida, usually around wetlands but sometimes in forested habitats. Specific Cumberland Island locations are Whitney Lake, Swamp Field, and the Sweetwater slough complex. It has been seen at the edge of the island salt marsh, although usually in the vicinity of a freshwater seep.

Activity on Cumberland Island peaks in April and May, with a smaller peak in August, and continues from February through November. I have no records of activity in December or January on Cumberland, and only one in February. It is likely that the snakes are active during warm periods throughout the winter but become inactive during cold spells.

These snakes mate in the spring and are viviparous, giving live birth in mid- to late summer. Embryos have been recorded on Cumberland Island at the end of July and mid-August, and a newborn was found on 4 August. On Cumberland Island, mosquitofish, leopard frogs, and tadpoles have been recorded in their diet.

Several Cumberland Island animals have been found dead with wounds suggesting an avian predator. More frequently than vehicle fatalities, the island water snakes are deliberately killed by humans. A few have been killed on Cumberland Island by wildfire.

_____. Family Colubridae. **Florida Red-bellied Snake.** *Storeria occipitomaculata* Trapido, 1944. This very small, secretive snake averages only 189 millimeters (7.4 inches) total length on Cumberland Island, with the largest record at 209 millimeters (8.2 inches). Both color and dorsal pattern are variable. Typically the color is brown or gray with faint or bold or no longitudinal stripes. Four stripes may be present, two on the back and two on the sides. The dark head is separated in color from the dorsum by light spots or an irregular band at the neck. The belly is unmarked and typically reddish or orange. Young are similar in coloration to the adults.

Cumberland and Sapelo are the only Georgia barrier islands on which this species has been reported, but it is also on Amelia Island, Florida. These diminutive snakes usually stay in thick leaf litter, underground, or under debris in moderately moist woodlands and around freshwater wetlands.

This terrestrial species sometimes moves relatively long distances, governed by soil moisture and its effect on the snake's prey (slugs and earthworms). On Cumberland Island, the majority of activity has been noted from May through June, with no records from November through February except for inactive animals.

On Cumberland Island, one was recovered from the stomach of a cottonmouth. Despite the low number of specimens encountered on Cumberland (ten), one was found killed by a vehicle and one was killed by wildfire.

_____. Family Coluber. **Ribbon Snake.** *Thamnophis sauritus* (Linnaeus, 1766). Ribbon snakes are relatively long and very thin, with their whip-like tail making up one-quarter to one-third of their total length. The greatest length of individuals measured on Cumberland Island was 965 millimeters (37.9 inches), but the average length is 609 millimeters (24 inches). The ground color is soft shades of brown with a light longitudinal stripe on each side and often a central stripe or remnants of a stripe. The belly is unmarked and off-white to light tan. The eyes are large and there is frequently a vertical white bar in front of each eye.

It has been recorded on Ossabaw, St. Catherines, Sapelo, Little Cumberland, Cumberland, and Amelia islands. Wetlands and adjacent habitats are home to this semiaquatic species in the Sweetwater complex, the scrub ponds, and most freshwater wet areas on the island.

Activity on Cumberland Island is highest from April through June, but observations have been made throughout the year. They have been found inactive under cover during cold weather. Two individuals have been found missing the ends of their tails; they may have the ability, like their relative the garter snake, of tail autotomy.

H. B. Jordan found that captives readily fed on newly metamorphosed toads, and they have been observed catching a green treefrog on the island. H. B. Jordan (pers. comm.) found an intracellular parasitic blood protozoan to be common in Cumberland Island ribbon snakes. See Appendix VI. A.

Ribbon snakes are viviparous, mating in the spring and giving live birth in July and August. A Cumberland Island female caught on 6 August gave birth to twelve offspring on 17/18 August. There are usually ten to fifteen young. Newborn or very small individuals have been recorded on Cumberland primarily in August and occasionally throughout the winter.

On Little Cumberland Island, an armadillo was observed biting the tail of a live ribbon snake, which was struggling to escape. The observer intervened, but the snake died overnight. One ribbon snake was found killed by wildfire on Cumberland Island, and four were vehicle fatalities.

_____. Family Colubridae. **Garter Snake.** *Thamnophis sirtalis* (Linnaeus, 1758). Both the color and pattern are highly variable in this species, but the most common form has a background color of greenish brown to dark brown with dark checkered-type markings and three clear longitudinal stripes; the stripes may be yellowish to very blue. There is usually a center stripe with one on each side. Some individuals may have a dominating checkered pattern in which the stripes are deemphasized or lacking completely. The belly is light, off-white to yellowish, with dark spots down each side. The young are similarly colored and patterned as adults. The average size for Cumberland Island garter snakes is 672 millimeters (26 inches) total length, and the largest individual measured was 940 millimeters (37 inches).

They have enlarged teeth in the rear of the upper jaw and mildly venomous saliva, which aids in capturing prey.

The garter snake has been recorded on Ossabaw, St. Catherines, Sapelo, Little Cumberland, and Cumberland islands in Georgia and on Amelia Island, Florida, using most habitats. They avoid the open interdune during the heat of the day, preferring moist woodlands, especially adjacent to wetlands. Garter snakes have been seen in the high salt marsh on Cumberland Island, although infrequently. They are more likely to be observed around the Sweetwater complex, the Cedar Dock area, and in wooded uplands.

Activity has been noted in all months on Cumberland Island, although it is reduced from November through February. Greatest activity occurs from April through June. As with other snakes with enlarged upper rear teeth, they sometimes appear to chew their food while maneuvering the enlarged teeth into a position to effectively hold prey. They also use these enlarged teeth while biting in defense. Once, while holding a garter snake loosely behind the head, I watched it squirm and wiggle with its mouth partly open until I saw the large tooth maneuvered into a position to reach my hand. They have the capability for tail autotomy. However, like nearly all snakes, their first choice is always to escape. Two animals have been found on Cumberland Island missing the tips of their tails.

On Cumberland Island, southern toads, eastern spadefoots, and leopard frogs have been documented as prey. One snake was observed tugging a resisting toad from its burrow. The intestinal nematodes *Physaloptera abject* and *Ophidascaris ashi* have been identified in garter snakes from Cumberland Island (C. Bursey, pers. comm.).

Mating on Cumberland Island has been observed in April and gravid females seen in June and July. Garter snakes are viviparous; very small and/or newborn snakes have been recorded from July to September.

On Cumberland Island, cottonmouths and American alligators have been verified as predators. Two unusual sources of mortality have also been documented: horses and an electric fence. The horse smashed a small garter snake by stepping on it. Two Cumberland Island animals were deliberately killed by people in the last decades, and eighteen were roadkills.

_____. Family Viperidae. **Cottonmouth**. *Agkistrodon piscivorus* (Lacepède, 1789). The color and pattern of this snake are variable. Across the back, dark crossbands and blotches of irregular shape are separated by light areas. Colors range from a beautiful rusty brown and light tan to an olive brown with a very dark pattern; some individuals may be black with no obvious dorsal pattern. The young are usually more brightly colored, but their pattern fades with age. There is a dark stripe through the eye to the corner of the mouth, and two vertical stripes are present on each side of the front of the snout. There may be faded markings or blotches on the light belly. The underside of the tail is frequently black except in very young animals, when the tip is a sulphur yellow. Pupils of the eye are vertically elliptical.

This is a heavy-bodied snake with a small neck, which emphasizes the large size of the head. The largest specimen from Cumberland Island, as measured by landowners in 1912, was 1,295 millimeters (51 inches), but the average total length on the island is 852 millimeters (33.5 inches). All members of this family are venomous.

Cottonmouths may be found around any type of aquatic habitat, but they also sometimes occur well away from water. On Cumberland Island, habitats frequented are the Sweetwater sloughs, the north end scrub, and along streams draining the interior to the west and seeps at the western edge of the island.

Activity on Cumberland Island has been recorded in every month but February. The earliest spring date is 6 March, with April through September the peak months of activity. Cottonmouths are normally not aggressive toward humans, but unless they have an easy escape route, they will attempt to intimidate by threatening with an open-mouth display. The yellow tail tip in very young animals is used as a lure for small prey, such as frogs (Wharton, 1960). With the end of the tail held vertically off the ground, the tip is provocatively wiggled, resembling a larval insect.

On Cumberland Island, the following species have been documented as prey: spadefoot toad, ground skink, broad-headed skink, garter snake, Florida red-bellied snake, and the southern short-tailed shrew.

Chiggers are occasionally found on Cumberland Island cottonmouths. Internally, a fluke, *Renifer ellipticus*, and a cestode, *Ophiotaenia agkistrodontis*, have been recorded (C. Bursey, pers. comm.). Pentastomes, parasitic tongue worms, frequently occur internally.

Cumberland Island road fatalities have increased since 1990. Prior to that (1974 to 1990), no cottonmouths were found dead on the road, but each decade since then has seen an increase (1991 to 2000 = 4, 2001 to 2010 = 8). Also, a few of these snakes are killed in temporary ponds by natural wildfires.

_____. Family Viperidae. **Eastern Diamondback Rattlesnake.** *Crotalus adamanteus* Beauvois, 1799. Eastern diamondbacks are the largest rattlesnakes in North America. The dorsal pattern is characterized by large dark diamonds strung down the back, point to point, each extending part way down the side; they usually fade near the tail. The background color is light brown to tan, and each diamond is outlined with a narrow band of yellowish-cream color. Variations in color and pattern are common. The large head is clearly distinct from the much smaller neck. The head has diagonal stripes on the side, a narrow, light one followed by a wide, dark band through the eye, followed by another narrow, light stripe. The snout has vertical, light stripes and the belly is off-white. This is a heavy-bodied snake. The average total length of Cumberland Island diamondbacks is 1,257 millimeters (49.5 inches), and the largest snake measured was 1,828 millimeters (72 inches).

The diamondback, a coastal plain form, is found from southeastern North Carolina to eastern Louisiana and occurs on most of the Georgia barrier islands. Sand hills, pine/oak communities, and palmetto flatwoods are home to this species, and on the island they may be found in any upland area and are not uncommon. Several have been found alive on the beach.

Activity on Cumberland Island has been observed in every month, with a slight peak in October and less activity from December through February. Diamondbacks take refuge from cold weather usually in a stump hole or somewhere underground, although they will emerge on warm days to bask. With so many heavy-footed feral livestock on the island, diamondbacks are accustomed to crashing and stomping by large animals and sometimes show very little fear of humans.

Because of their size, these diamondbacks can take fairly large prey, such as marsh rabbits, which were common before the park service introduced bobcats to the island. These rattlesnakes also take smaller mammals and seem to know when nuts are ripe in order to ambush intently foraging squirrels. I have found them inside my chicken pen causing the chickens no alarm, although a half-grown hen was once killed by a rattlesnake. Songbirds may be taken for food, as when a northern cardinal was caught and eaten in my yard (Mitchell and Ruckdeschel, 2008). Pentastomes (internal parasites of the respiratory system, commonly called tongue worms because of their resemblance to tongues) are common in Cumberland Island diamondbacks.

Eastern diamondbacks have been seen mating on the island in September; one individual had ova 12 to 20 millimeters (0.47 to 0.78 inches) long on 19 October, and another had seventeen ova on 29 April. They are viviparous, with newborn or very small young animals seen in June, September, and November. Females may not reproduce until they are four years old, and then do so only every two or three years.

On Cumberland Island, twenty-four diamondbacks have been recorded as deliberately killed by people in the last few decades. Mortality has also resulted from vehicles, a few have been killed by National Park Service machinery, and a few by wildfires.

_____. Family Viperidae. **Canebrake Rattlesnake**. *Crotalus horridus* Linnaeus, 1758. Canebrakes are large, heavy-bodied snakes, pinkish gray to light tan with narrow zigzag dark-brown crossbars along the back and a bright, contrasting rusty stripe down the midline. The tail is black. As with most snakes, the background coloration is variable, ranging from light individuals to almost black. The belly is off-white to grayish with some dark mottling, and there is a dark stripe from the eye to the angle of the mouth. We have measurements of only two Cumberland Island specimens, about 762 millimeters (30 inches) and 1,148 millimeters (45 inches) total length.

Canebrakes have been reported from St. Catherines, Sapelo, and Cumberland islands of the Georgia barrier chain. The name "canebrake" suggests its habitat preference. Rather than the dry uplands that the eastern diamondback prefers, the canebrake is a denizen of the lowlands, wet pine flatwoods, and swampy areas. Specific Cumberland Island locations are around Whitney Lake and the ponds around Stafford. Two have been found on the beach.

Observations on Cumberland Island are not frequent enough to show activity periods; all sightings have been in late summer, except for one in early October. At least two were deliberately killed on the island (1973 to 2010).

ORDER TESTUDINES. Family Cheloniidae. **Sea Turtles**.

Introduction. Cattle and a three-mile eastward-extending rock jetty bordering the St. Marys River on the south end of the island, constructed during the 1880s, had a profound effect on sea-turtle nesting on Cumberland Island. Prior to the 1990s, few sea turtles nested on the southern half of the beach due to the instability and poor development of the dune system. Cattle were removed in the late 1980s, allowing some dune recovery, and turtles now nest the full length of the ocean beach. Feral horses, however, continue to degrade the habitat and feral hogs always threaten eggs.

Four species of sea turtles have been recorded nesting along the Georgia coast, but only the loggerhead nests regularly and in relatively large numbers. Nesting turtles were tagged on Cumberland Island for many years, but the state presently requires only a daily survey to monitor the success of the nests. Protective screen, which deters raccoons and small mammals, is put over each nest, and each nest is monitored through the incubation period. Nest chambers are then excavated following emergence of the hatchlings.

Five species of sea turtle have washed ashore dead on Cumberland Island as a result of commercial fishing operations: loggerheads, Kemp's ridleys, greens, leatherbacks, and hawksbills. Sea turtles are all listed as endangered by the US government and the International Union for the Conservation of Nature (IUCN). Sea turtles must breathe air, and if incidentally caught in a trawl net, may succumb to anoxia before being ejected by a turtle excluder device (TED) in the net, which handles passive objects much better than struggling ones. Depending upon the size of the turtle, the energy depleted in struggling for air, the water temperature, and the health of the animal, some individuals may survive the ordeal, although many do not. Fortuitously, data on Cumberland Island sea-turtle strandings were collected for thirty years (1979 to 2009), fifteen years of which were prior to the implementation of TEDs and fifteen years following implementation. These data allow evaluation of the effectiveness of the device purported to reduce mortality. The results clearly indicate that TEDs did not lessen local sea turtle mortality during that time (Table 4).

The number of strandings for most species increased over the time surveyed. Kemp's ridleys, with the second highest number of strandings on Cumberland Island, increased from eighty-nine during the first fifteen years (no TEDs) to 197 individuals the latter fifteen years (TEDs mandatory). The number of greens similarly increased from ten to fifty-eight. Conservation programs have focused on greens and Kemp's ridleys, and the increased stranding numbers may reflect past conservation efforts and protection. Loggerhead numbers dropped from 1,017 during the first fifteen years to 922 the second fifteen years, and leatherback numbers have remained constant. Since there was no decrease in general sea-turtle mortality in this area for the thirty years mentioned, the decline in the number of loggerheads may have reflected a local population decline. Trawling is undoubtedly a major factor in local loggerhead mortality. The reduction in strandings beginning in 2006 also coincides with less trawling along this coast, likely involving the competition of farm-raised imports with locally caught shrimp, as well as financial constraints, including rising fuel costs imposed on fishermen by our faltering national economy. Simply put, less shrimping effort has resulted in a decrease in sea turtle strandings.

The standard measurement for turtles is a straight-line carapace measure (SL or SCL), but because carrying a large caliper in the field is difficult, many projects use curved length (Curved Carapace Length [CCL]), which can be easily taken with a simple measuring tape. Cumberland Island sea turtles were all measured "over the curve" rather than with a caliper. Measurements can be converted.

_____. Family Cheloniidae. **Loggerhead Sea Turtle.** *Caretta caretta* (Linnaeus, 1758). Adult loggerheads get quite large, up to 122 centimeters (48 inches) curved carapace length; females nesting on Cumberland Island average 102 centimeters (40 inches). The rufous color of the carapace and top of the head and limbs is the most immediate diagnostic character, but coloration is variable and can be obscured by epibiotic growth. The head is relatively larger than that of any of the other sea turtles, continuing to grow with age. Hatchlings are silver-dollar sized, oval, and of variable coloration.

A genetically distinct subpopulation, the females of which nest only from North Carolina to northeast Florida, nests on Cumberland Island. Ideally, stable primary dunes above the high-tide line are selected for nesting.

When choosing a nest site, females are sensitive to light and movement and may abort the nesting attempt if a threat is perceived. Once they have completed depositing eggs and covered and secured the nest, the opposite is true; that is, they are attracted to light, typically drawing them to the reflective ocean. Hatchlings are also attracted to light. Hatchlings, ready to emerge, wait for temperature at the ground surface to cool, which usually signifies that the sun has set. While most emergences occur at night, hatchlings may infrequently leave the nest during daylight hours after a brief shower cools the sand (Ruckdeschel et al., 2000).

Animals stranded on Cumberland Island have had moon snails, whelks, and various species of crabs in their gut (Ruckdeschel and Shoop, 2006). To demonstrate that they are opportunistic, they occasionally have individuals of only one species, such as a brittle star.

Nesting season on Cumberland Island begins the first of May and continues into August and sometimes September. Hatchlings emerge from late June through October and into November.

The greatest mortality occurs to eggs and hatchlings; to many predators, loggerheads are a seasonal resource. Ghost crabs, raccoons, and coyotes predominate as natural predators on the island at this time, but exotic feral swine, if not controlled, can eliminate every clutch of eggs and hatchlings on the island in a season. Historically, black bears were notorious egg poachers.

Locally, shrimp trawling is the greatest hazard for sea turtles. Only about a quarter of the animals killed wash ashore to be counted. Still, for the thirty years between 1979 and 2008, 1,939 dead loggerheads were recorded on Cumberland Island alone.

When Cumberland Island was in private ownership in the 1960s and 1970s, no protection from feral hogs was afforded nesting loggerheads and very few eggs escaped predation (Ruckdeschel et al., 2000). Nesting was also relegated to roughly the northern 5 miles of the island at that time, due to unsuitable physiographic conditions to the south. Nesting is now more equitably distributed along the entire beach with the dune system more stabilized and the feral hog population kept to a minimum. Presumably a higher percentage of hatchlings make it into the sea.

_____. Family Cheloniidae. **Green Sea Turtle**. *Chelonia mydas* (Linnaeus, 1758). Cumberland Island-stranded specimens have ranged from 22.5 to 87.5 centimeters CCL (8.9 to 34.4 inches), with the average at 42.5 centimeters (16.7 inches). The carapace is dark brown and may have light and dark streaks radiating out from a point at the posterior margin of each scute (horny scale covering the carapace); this pattern is frequently obscured in older animals. The animals associated with Cumberland Island are mostly small juveniles on which the pattern is clearly visible. The skin is light brown to yellowish and the ventral surface is light to white. The "green" is in reference to the color of the flavorful fat of the animal, which is not apparent externally. Diagnostic characters are the reduced number of pleural scutes (four), one claw on each front flipper, and the edge of the lower jaw serrated. The flippers and carapace of hatchlings are beautifully trimmed with white.

There is a substantial nesting population along the southeast coast of Florida, with occasional rare nesting in Georgia and on Cumberland Island. Their bones have been found in aboriginal middens along our coast.

Activity in the vicinity of the island, as reflected by strandings, occurs in all months, with a peak in June and July. Nesting occurs throughout the year in tropical areas, but only from June through September along the Southeast US coast.

Hatchlings in the pelagic stage are carnivorous, but change to a diet of mostly sea grasses when they return to the near-shore environment. Marine grasses and algae are readily available in the salt marshes, where the only other marine vertebrate herbivore, the manatee, also feeds.

Humans have inflicted the greatest losses on the species for food; both eggs and large turtles are valued. The fat and cartilaginous material on the carapace and plastron, which thickens soup, is world renown, and was even served on Cumberland Island by Caty Greene in the early 1800s. From1980 to 1989, only six green sea turtles stranded on Cumberland Island, but between 1990 and 1999, as populations slowly increased, there were seventeen, and from 2000 to 2008, forty-five.

_____. Family Cheloniidae. **Hawksbill Sea Turtle.** *Eretmochelys imbricata* (Linnaeus, 1766). The single adult stranded on Cumberland Island measured 87.5 centimeters CCL (34.4 inches) and one juvenile was measured at 34 centimeters CCL (13.6 inches). Distinguishing this species from the other sea turtles are the number of pleural scutes on the carapace, four per side, in combination with two pairs of prefrontal scales over the snout.

Hawksbills nest in low numbers in Florida; their nearest major nesting area to Cumberland Island is in the Caribbean. They have stranded dead on Cumberland Island (Ruckdeschel and Shoop, 1998a), both specimens having incurred head trauma. From hawksbill carapacial scutes, traditional "tortoiseshell" was acquired and fashioned.

_____. Family Cheloniidae. **Kemp's Ridley Sea Turtle.** *Lepidochelys kempii* (Garman, 1880). Kemp's ridley is a round turtle with a rather flat, flaring, greenish-gray carapace, and skin and head of the same color. The plastron and ventral surfaces are usually creamy white with a yellowish tinge around the head and neck. There are five pleural scutes, horny scales covering the carapace, but usually four inframarginals (loggerheads usually have three). The tip of the beak is decidedly hooked. Adults are relatively small and agile, reaching only 75 centimeters (29.5 inches) curved carapace length. Juveniles stranded on Cumberland Island have ranged from 21.5 to 60 centimeters (8.5 to 24 inches) curved carapace length.

Adults tend to be confined to the Gulf of Mexico, but juveniles are found seasonally from Massachusetts southward along the US coast and Gulf of Mexico. There have been several isolated nestings along the Atlantic Coast, including Georgia, but they are rare.

Humans have by far been the most influential predator of Kemp's ridley. Exploitation of eggs resulted in serious population declines until protective measures were promulgated and enforced. Today, commercial fishing techniques continue to threaten the species. Between 1979 and 2008, 286 Kemp's ridleys washed ashore dead on Cumberland Island, the result of mortality in shrimp trawl nets. During the first fifteen years, eighty-nine dead ridleys were documented, but between 1994 and 2008, that number jumped to 197, despite the fact that TEDs were mandatory. Perhaps the increased mortality reflects conservation success elsewhere—a sad irony. In addition to trawling, the massive BP Deepwater Horizon oil spill in 2010 has had a suspected but uncertain impact on the long-term status of this species in the Gulf of Mexico.

_____. Family Dermochelyidae. **Leatherback Sea Turtle**. *Dermochelys coriacea* (Vandelli, 1761). The average size of leatherbacks stranded in the vicinity of Cumberland Island between 1987 and 2003 was 150.5 centimeters (59.3 inches CCL), and the largest recorded was 180 centimeters (70.9 inches CCL). The largest of the sea turtles, the leatherback is easily identified by its ridged, black to dark-gray, skin-covered carapace, which is easily scratched and is smooth and dry to the touch. There is frequently some light spotting, and the head is typically mottled with bluish white. Most females and a few males may have an irregular pink blotch on the top center. The flippers are heavily flecked with bluish white, white, or pinkish spots, and the plastron and ventral surfaces are basically light with dark flecking. Seven distinct ridges/keels run from the anterior end of the carapace, one down the center and three to each side, and converge at the pointed terminal extension. The carapace is bone, but not the ridged, fused bones of the hard-shelled carapace. Instead there are many small, dime- to quarter-sized bones sutured together on a fibrous cartilage layer, which accommodates the deep diving habits of this species by being relatively flexible. The upper beak is deeply notched on each side and the jaws are shiny black and knife-edged. The flippers are massive, extremely long, and without claws. The disproportionate size of the flippers is also evident in hatchlings.

The first nest documented on Cumberland Island was on 24 April 1981 (Ruckdeschel et al., 1982); at that time, Flagler Beach, Florida, was the northernmost confirmed nesting site along the East Coast.

Activity in the vicinity of Cumberland Island, as judged by strandings, occurs in two periods of the year, from March to May and October to December. Infrequent nesting has been reported from April through July. Hatchling leatherbacks, with seven keels on the carapace, resemble adults. Unlike other sea-turtle hatchlings, they can dive and remain well below the surface immediately after entering the water.

In Florida, eggs are oviposited primarily from March through June, but nesting in Georgia may begin in April before the loggerheads begin. Fewer eggs are deposited by this giant species than the other sea turtles, averaging about eighty-five (range 58 to 160) per clutch plus numerous small, odd-shaped inviable eggs. There may be six to seven clutches per season, with the record at thirteen. Incubation usually takes fifty-six to seventy-two days, but a clutch on Cumberland Island deposited low in the dunes, and thus more likely to have had low incubation temperatures, took ninety-eight days for the first emergence to occur.

In the vicinity of Cumberland Island, shrimp trawl nets are the main threat, but leatherbacks usually migrate through state waters only twice a year. Seventeen stranded leatherbacks were recorded on Cumberland Island between 1979 and 2008.

_____. Family Chelydridae. **Snapping Turtle.** *Chelydra serpentina* (Linnaeus, 1758). The snapping turtle is a stout, robust animal that has a rough carapace with keels of the vertebral and pleural scutes forming three longitudinal rows. The rear marginal scutes are pointed, coarsely serrating the rear of the carapace. The carapace is black or dark brown, and the skin is gray to black or tan to yellowish, especially on the ventral surface. The small plastron is usually light yellow and leaves much more flesh exposed than on other freshwater turtles. Keels on the carapace may be obscured with age. The relatively large head has a hooked beak, and the long, ridged tail is proportionate to the body, especially as the turtle grows large; in hatchlings it is quite long. The largest snapper measured on Cumberland Island between 1979 and 2007 was 37.5 centimeters (14.8 inches CCL), the average was 26.5 centimeters (10.2 inches).

The common snapping turtle is found throughout the entire eastern US and occurs on Wassaw, Ossabaw, Sapelo, Cumberland, and Amelia islands. It will inhabit almost any available freshwater wetland but prefers shallow water with a muddy bottom. Snappers are occasionally found in or near brackish water, such as the edge of the high marsh where freshwater seeps occur. Cumberland Island localities include Whitney Lake, the Sweetwater complex, and Stafford Place.

Activity on Cumberland Island peaks in March but has been recorded from January through May and August through October. During times of drought, they aestivate buried in mud or move to another water source.

While the origin of individuals found DOB is questionable, fiddler crabs, a dark bird, and a "crab" were found in two such animals on Cumberland Island. On the island, alligators have been implicated in snapping turtle deaths.

_____. Family Emydidae. **Chicken Turtle**._Deirochelys reticularia_ (Latreille, 1801). The chicken turtle is a small to medium-sized turtle with a long neck and a smooth-edged carapace that is widest over the hind legs, and longer than wide. Cumberland Island animals have averaged 12.9 centimeters (5.1 inches) in straight carapace length, and the largest was 2.15 centimeters (8.5 inches). Carapace color is between olive, brown, and almost black, with a thin yellow reticulated pattern of a large meshed net; the carapace may be finely engraved with longitudinal grooves. The plastron is yellow and may have dark blotches along the scute seams and at the bridge. Yellow stripes follow the neck onto the head, and there is a broad yellow stripe on the anterior part of the front legs, which is characteristic of this species.

It occurs on St. Catherines, Sapelo, Cumberland, and Amelia islands. Temporary ponds are favored habitats, and chicken turtles are found on Cumberland Island in the Sweetwater sloughs and vegetated interdune areas, which occasionally hold water.

Chicken turtles are not common on Cumberland Island, so observations are few but peak in March. In Florida, they are active all year on warm days. One was killed by a vehicle on Cumberland Island.

_____. Family Emydidae. **Diamond-backed Terrapin**. _Malaclemys terrapin_ (Schoepff, 1793). The carapace of this medium-sized turtle is variably colored between an unmarked olive, brown, or gray to one with dark concentric lines on each scute emphasizing the growth layers, which are apparent on all terrapins. The plastron is yellowish and may have dark spots, but there is no hinge. The skin is light gray with a range of dark speckling from a few large spots to moderately small flecking, to an almost equal ratio of dark to light. The head is relatively large and the jaws are usually light yellowish and horn-colored.

Diamond-backed terrapins occupy a narrow coastal range along the Atlantic and Gulf coasts from Massachusetts to Texas and occur around all the Georgia barrier islands. Appropriate habitat is salt and brackish marshes in estuarine habitats. They nest well above the tide line and sometimes well away from the water in open sandy areas.

Activity around Cumberland Island peaks in April and May and has not been recorded from December through February. Diamond-backed terrapins become dormant during the winter when water temperatures fall below 10°C (50°F). Osmotic regulation (a balance between salt and water concentration in body tissues) is a problem for all reptiles in a marine environment, and while adult diamond-backed terrapins adjust to the salinity, juveniles are largely intolerant of salts and require more freshwater. Freshwater in the form of rain forms a film (lens) on the surface of saltwater and may be utilized by juveniles; they also find freshwater along the edges of the island adjacent to the salt environment in seeps or in small streams. The physiological requirement for freshwater may contribute to our lack of understanding of juvenile habitats during the first several years of life.

An adult male found DOB on Cumberland Island had eaten many individuals of a minute species of clam, *Gemma gemma*.

Cumberland Island nesting has been recorded from May through July. Hatchlings have been found in the vicinity of the island in March, April, and August, and one was accidently excavated eight to ten inches deep on 30 August. Late young may overwinter in the nest.

Discussion. Historically, many nesting females and eggs were no doubt inadvertently protected by the presence of alligators in tidal creeks and sunning on nesting beaches, but alligators, too, would have been predators.

The most devastating mortality for diamondback terrapins has come at the hands of humans. By the 1800s, they were in markets in Philadelphia and their popularity grew through the nineteenth century as their esculent fame spread. Finally, overexploitation caused severe population declines and some populations were eliminated. Remnants of a terrapin pen may be found on Cumberland Island beside the Brickhill River at Plum Orchard and another at Stafford. People on the north end of the island had a diamondback terrapin pen in the marsh at Half Moon Bluff in the early 1920s or 1930s. Terrapins would be held until enough were accumulated to be taken to market. Diamond-backed terrapins are protected or managed throughout their range, and the fad of terrapin soup has long since faded.

Diamond-backed terrapins are incidentally caught in crab traps, attracted by the bait. They usually die in the trap from lack of air, or, if caught alive by a commercial crabber, they are killed. I once found three terrapins dead in a neglected commercial trap in Christmas Creek. Presently, crab traps are the largest cause of mortality besides roadkills. Regulations should ensure that crab traps be regularly attended, and the traps should be equipped with an escape device allowing terrapins to get away, while retaining crabs.

_____. Family Emydidae. **Florida Red-bellied Cooter.** *Pseudemys nelsoni* Carr, 1938. This freshwater turtle is relatively large and becomes particularly heavy with age. A freshly killed animal on Cumberland Island, devoid of all internal organs, weighed 7 pounds 12 ounces. Average island carapace length is 26 centimeters SL (10.2 inches), and the largest specimen measured was 34.4 centimeters (13.5 inches). The basic color of the animal is dark to black. The domed carapace pattern is variable and changes with age, but typically has a wide, light vertical band, frequently a dull red, down the center of each pleural scute and onto the marginals. The rear margin of the carapace is serrated. The unpatterned plastron is light yellow with an orange tinge and lacks a hinge. The black head is streaked with a few narrow yellow lines. On top of the snout in the center is an arrow-shaped line pointing forward, which is diagnostic for the species. The nearly round hatchlings are colorful with dark markings on a bright orange plastron.

Outside of Florida, this species is only found on Cumberland Island (discovered in 1979) and in the Okefenokee Swamp. Until recently, it was thought restricted to Florida. Florida red-bellied cooters use temporary ponds and sloughs on Cumberland Island but are said to occasionally use brackish water. Several have been found alive on the ocean beach.

This is a diurnal, basking turtle and one of the two species seen on logs in wetlands on Cumberland Island. They appear to be active on the island most of the year, with a peak of activity in May, although there are no local records for February or November. Nesting females have been encountered in May and June on Cumberland Island.

Young turtles eat insects along with vegetation, but adults are entirely herbivorous. A small Cumberland Island red-belly ate the plant frogbit in captivity.

Eggs and hatchlings are subject to predation from all the Cumberland Island vertebrate predators, but predators of adults are mainly alligators. The carapace and plastron thicken with age, which is thought to be an adaptive response to alligator predation, and the carapaces of most adults show signs of attacks by alligators. As with other reptile and amphibian species, drying of the temporary wetlands exposes these turtles to predation by exotic feral swine.

_____. Family Emydidae. **Yellow-bellied Pond Slider**. *Trachemys scripta* (Schoepff, 1792). This is a medium-sized turtle with a dark rugose carapace and a yellow vertical stripe on each pleural scute. The plastron is yellow with a dark spot on each anterior scute. All patterns and coloring fade with age, and males become melanistic. Good diagnostic characters are the large yellow blotch on the head behind or below the eye and the vertically striped "pants" on the rear of the thighs. The rear of the carapace is moderately serrate, and all toes are webbed. The anterior side of the front limbs has narrow yellow stripes. There is a notch in the center of the upper jaw but the jaw edges (tomia) are smooth. The largest animal recorded on Cumberland Island was 28 centimeters (11 inches) in straight carapace length, although the average size was 24.7 centimeters (9.7 inches).

Yellow-bellies prefer quiet water, plenty of aquatic vegetation, and a mucky bottom, but they make use of a wide variety of habitats. Cumberland Island localities include Whitney Lake, Serendipity Pond, and the Sweetwater sloughs.

This is the most common turtle seen basking on Cumberland Island. They do not aestivate, so when their temporary wetland dries, they must emigrate. Unfortunately, options are limited on the island. During drought conditions, I have seen several turtles grouped together sharing a small alligator hole with three to four small, one-and-a-half-foot alligators. Presumably the turtles moved on when that water dried down to a den hole. Activity on Cumberland Island has been recorded in all months except January and October, with a peak in April and May.

Mating occurs in spring and nesting on Cumberland Island peaks in May and June, although there is a single record each for March and August. Hatchlings may emerge in the late summer or early autumn or may delay emergence until the following spring. Hatchlings have been recorded from Cumberland Island in August and October.

Alligators are the main predators of adults, and many Cumberland carapaces show scars from an alligator encounter. Harsh environmental conditions, especially drought, force many yellow-bellied sliders into life-threatening situations that result in mortality. In the past, this species was eaten locally on this and other barrier islands and was apparently sold in Southern markets.

_____. Family Kinosternidae. **Eastern Mud Turtle**. *Kinosternon subrubrum* (Lacepède, 1788). The carapace of this species is generally oval with an unmarked brown, olive to almost black coloration. The double-hinged plastron is light yellowish to tan. The average size on Cumberland Island is 89 centimeters SL (3.5 inches), and the largest animal measured was 10.5 centimeters (4 inches) in length. Markings on the side of the head are variable and range from none to mottling, or even faint stripes; the stripes are not clear and do not continue past the eyes onto the snout. The young are more colorful and each marginal scute has an orange spot; the plastron also is bright orange with dark mottling.

It occurs on most of the Georgia barrier islands and Amelia Island, Florida. Swamps, sloughs, and sluggish waters are preferred; they avoid fast-flowing water. Brackish water at the mouths of small streams and at freshwater seeps along the edge of the salt marsh is frequently used. Cumberland Island localities include Stafford Place and the Sweetwater sloughs.

Eastern mud turtles are active all year in southern latitudes, but activity on Cumberland Island has not been recorded for December or January. Activity peaks in March and April and continues to a lesser extent for the remainder of the year. Loss of individual body water can be a physiological problem, so they burrow underground during droughts. Mud turtles have been recorded basking on the island, although they rarely do so.

Eggs have been found on Cumberland Island in June and July. There may be two or more clutches, but most females have only one, and not all reproduce every year. The eggs are elongate and have a brittle shell that helps minimize water loss.

While walking in a swamp once with a pet otter, the young otter found an eastern mud turtle and was very interested in it, carrying it around for a while. He tried to get to the animal inside with his teeth but could not do so and soon lost interest. One island mud turtle was found smashed on the firm bank near a small stream. There were many feral horses in the area, and the turtle was likely stepped on by a horse.

_____. Family Kinosternidae. **Striped Mud Turtle**. *Kinosternon baurii* (Garman, 1891). This small, generally oval turtle usually has three light parallel stripes down its carapace. These stripes are evident on young turtles, but they may fade with age and be completely absent on old adults. The average length of striped mud turtles on Cumberland Island is 7.9 centimeters SL (3.1 inches), with the largest recorded at 9.8 centimeters (3.8 inches). The carapace color is a shade of brown, and the double-hinged plastron is light yellow or pale. The most reliable characteristics to distinguish this species from the eastern mud turtle are the two yellowish stripes on the side of the head, which continue from the eye to the snout. Hatchlings have been found on the island in May.

Cumberland is the only Georgia barrier island on which this species has been reported. Striped mud turtles prefer quiet waters in shallow sloughs and ponds. Cumberland Island localities include Whitney Lake and the Sweetwater slough complex.

During warm winters, they may be active all year, but on Cumberland Island their activity peaks in May and June; none have been recorded in December or February. One individual marked in July of 1985 measured 8.3 by 6.0 centimeters SL and was recaptured in May of 1988 when it was measured at 8.7 centimeters by 7.3. The specimen was estimated to be 12 years old at that time.

_____. Family Testudinidae. **Gopher Tortoise**. *Gopherus polyphemus* (Daudin, 1802). This herbivorous terrestrial species has a high-domed, boxy carapace that is brown to tan; in young animals, the center of each scute is frequently off-yellow to light tan, and growth rings are obvious. With age, the rings become obscured. The skin is grayish brown and without pattern in adults and yellowish brown in young. The front limbs are flattened and stiff with heavy scales, and the wrist is immobile so they can effectively seal the opening between the carapace and the plastron when the limbs are pulled tightly inward. These features, plus wide claws, also aid in digging. The rear limbs are elephantine in appearance yet are well able to dig a nest cavity. On Cumberland Island, the average carapace length was 22.0 centimeters SL (8.7 inches) for tortoises measured between 1985 and 2009.

They presently are found on Tybee, St. Catherines, St. Simons, Cumberland, and Amelia islands. Sandhills, long leaf pine uplands, and any open, dry, sandy habitat, the type usually maintained by fire, meets their needs.

Cumberland Island localities include Stafford Field, Davisville, the edge of the north end scrub, and the uplands mid-island.

Gopher tortoises are active all year in Florida, but on Cumberland Island, activity peaks in July and August and is low the rest of the year, with no activity recorded in January or February (records from 1971 to 2010). One burrow was seen plugged with sand in February.

There are no reproductive data for island gopher tortoises, but I have observed very small tortoises in an island colony.

A tick has been identified (Amblyomma Americana) from a Cumberland Island tortoise. (See Appendix VI A.)

Vehicle mortality occurs everywhere, including on Cumberland Island, and several individuals have been found dead on the beach. The fire suppression policy of the National Park Service from 1972 through 2014 has considerably altered available habitat. In other parts of its range, fire suppression has led to significant population declines, as the shrub layer became extremely dense.

Discussion. It is often stated in the literature that the gopher tortoise was "recently introduced" on Cumberland Island, but details are lacking. In his second edition of *A Field Guide To Reptiles and Amphibians of Eastern and Central North America* (1975), Roger Conant said that the gopher tortoise had been "introduced on Cumberland Island, Georgia." In May 1985, C.R. Shoop of the Cumberland Island Museum wrote to Dr. Conant asking where he had obtained that information. Conant responded that the information had come from C. H. Wharton in a letter dated 3 February 1972. We asked for a copy of the letter, which Conant was unable to locate. In June 1985, I wrote C. H. Wharton, explaining our inquiry into the island's gopher tortoise question, but he could not remember discussing it with Conant. He further stated that he had no concrete information regarding the distribution of gopher tortoises on Cumberland Island. In October 1971, S. Candler commented that he had never seen a tortoise on the island before that time, but this comment is inadequate to establish that the origin of the gopher tortoise population resulted from an introduction. Gopher tortoises occur on many barrier islands and near shore islands in Florida, and it seems likely that they could be native to Cumberland.

Archaeological investigations at Table Point by Milanich (1973) uncovered the remains of two individual gopher tortoises. The site had been occupied about 100 AD. Other relict sandhill inhabitants are present on the island today, further suggesting that gopher tortoises could be native to Cumberland. Several people associated with Cumberland Island were interviewed and early observations consulted. There is no mention of the tortoise in observations recorded between 1885 and 1949. In 1985, Lucy S. Foster recalled no warning issued by her parents to be on the lookout for burrows when horseback riding, which was significant to her. She thought she recalled Lucy R. Ferguson releasing some individual tortoises. J. B. Peeples, L. R. Ferguson's foreman, said in 1985 that he had released five or six at Greyfield about thirty years ago (1955?), but L. R. Ferguson did not remember the release nor was she familiar with the tortoise when asked in 1985 (she was 86 years of age at the time). Since that time, several gopher tortoises, at least four, have been released or escaped captivity on the island.

The colony at Davisville was mapped in April 1985, and five active and two inactive burrows were noted. In 1990, twenty-two active burrows were recorded there. One animal encountered north of the Red Bridge on 26 July 1990 was found again in June of 1993 in the north end scrub. Reproduction was noted in the Davisville colony in 2011.

_____. Family Trionychidae. **Florida Softshell**. *Apalone ferox* (Schneider, 1783). Florida softshells are medium to large turtles that on Cumberland Island average 38 centimeters (15 inches) in straight carapace length; the largest measured was 47.5 centimeters (18.7 inches). The carapace is flattened, without scutes, and has a marginal ridge, more apparent in juveniles than adults. There are many rounded tubercles at the anterior end of the skin-covered, brownish-gray carapace. The plastron may extend farther forward than the carapace in adults, and it is light colored. Juveniles are especially colorful, with bright yellow head markings and a thin line of orange and yellow around the margin of the carapace. The ventral surface is brown and the carapace has irregular dark brown spots, all of which fade with age. A snorkel-like proboscis extends well beyond the fleshy lips covering the jaw and has median lateral projections off the septum. Hatchlings have been found on Cumberland in August.

This species is on Cumberland Island and perhaps Little Cumberland Island of the Georgia barrier islands. Sloughs and lakes with mud or sand bottoms are preferred habitats, but softshells are also active on land and may be found in surprising places, probably en route between wetlands. They have been found in brackish water at the mouths of small streams, and they willingly run into the surf rather than confront a human.

Florida softshells become inactive in cold weather; they have been noted on Cumberland Island from March through October, with most activity occurring from April through June. When submerged or buried on the bottom of a wetland, they may "breathe" by exchanging gasses through their skin. If caught on land by a compromising environmental situation, they burrow. A fresh turtle track that came to a dead end in hot, loose sand (surface 91.4°F) in the vicinity of Whitney Lake was made by a softshell, which took refuge between 6.4 centimeters (2.5 inches) and 6.8 centimeters (2.75 inches) deep, where the sand was damp and much cooler.

Florida softshells frequently have freshwater leeches on them, possibly *Erpobdella punctata*, which is not parasitic but has been identified in Cumberland Island wetlands.

Several softshells have been found at the beach wrack line alive, only one dead. One road fatality has been documented on the island. Several carcasses have been found at temporary ponds following droughts.

Birds

Introduction.

My focus has mainly been on other classes of vertebrates, but I have accumulated a great amount of information on class Aves, much of which is here presented. This section is not intended as a primer on the birds of the island, but rather a means to share my observations while providing a list of birds that use or are known to have used the island. Since Cumberland Island differs from the adjacent mainland in environmental conditions and available habitats, I have limited species to those with actual evidence of a connection to the island, with few exceptions that are clearly noted. Literature references, museum specimens, and the Audubon Christmas Bird Counts were considered reputable sources, along with observations provided by recognized experts.

Many avian species migrate, some extreme distances, and knowledge of their seasonal distribution gives an understanding of the likelihood of seeing them on Cumberland Island at a particular time. Breeding and wintering ranges for each species listed have been roughly delineated, and resident species indicated.

The varied habitats available on Cumberland Island, from ocean beach through the interdune, freshwater wetlands and upland maritime forest to the salt marsh, offer a wide variety to species. Weekly beach surveys have provided information on species associated with the beach and ocean environment. Pelagic species are recorded when they wash ashore dead, and many banded birds are recovered on the beach.

During my island tenure, the abundance of many species has changed or fluctuated. Habitat changes due to environmental conditions and the National Park Service's policy of total fire suppression (until 2015) have altered some nesting habitats. Bobcats and coyotes, both relatively new additions to the island fauna, impact shorebird nesting success, and the increasing amount of people and vehicle traffic has reduced the number of shorebird species which use the island for roosting and nesting.

A list of avian museum specimens from Cumberland Island was compiled by D. W. Johnston and is included as an appendix. S. Willis, an indefatigable "birder," who heads the Cumberland Island Audubon Christmas Bird Count and is a fountain of knowledge, gave freely of her time and extensive records to help fill in gaps of this list, as did M. Hodges. Much of the information on nesting distribution came from Burleigh (1958) and Imhof (1976).

The Audubon Christmas Bird Count was begun by F. M. Chapman in 1900 as a species census. Each census is conducted within a 24-kilometer (15-mile) circle, following an established route, for a one-day period each year. The Cumberland Island survey was started in 1986 and the data are included with those of Kings Bay on the mainland, both areas within the survey circle.

Heronries.

Two locations on the island have been identified as nesting areas for colonial wading birds, Heron Pond (Nightingale Pond) and an area in the Sweetwater complex south of South Fraser Road (South Cut Road.). The artificial pond at Plum Orchard once provided nesting habitat but has since become overgrown.

Heron Pond has been used by the birds for many years; at least seventy. In 1987, N. C. Rockefeller (1900–1994) said nesting birds had used it as long as she could remember. Hillestad et al. (1975) reported twenty to thirty pairs of great egrets nesting there in 1973, and in 1985, in order of abundance, great egrets, cattle egrets, snowy egrets, tricolor herons, little blue herons, and, in fewer numbers, wood storks, water turkeys, and black-crowned night herons nested there, and nesting continued until 1990. Diminishing water level in the pond was the initial cause for abandonment. Coupled with increased understory vegetation, the decreased water level facilitated predation and the site was abandoned.

The Sweetwater nesting colony was first monitored in 1987 and was intermittently successful, depending upon water level, until 2002, when it was abandoned due to dropping water level and encroachment of thick vegetation. Nesting there were wood storks, great egrets, snowy egrets, cattle egrets, black-crowned night herons, little blue herons, water turkeys, and white ibis.

The requirements of a colonial wading bird nesting area are trees or shrubs strong enough to support a nest with adults and young above standing water and an open area so no limbs from adjacent vegetation on high ground touch the nesting area (Fig. 27). The deeper the water is, the better, but even five centimeters (two inches) will do. Although several predators prey on nesting birds, on the island the raccoon is the foremost threat. Groups of large birds create an unmistakable environment, advertising their presence by sight, sound, and odor. That, and the fact that they reuse successful nesting areas, assures there will be an alligator in attendance beneath the colony. Whether the alligator secures a fallen nestling or a careless intruder, such as a raccoon, the potential for food is enough to guarantee its continued presence. Most raccoons recognize the danger associated with entering even shallow water and avoid it. Perhaps they can smell the alligator's presence or they associate the melee of a colonial nesting group of birds with the threat, but they keep their distance as long as water intervenes.

The National Park Service's fire-suppression policy for the last forty years, 1973 to 2014, changed wetland community dynamics, which had included periodic natural fires, and the habitat is now less acceptable for colonial wading bird nesting. Willows and other fast-growing species were previously checked by frequent wildfires, but today they crowd out nest trees and provide raccoons access avoiding the water. However, the navy has constructed a safe place for nesting just across the river at King's Bay, which helps ameliorate the habitat loss on Cumberland Island.

Nomenclature follows the American Ornithologists' Union Checklist, 7th Edition (incl. 52nd Suppl.).

Species Accounts

ORDER ANSERIFORMES. Family Anatidae. **Fulvous Whistling Duck.** *Dendrocygna bicolor* (Vieillot, 1816). The first record for Florida of this uncommon transient was in 1931, and numbers in Florida increased from 1960. This is a bird of the Southwest US to the Rio Grande Valley of Texas and Mexico; it winters to south Mexico. A group of eighteen to twenty were observed on the Cumberland Island beach near the outlet on 18 November 1982. They have not been documented on the island Christmas bird counts.

_____. Family Anatidae. **Snow Goose.** *Chen caerulescens* (Linnaeus, 1758). An autumn and winter visitor, this goose breeds on Arctic islands and winters south to Florida. Cumberland Island records are from October through January plus infrequent sightings on Christmas bird counts.

Two animals have been found dead on the beach (28 November and 1 December).

_____. Family Anatidae. **Brant.** *Branta bernicla* (Linnaeus, 1758). Brant breed in Arctic regions of eastern North America and winter along the Atlantic Coast. A Brant was recorded on the 2004 Cumberland Christmas bird count.

_____. Family Anatidae. **Canada Goose.** *Branta canadensis* (Linnaeus, 1758). There are at least eight recent records of this species on Cumberland Island, plus infrequent sightings on the Christmas bird count (1994, 1995). Because of declining populations, the Georgia Department of Natural Resources (DNR) stocked a nonmigratory form in Georgia, and that feral form is what is now seen, as island records are primarily from April through July. In February 1901 and January 1924, migratory birds were shot on the island.

_____. Family Anatidae. **Tundra Swan.** *Cygnus columbianus* (Ord, 1815). The tundra swan is listed as a rare, irregular winter visitor. Two birds were seen over the Cumberland Island beach in April of 1932 (Sprunt, 1936). The species breeds mostly north of the Arctic Circle and winters along the Atlantic Coast to Florida.

_____. Family Anatidae. **Wood Duck.** *Aix sponsa* (Linnaeus, 1758). There are records of this beautiful permanent island resident beginning February 1889 to 1901, when it was hunted on Cumberland Island, and from 1903 to 1909, when specimens were collected for science. It is regularly seen on the island Christmas bird counts, and chicks have been recorded in island freshwater wetlands April through June.

_____. Family Anatidae. **Gadwall**. *Anas strepera* Linnaeus, 1758. This winter visitor breeds from Canada into the northern US and winters from Maryland south to Mexico. It is a freshwater duck and is rarely seen in the salt marshes. One was collected on Cumberland Island by Helme in March 1903.

_____. Family Anatidae. **Eurasian Wigeon**. *Anas penelope* Linnaeus, 1758. An uncommon or rare transient and possible winter visitor to Cumberland Island, the Eurasian wigeon breeds north to Iceland, Europe, and Asia and may winter south to Florida. Sprunt (1936) reported that Helme had told him that a "Eurasian wigeon" had been procured from a "gunner on Cumberland Island." Sprunt suggested that was the only record for Georgia at that time. This species was recorded on the 1994 Cumberland Island Christmas bird count.

_____. Family Anatidae. **American Wigeon**. *Anas americana* Gmelin, 1789. The American wigeon breeds far to the north and winters from Chesapeake Bay to Central America. It will use brackish water, but on Cumberland Island it has been seen in freshwater areas. Limited numbers were shot on the island between1896 and 1924, and the species was recorded on the 1994 Cumberland Christmas bird count. One was recorded dead on the beach (December 1978).

_____. Family Anatidae. **American Black Duck**. *Anas rubripes* Brewster, 1902. Breeding from Canada south to North Carolina and wintering from New England south to Florida, this species is declining. They were hunted on Cumberland Island from December through February, from 1889 on, but the numbers taken were never as great as mallards. A group of fifteen to twenty was seen in Plum Creek in 1989, and the species was recorded on three Christmas bird counts as of 2010.

_____. Family Anatidae. **Mallard**. *Anas platyrhynchos* Linnaeus, 1758. A winter visitor, the mallard breeds from Virginia north and winters south to Florida and Mexico. It prefers freshwater and was heavily hunted on Cumberland Island from November into March, with records beginning in the 1890s. It was formerly more numerous throughout its range, but none were recorded on the Cumberland Christmas bird counts through 2010.

_____. Family Anatidae. **Mottled Duck**. *Anas fulvigula* Ridgway, 1874. This uncommon species interbreeds with the black duck and is found along the Gulf Coast from Texas to Florida. A specimen was collected on

Cumberland Island by Helme in December 1902 (Burleigh, 1958), and it has been recorded on one Christmas bird count, 2001.

_____. Family Anatidae. **Blue-winged Teal.** *Anas discors* Linnaeus, 1766. Listed as a transient and mainly winter visitor, this small duck breeds in Canada and the northern US, and most winter in Central and South America, but some use the Southern US from North Carolina south. Most Cumberland Island observations have been in spring, with the remainder from summer into autumn, July to October. Sprunt (1936) first reported blue-winged teal on Cumberland Island, Helme collected specimens in April 1903 and December 1904, a few were taken sport hunting in the early 1900s, and they have been frequently recorded on the Christmas counts. Six have been found dead on the beach.

_____. Family Anatidae. **Norther Shoveler.** *Anas clypeata* Linnaeus, 1758. An uncommon winter visitor, the shoveler breeds from Canada to North Carolina and Alabama and winters south to Mexico and the West Indies. Cumberland Island records begin in 1896, and there was a specimen collected by Helme on 28 December 1904. None have been recorded on the Christmas bird counts.

Reports conflict as to its culinary qualities.

_____. Family Anatidae. **Northern Pintail.** *Anas acuta* Linnaeus, 1758. A freshwater winter visitor, the pintail breeds from Labrador south to Iowa and winters south to the Gulf Coast, West Indies, and Central America. It was taken on Cumberland Island for sport and science early in the 1900s, and Willow Pond was a locality it frequented.

_____. Family Anatidae. **Green-winged Teal.** *Anas crecca* Linnaeus, 1758. The green-winged teal is a small, common winter visitor that prefers freshwater ponds on the island. It breeds from Canada to the northern US and winters from Maryland south to Mexico, Central America, and the West Indies. Few were reported from early hunting parties on Cumberland Island; rather they were lumped as "teal." They are often reported on the island Christmas counts.

_____. Family Anatidae. **Canvasback.** *Aythya valisineria* (Wilson, 1814). The canvasback is a winter visitor to Cumberland Island. Its breeding in the US extends into southern Wisconsin and Minnesota and it winters south to the Gulf Coast and northern Florida. A specimen was collected on Cumberland Island by A. Helme, the species was shot for sport on the island in 1914, and six were observed in the surf on 14 February 2002. It is occasionally seen on the Christmas bird counts. The generic name of this species is taken from its preferred food and the one to which its extraordinary flavor is attributed, wild celery, *Vallisneria spiralis*.

_____. Family Anatidae. **Redhead**. *Aythya americana* (Eyton, 1838). An uncommon winter visitor and transient, the redhead breeds in Canada and the northern US and winters south to the West Indies. It inhabits both fresh- and saltwater habitats. There was a Cumberland Island specimen taken 17 November 1903, and the species has been recorded on the island Audubon Christmas Bird Counts.

_____. Family Anatidae. **Ring-necked Duck**. *Aythya collaris* (Donovan, 1809). A transient and winter visitor, this species breeds from Canada to southeast Maine and winters to south Florida, Central America, and the Bahamas. It is more frequent in freshwater than salt. Helme saw six on Cumberland Island on 7 March 1902 (Burleigh, 1958), and the species has been recorded on several island Christmas counts.

_____. Family Anatidae. **Greater Scaup**. *Aythya marila* (Linnaeus, 1761). Greater scaup breed along the Arctic coast of Alaska and in Canada and winter along the Atlantic Coast to Florida and the Gulf Coast, southern Texas, and the Bahamas. This is an uncommonly recorded winter visitor, but the species is difficult to differentiate from its smaller relative, the lesser scaup, and hunters usually lumped together the two species of scaup, "bluebills," and *Aythya* sp. They were taken in moderate numbers on and around Cumberland Island from 1891 through 1925. Three greater scaup were found DOB on December 1977, November 1980, and March 1985.

_____. Family Anatidae. **Lesser Scaup**. *Aythya affinis* (Eyton, 1838). The lesser scaup is a common winter visitor and transient that breeds in Canada and some northern US states and winters south through Florida and the Gulf Coast to Texas and the Bahamas. They were hunted on Cumberland Island, presumably for food, from 1891 through 1925, although the two scaup species were not differentiated. Specimens for scientific study were collected in 1904 by I. Arnow. Rafts containing hundreds of scaup have been observed just beyond the surf from December through March, and the species is regularly recorded on the Cumberland Christmas bird counts. Dead animals have been found on the beach from November through April.

_____. Family Anatidae. **King Eider**. *Somateria spectabilis* (Linnaeus, 1758). This heavy-bodied sea duck is considered a casual or incidental visitor around Cumberland Island. It breeds far north in Canada and winters from Greenland south to New England and occasionally to Florida. One was seen with a small group of scaup south of Dungeness on 13 December 1984 (Moore, 1986).

There are no sightings from the Christmas bird counts.

_____. Family Anatidae. **Common Eider**. *Somateria mollissima* (Linnaeus, 1758). An irregular, incidental visitor, the common eider breeds from Canada to Maine and winters south, occasionally as far as Florida. This duck is commercially valuable for its feathers. There are observation records from the island (S. Willis, pers. comm.).

_____. Family Anatidae. **Surf Scoter**. *Melanitta perspicillata* (Linnaeus, 1758). This sea duck breeds in northern Canada and winters south to Florida, preferring the open ocean. Pearson (1922) reported it on Cumberland Island on 6 May 1921, and there are specimens from 17 November 1903 and 19 March 1904 (eight). Animals have been found DOB from October through December and in May, and surf scoters have been observed on the island Christmas bird count.

_____. Family Anatidae. **White-winged Scoter**. *Melanitta fusca* (Linnaeus, 1758). The white-winged scoter is an uncommon winter visitor to Cumberland Island that breeds from northwest Alaska and Canada south to central North Dakota and winters south to the Gulf Coast and Florida. It is an offshore duck and has frequently been recorded on the Cumberland Christmas bird counts. An individual was found DOB 31 October 1988, and three were observed on the beach 15 June 2006.

_____. Family Anatidae. **Black Scoter**. *Melanitta nigra* (Linnaeus, 1758). The black scoter, a common visitor to Cumberland Island from November through June, breeds in northern North America and winters down the East Coast to Florida. There are two specimens from Cumberland Island, 17 November 1903 and 28 November 1969, and stranding records, predominately females, delineate temporal distribution from October into July (N=654). November (104), December (281), and January (91) were months of highest strandings (1972 to 2009). This species is regularly recorded on the Christmas counts.

_____. Family Anatidae. **Long-tailed Duck**. *Clangula hyemalis* (Linnaeus, 1758). Primarily a coastal species, the oldsquaw or long-tailed duck is an uncommon winter visitor to Georgia. The species breeds from the Arctic Coast south to Canada and winters south to Florida and the Gulf Coast. It has been recorded on Cumberland Island Christmas bird counts.

_____. Family Anatidae. **Bufflehead**. *Bucephala albeola* (Linnaeus, 1758). A common transient and winter visitor, this small, primarily saltwater duck breeds in western Canada to Wisconsin and southern Maine and winters south to Florida and central Mexico. A. Helme collected a specimen on Cumberland Island 24 March 1902. They are known to use Christmas Creek marsh on Cumberland Island and have been documented many times on the Cumberland Island Audubon Christmas Bird Counts.

_____. Family Anatidae. **Common Goldeneye.** *Bucephala clangula* (Linnaeus, 1758). This maritime species is an uncommon transient and winter visitor that breeds in Canada and the northern tier of the United States and winters from Maine to Florida along the East Coast. There are no specimens from Cumberland Island and no early records. It was recorded on the 1993 Cumberland Island Christmas bird count.

_____. Family Anatidae. **Hooded Merganser.** *Lophodytes cucullatus* (Linnaeus, 1758). The hooded merganser is a regular winter visitor on Cumberland Island seen in tidal creeks and freshwater wetlands. Sprunt reported them in 1936, and island observations fall between November and April, most December to March. A specimen from Cumberland Island was collected on 25 December 1902 by A. Helme, and the species is occasionally recorded on the Christmas count.

Three have been found DOB, 1974 to 2011, and all were females.

_____. Family Anatidae. **Common Merganser.** *Mergus merganser* Linnaeus, 1758. The common merganser is an irregular transient and winter visitor in both Florida and Georgia. It breeds in Canada and the northern US states from Minnesota east, including New England and winters south to the Gulf Coast and to northern Mexico. There are no specimens from Cumberland Island, but there is an observation of the species (S. Willis, pers. comm.).

_____. Family Anatidae. **Red-breasted Merganser.** *Mergus serrator* Linnaeus, 1758. A common winter visitor to Cumberland Island, this species breeds from Alaska east to the northern US states and the coast of Maine and winters south to Florida and Texas. It is commonly seen on the Christmas bird counts, and other observations on Cumberland Island have been in November, December, February, and March. Seven have been found dead on the beach, and A. Helme collected one for a museum specimen on the island on 3 April 1903.

_____. Family Anatidae. **Ruddy Duck.** *Oxyura jamaicensis* (Gmelin, 1789). A small duck, the ruddy breeds from Canada to Minnesota, Iowa, and east to New England, and it winters on the East Coast to Florida, the Bahamas, and West Indies. It is considered an uncommon winter visitor in Georgia and a regular winter visitor to Florida. Hunters on Cumberland Island in January 1920 identified two shot in the Big Slough. There are no museum specimens from the island, but the species has been recorded on several island Christmas bird counts.

ORDER GALLIFORMES. Family Odontophoridae. **Northern Bobwhite.** *Colinus virginianus* (Linnaeus, 1758). The northern bobwhite breeds across the central eastern US, and there have been many introductions for hunting purposes. In 1846, Elliott commented that quail were particularly numerous along the coast and among the cultivated islands, but in 1936 Sprunt reported their absence on Cumberland Island. They were hunted on Cumberland Island, with over fifty taken between 1899 and February 1911, and the last one recorded shot was in March of 1975. They are resident locally on the mainland but numbers have declined there also, and few are to be seen on this or other Georgia barrier islands at this time.

_____. Family Phasianidae. **Wild Turkey.** *Meleagris gallopavo* Linnaeus, 1758. Helme collected two museum specimens of this Cumberland Island resident in the early 1900s, and Pearson (1922) and Sprunt (1936) reported turkeys to be abundant on the island. In 1898, sixty-three birds were shot, and between 1885 and 1911, 399 were taken on Cumberland Island. By 1939, they were getting scarce, and in 1949, none were seen by hunters. Pen-reared birds were released on the island in the 1970s, and today turkeys are once again common. Breeding occurs March through May, with the earliest chicks seen 16 April.

For external parasites see Appendix VI. B. Mycoplasmosis, a respiratory disease, was diagnosed in some island birds in 1982 (Davidson et al., 1982). The disease is rare in wild populations and occurred at the time L. R. Ferguson had many captive gallinaceous birds, which could have introduced the problem.

ORDER GAVIFORMES. Family Gaviidae. **Red-throated Loon.** *Gavia stellata* (Pontoppidan, 1763). This species is an uncommon winter visitor, which breeds from the Arctic through Canada and winters along the Atlantic Coast to Florida. A total of thirty-seven specimens have been recorded on Cumberland Island between 1983 and 2011, during November through April, with a peak in January and February. None have been found from May through October. There is a museum specimen from Cumberland Island, and the species has been observed on the Cumberland Island Christmas bird counts.

_____. Family Gaviidae. **Common Loon.** *Gavia immer* (Burn-nich, 1764). The loon is a common offshore winter visitor, which breeds from the Arctic to northern US and winters south to the Gulf of Mexico. This species uses shelf waters up to 100 kilometers from shore and avoids near-shore turbid waters. Most island records are from birds found dead or dying on the beach, two to ninety per month, per year (700 animals, 1973 to 2010). It has been suggested that during molt they may lose all primaries at once. Hundreds of birds have been reported at a single time by fishermen 16 to 24 kilometers (10 to 15 miles) offshore. Most records occur from December through April, with absence in August and September. Carcasses have been found from February to April that were obviously molting, missing primaries.

ORDER PODICIPEDIFORMES. Family Podicipedidae. **Pied-billed Grebe.** *Podilymbus podiceps* (Linnaeus, 1758). This grebe is a resident and uncommon, although its numbers may be augmented during the winter by migrants from the north. The species breeds from Canada through the US and winters in the southern part of the range. It prefers freshwater and reportedly has an interesting association with alligators (Stoddard in Burleigh, 1958). There is a specimen from Cumberland Island taken in October 1903, and Sprunt (1936) reported the species on Cumberland Island. They are frequently seen on the Christmas counts. Six have been found DOB from 1981 to 2003, all in autumn, from September through December. Island localities they frequent include temporary ponds in the north end scrub and Big Slough.

_____. Family Podicipedidae. **Horned Grebe.** *Podiceps auritus* (Linnaeus, 1758). This common winter visitor to Cumberland Island breeds from Alaska south to the northern US and winters to the Gulf Coast and Florida. There are Cumberland Island records from February 1902, February 1904, and March 1971, and it has frequently been recorded on the Christmas bird counts. The horned grebe has also been found DOB in January, March, April, and November and seen in tidal creeks in March.

_____. Family Podicipedidae. **Red-necked Grebe.** *Podiceps grise-gena* (Boddaert, 1783). The red-necked grebe is a winter visitor along the Georgia coast. It breeds from Alaska into the northern US and winters south to Florida. I. Arnow collected this species at the mouth of the Cumberland River on 18 February 1904 (Burleigh, 1958). None have been recorded dead on the Cumberland Island beach. They were observed on the 2003 Cumberland Audubon Christmas Bird Count.

ORDER PROCELLARIIFORMES. Family Procellariidae. **Cory's Shearwater.** *Calonectris diomedea* (Scopoli, 1769). This large shearwater is common offshore, sometimes seen in the hundreds during summer and autumn. They breed in the Azores, Madeira, and Canary Islands. On Cumberland Island, thirty-three were recorded DOB between May and October 1984 to 2010.

_____. Family Procellariidae. **Cape Verde Shearwater.** *Calonectris edwardsii* (Oustalet, 1883). The first Georgia specimen of the Cape Verde shearwater or Scopoli's shearwater, a subspecies of Cory's shearwater, was collected on Cumberland Island on 24 August 2008 following winds associated with a tropical storm. The identification was confirmed by R. Clapp and C. Angel at the Smithsonian National Museum of Natural History (Ruckdeschel, 2008).

_____. Family Procellariidae. **Great Shearwater.** *Puffinus gravis* (O'Reilly, 1818). While these large shearwaters do not usually come near land except to breed, which they do along the South Atlantic, storms occasionally force them ashore. Weather patterns apparently influence seasonal upwelling, which brings nutrients to the surface and periodically affects the availability of food for this species. All of our records (363 animals, 1978 to 2007) are from animals found dead on the beach between May and September, with one outlier in November. June and July are the months of most island activity. The highest number found DOB on Cumberland Island for any year was 280 in 2007. Hebard reported seeing four or five at the end of the jetty in February 1949 (Burleigh, 1958), and there are several museum specimens: June (1983), June and July (1972), July (1973). Lice were documented on several animals, and nematodes that had perforated the gut were observed. Many gizzards were found to contain plastic (78%, 23 animals) along with squid beaks. Most carcasses had been emptied by vultures by the time they were found.

_____. Family Procellariidae. **Sooty Shearwater.** *Puffinus griseus* (Gmelin, 1789). A summer visitor only, the sooty shearwater breeds in burrows in New Zealand and southern South America. Seasonally the population shifts north in winter to the warmer climes of the Northern Hemisphere, and being a cold-water species, hurriedly crosses the Tropics. They are reported to be susceptible to diseases associated with high ocean temperatures (Murphy, 1936). Island specimens have been found DOB between May and July, 1991 to 2006 (Ruckdeschel and Shoop, 1998b).

_____. Family Procellariidae. **Audubon's Shearwater**. *Puffinus lherminieri* Lesson, 1839. The smallest of the shearwaters, this species breeds in Bermuda, the Bahamas, and Lesser Antilles but is considered an uncommon visitor due to its pelagic habits. There are two museum specimens from Cumberland Island, and on the island, stranded specimens numbered sixty-three between 1974 and 2008. The majority stranded in July and August, but dates ranged from May through October.

_____. Family Hydrobatidae. **Wilson's Petrel**. *Oceanites oceanicus* (Kuhl, 1820). This petrel occurs along the eastern US coast only between its breeding seasons, which occur far south in the sub-Antarctic off South America, November through April. Bad weather sometimes forces it ashore, and there are two stranding records for Cumberland Island, one in May 2001 and another in May 2009.

_____. Family Hydrobatidae. **Leach's Storm Petrel**. *Oceanodroma leucorhoa* (Vieillot, 1818). Leach's storm petrels are considered offshore transients and breed from Maine north to Greenland on the East Coast and wander as far as South America after nesting. Between 22 May and 2 June 1991, seventy-two Leach's storm petrels were found dead or dying on Cumberland and Little Cumberland islands. This was the first reported mass stranding of this species along the Southeast US coast and the first record for the state (Ruckdeschel et al., 1994). Since then, one to three individuals have stranded other years, in May and June.

_____. Family Hydrobatidae. **Band-rumped Petrel**. *Oceanodroma castro* (Harcourt, 1851). Authorities use words like "straggler," "vagrant," and "accidental" to describe this bird in the eastern US. It breeds colonially in burrows on islands around the tropical Atlantic and Pacific. Two have been found DOB on Cumberland Island, 14 June 2005 and 22 May 2009, with species identification verified by J. Gerwin and R. Clapp.

ORDER PHAETHONTIFORMES. Family Phaethontidae. **White-tailed Tropicbird**. *Phaethon lepturus* Daudin, 1802. These beautiful birds nest in Bermuda and islands in the West Indies yet are relatively rare in Florida and off the East Coast. Two specimens were found DOB on Cumberland Island, one in August of 1995 and the other in May of 2004. The 1995 specimen was the first for Georgia, although there had been offshore sight records (Ruckdeschel, 1996).

ORDER CICONIIFORMES. Family Ciconiidae. **Wood Stork**. *Mycteria americana* Linnaeus, 1758. Sprunt (1936) reported wood storks on Cumberland Island. The species ranges from South Carolina to South America. The first recorded wood stork nesting on a Georgia barrier island was on Cumberland Island in 1985 (Ruckdeschel and Shoop, 1987), and island nesting continued into 2002, with up to thirty-five nests observed per year. Two areas on the island were used for nesting, but drought conditions and the National Park Service's fire-suppression policy ultimately rendered conditions unacceptable for nesting at both places. Ectoparasite infestations of nestlings by *Dermestes nidum* Arrow, 1915, were evident but seemed to have little impact on juvenile survival. One bird observed on 13 July had been banded in May of the same year as a nestling at Pelican Island or Merritt Island, Florida.

In the past, barrier island residents referred to the wood stork as "Gannet," and they used to regularly eat them. One island person told me that this was his favorite bird to eat, yet Burleigh (1958) reported the flesh to be tough and said it was rarely eaten. In my experience, it is quite delicious, with giant perctoral muscles dark and rich tasting, almost like liver.

ORDER SULIFORMES. Family Fregatidae. **Magnificent Frigatebird**. *Fregata magnificens* Mathews, 1914. Described as a rare visitor to Georgia, this species breeds in the Bahamas and West Indies to Venezuela. It has been recorded flying over waterways adjacent to the island.

_____. Family Sulidae. **Masked Booby**. *Sula dactylatra* Lesson, 1831. Masked boobies are occasional in offshore waters to the Gulf Stream, but rare inshore in Georgia. One was reported dead on the beach at Cumberland Island in May 1986 (Brisse, 1986). This largest of the boobies nests on the ground on islands in the tropical seas of the Atlantic, Pacific, and Indian oceans.

_____. Family Sulidae. **Brown Booby**. *Sula leucogaster* (Boddaert, 1783). Breeding of this species occurs in the West Indies and much of the tropics, and it is considered uncommon off the Florida coast. There were offshore sight records (May 1983) and photographs (August 2002) from Georgia, but the first specimen from the state was found on Cumberland Island in September 2004 (Ruckdeschel, 2005).

_____. Family Sulidae. **Northern Gannet**. *Morus bassanus* (Linnaeus, 1758). A common offshore winter visitor, the gannet breeds in Newfoundland and the Gulf of St. Lawrence area and winters from New England south to the Gulf of Mexico and Cuba. Helme found one DOB on

Cumberland Island in 1903 (Burleigh, 1958), Sprunt (1936) reported them on Cumberland Island, and there are museum specimens (see Appendix IV. B.). Prior to 1992, there were no summer island records. The first August record was in 2007, and the first September record in 2009. The majority of records are from November through May (N=559, 1974 to 2010).

_____. Family Phalacrocoracidae. **Double-crested Cormorant**. *Phalacrocorax auritus* (Lesson, 1831). Numbers of the double-crested cormorant in the vicinity of Cumberland Island are greatly reduced during the summer months, June through September. Breeding occurs from Newfoundland to Maine, and these cormorants winter south to Florida. Migrations northward are primarily during March and April, with the earliest date observed here 27 February. Autumn migrations south occur mainly during September and October, with the earliest noted here on 3 September and the latest 30 December. More individuals are found dead, stranded on the beach, during the autumn migrations and winter months (178 animals) than during spring and summer (73 animals, 1973 to 2010). Two banded birds have been found dead. One found 12 November 1990 had been banded by F. E. Ludwig near Cedarville, Michigan, on 19 January 1989 as a nestling, and the other, recovered 19 October 1992, was only four months old and had been banded on Mackinac Island, Michigan.

_____. Family Anhingidae. **Anhinga**. *Anhinga anhinga* (Linnaeus, 1766). The "water turkey" or "snake bird" is an island resident and frequents most inland wetlands, breeding in at least two localities on Cumberland Island. The earliest nesting recorded was 19 April and nesting continued through May. The latest young were seen was on 26 June. Our observations are for spring and summer only, with one in September. We have no records from October through February, except for a Christmas bird count, 2007. Both Pearson (1922) and Sprunt (1936) reported this species on Cumberland Island, but Sprunt and Chamberlain (1949) said that the species rarely visited the South Carolina barrier islands.

ORDER PELECANIFORMES. Family Pelecanidae. **White Pelican**. *Pelecanus erythrorhynchos* Gmelin, 1789. White pelicans migrate east from their breeding grounds in British Columbia, Southern California, and the Texas coast to spend the winter in the southeast US and south to Panama and Trinidad. They are colonial but may have as few as three or four in a group. Sprunt (1936) reported them around the island in 1933. They have been recorded in the vicinity of Cumberland Island in all months, but breeding has not been noted in this area.

_____. Family Pelecanidae. **Brown Pelican**. *Pelecanus occidentalis* Linnaeus, 1766. The brown pelican is a common island resident. It nests on islands from Maryland to Texas, along the Gulf Coast to Central and South America, and it winters in the southern part of its range. Helme (Burleigh, 1958), Pearson (1922), and Sprunt (1936) recorded it on Cumberland Island. Nesting in Georgia was not recorded until 1988 (Ruckdeschel et al., 1990), and the closest nesting area to Cumberland is a small island in the Satilla River. Forty banded birds have been found dead on the ocean beach, with data available for thirty-six. The majority came from North Carolina (twenty-five), with Florida (four) and Maryland (four) tied for second, and South Carolina (three) last. The oldest bird was 16 years 8 months, with 72% of the birds less than one year old and 21% more than two years old. Between 1974 and 2010, 439 pelicans were found dead on the beach, and of those that could be generally aged, 68% were juveniles and 32% adults.

_____. Family Ardeidae. **American Bittern**. *Botaurus lentiginosus* (Rackett, 1813). The American bittern is more numerous in winter on Cumberland Island when its numbers are increased by migrants. It breeds from Canada to New Jersey and less frequently farther south. It was first reported on Cumberland Island by Sprunt (1936), and Helme collected two specimens in April 1903. One was found DOB 28 October with a broken neck.

_____. Family Ardeidae. **Least Bittern**. *Ixobrychus exilis* (Gmelin, 1789). The least bittern is a summer resident that uses both fresh- and salt-water wetlands and occasionally nests along the coast. Breeding occurs from Canada to southern Mexico and the West Indies, and they winter from Florida south to South America. There are no literature references to this species on Cumberland Island, no museum specimens, and none have been seen on the island Christmas bird counts.

_____. Family Ardeidae. **Great Blue Heron**. *Ardea herodias* Linnaeus, 1758. This permanent island resident nests colonially in tall, mostly live pines, usually in proximity to a freshwater wetland. Cumberland Island nesting locations include Swamp Field, Ashley and Johnson ponds, Table Point pond, and ponds in the north end scrub. The nesting season is long, and nesting activity on Cumberland Island has been recorded from March through June. Observations peak in April.

Great blue herons frequently forage in surf at the beach. The extent of mortality on Cumberland Island is unknown, but five individuals have been found dead on the beach and three dead inland. Most had been eaten by predators. One was shot unsolicited and brought to me for food by an island friend. Most avian species are considered edible and have had human pressure on populations in the past.

_____. Family Ardeidae. **Great Egret**. *Ardea alba* (Linnaeus, 1758). The great egret is a breeding resident of Cumberland Island. Sprunt (1936) reported it from the island and Helme preserved a museum specimen collected on the island. The species breeds from New England along the East Coast, up the Mississippi Valley, and south to South America. Nesting on Cumberland Island has been observed from the early 1900s, dependent upon water level. Artificial ponds, as well as natural ones, and sloughs provided nesting habitat. The earliest island nesting date noted is in March and the latest is the end of July. Full clutches of eggs were reported the first week of March and nesting may continue into July. Up to 100 nests have been estimated in one area on Cumberland Island. There had been much predation at the overgrown nesting sites, now abandoned. Two birds have been found dead on the beach,

_____. Family Ardeidae. **Snowy Egret**. *Egretta thula* (Molina, 1782). This common resident of Cumberland Island breeds from New England along the East and Gulf coasts south to South America. Nesting on Cumberland Island occurs April through June. Although the species has been recorded in every month, it is most often seen from April through September. Along with other colonial species, it nests either over a pond or slough when water and vegetation permit. Snowy egrets feed in brackish or saltwater as well as freshwater. Both Pearson (1922) and Sprunt (1936) reported the species on Cumberland Island, and A. Helme collected a museum specimen in April of 1903.

_____. Family Ardeidae. **Little Blue Heron**. *Egretta caerulea* (Linnaeus, 1758). The little blue heron is a permanent Cumberland Island resident but may be less numerous during autumn and winter.

They have nested on Cumberland Island from April through June at various freshwater habitats. Both Pearson (1922) and Sprunt (1936) reported the species on Cumberland Island. Three have been found DOB from 1988 to 2005.

_____. Family Ardeidae. **Tricolor Heron**. *Egretta tricolor* (Müller, 1776). The tricolor heron was reported from Cumberland Island by Pearson (1922) and Sprunt (1936), and Helme collected a museum specimen from the island. This species breeds from New England along the East Coast to Mexico and Central America. It is most common on the island from April through July, and it is uncommon from August through March. Two have been found dead on the beach.

_____. Family Ardeidae. **Reddish Egret**. *Egretta rufescens* (Gmelin, 1789). Populations of this species were greatly reduced by plume hunters in the early twentieth century but have rebounded and continue to increase. In 1958, there had been only one record for Georgia and that at St. Marys (Burleigh, 1958). From when they were first recognized on Cumberland Island in June of 1991, an average of ten separate sightings of between one and six birds per year were made through 2009, primarily on the beach. Activity was greatest from June through October, with no records for March or April. No breeding has been recorded in Georgia.

_____. Family Ardeidae. **Cattle Egret**. *Bubulcus ibis* (Linnaeus, 1758). This species is a fairly recent (1940s to 1950s) colonizer of the US from Eurasia and Africa and is now a common summer resident of Cumberland Island, especially from April through June. We first observed it on Cumberland Island in 1982 and recorded it nesting on the island from 1985 to 1997. The earliest Cumberland Island nesting date was 19 April. They winter south to South America and are infrequent on Cumberland Island at that time. Eleven were found dead on the beach from 1982 to 1999.

_____. Family Ardeidae. **Green Heron**. *Butorides virescens* (Linnaeus, 1758). This common, mostly summer resident breeds from Canada to southern Mexico and into Central America and winters from South Carolina south. On Cumberland Island it breeds in May and June around the edges of wetlands. The majority of observations are from March through June, with a few from November through February. The species was reported on Cumberland Island by both Pearson (1922) and Sprunt (1936), and seven have been found DOB (1981 to 2008).

_____. Family Ardeidae. **Black-crowned Night Heron**. *Nycticorax nycticorax* (Linnaeus, 1758). A permanent resident, this species nested on Cumberland Island with other wading birds from April through June; young sometimes remained in the area into August. Breeding occurs from Canada to Central and South America. Pearson (1922) and Sprunt (1936) saw this species on Cumberland Island, and A. Helme collected two museum specimens. Roosting on the island is frequent in trees at the edge of the salt marsh and freshwater wetlands.

_____. Family Ardeidae. **Yellow-crowned Night Heron.** *Nyctanassa violacea* (Linnaeus, 1758). Yellow-crowned night herons breed from New England to South America. They are breeding summer residents on Cumberland Island, often reduced in number during the winter. They are most frequently observed April through June. Nesting has been documented in the Sweetwater complex, with large young in the nest on 9 June. Pearson (1922) and Sprunt (1936) reported yellow-crowned night herons on Cumberland Island, and there is a museum specimen from April 1903. Two birds have been found dead on the beach.

_____. Family Threskiornithidae. **White Ibis.** *Eudocimus albus* (Linnaeus, 1758). The white ibis is a common resident of Cumberland Island, especially numerous March through August, and less numerous in autumn and winter. The species nested on Cumberland Island in the past: 1921 (Pearson, 1922), 1985 at Heron Pond, and 1989 in the Sweetwater heronry. An estimated 1,500 to 2,000 nests were noted in 1991 and 1992 on nearby Bird Island in the Satilla River. They are colonial both in feeding and nesting and typically nest from South Carolina along the Gulf Coast, West Indies, and South America. Sprunt (1954) referred to white ibis as "the great food bird of Florida," and indeed it is quite delicious, however distracting the intense, Day-glo-orange color of the liver. People on the islands, black and white, ate them regularly (Fig. 28).

_____. Family Threskiornithidae. **Glossy Ibis.** *Plegadis falcinellus* (Linnaeus, 1766). Nesting in North America occurs from southern Louisiana to Florida and the West Indies. The first record of the glossy ibis in Georgia was from Cumberland Island in 1933 (Sprunt, 1933). Our Cumberland Island records are from March through August, most often of a single sighting. Nesting on Cumberland Island in the Sweetwater complex occurred in May and June. Glossy ibis have been recorded on the island Christmas bird count (2008), and three have been reported DOB, one in October (1974 to 2008).

_____. Family Threskiornithidae. **Roseate Spoonbill.** *Platalea ajaja* (Linnaeus, 1758). A spectacular, uncommon bird in Georgia, the roseate spoonbill has recently been recorded breeding in Camden County, Georgia. The spoonbill is locally seen most often in July through September, although there are records from Cumberland Island May through November, and they are becoming more frequent visitors. Spoonbills are much more common just south of the state line, west of Fernandina, Florida, where an estimated 100 to 200 have been seen at a time (C. Fries, pers. comm.). On Cumberland Island, they are usually seen foraging in tidal creeks, but they sometimes roost over the Plum Orchard pond at midday. Breeding occurs along the Gulf of Mexico, south Florida, and Cuba.

ORDER ACCIPITRIFORMES. Family Cathartidae. **Black Vulture**. *Coragyps atratus* (Bechstein, 1793). Black vultures are a common species resident on Cumberland Island. Breeding occurs from Kansas and Maryland to South America, so autumn numbers are increased by migrants. Copulation has been noted on the island in March and April, and birds have been seen on nests with eggs and chicks from April through May. The earliest a fledged young has been recorded on the island is 21 June. They patrol the roads and beach, and have been recorded eating decomposing marine mammals and horseshoe crabs as well as terrestrial mammals. They show particular caution around carcasses of male opossums and male coyotes and have an intimate relationship with alligators. Black vultures have been found DOB (two) and DOR (three) on the island.

_____. Family Cathartidae. **Turkey Vulture**. *Cathartes aura* (Linnaeus, 1758). The turkey vulture is a permanent resident on Cumberland Island, common at all times of the year. Numbers may be augmented in autumn and winter by northern transients. They breed from Canada south to Mexico and winter in the southern part of their range. Young have been seen on Cumberland Island from August through October. They regularly scavenge the beach and have been recorded eating dead horseshoe crabs, fish, sea turtles, and marine and terrestrial mammals. They find many roadkills on Cumberland Island as well. Four birds have been found DOB.

_____. Family Pandionidae. **Osprey**. *Pandion haliaetus* (Linnaeus, 1758). Ospreys breed from northwestern Alaska east to Newfoundland and south to Florida, and they winter from Georgia and the Gulf states and the West Indies to Central America. They are most abundant on Cumberland Island in spring and summer, with numbers greatly reduced in winter. Large groups of transients have been seen in March. Nesting activity has been observed on Cumberland Island from the end of February through early August, with the earliest chick noted on 4 June and the latest 10 August. Both Pearson (1922) and Sprunt (1936) reported the species on Cumberland Island. Three have been found DOB and nests containing young have been toppled by wildfires in May and July and by wind.

_____. Family Accipitridae. **Swallow-tailed Kite.** *Elanoides forficatus* (Linnaeus, 1758). Cumberland Island records of this kite are in spring, March, April, and May. Helme saw it on the island in April 1902 (Burleigh, 1958). The species breeds from Texas to South Carolina and south into South America, and they winter in Central America. There are records of breeding in Camden County on the mainland.

_____. Family Accipitridae. **Mississippi Kite.** *Ictinia mississippiensis* (Wilson, 1811). These kites breed from Indiana to South Carolina, Texas, and Florida and winter from central Florida to Central America. They are said to be uncommon summer residents in Florida (Robertson and Woolfenden, 1992). There is an observation record from Cumberland Island from March of 1988 (S. Willis, pers. comm.).

_____. Family Accipitridae. **Bald Eagle.** *Haliaeetus leucocephalus* (Linnaeus, 1766). This eagle is a fairly common bird on Cumberland Island, seen in all months. Breeding is recorded prior to the 1940s and recently since 1999. Pearson (1922) reported that there were two nests on the island in 1921 and "understood there were others," and Sprunt (1936) also reported the species on the island. In 1880, F. Ober shot a bald eagle at Dungeness. Eagles were also killed because they took newborn livestock. A recently fledged bald eagle was found dead on the Main Road on Cumberland Island in April 2010, a roadkill. A freshly regurgitated pellet found in November contained remnants of a coot.

_____. Family Accipitridae. **Northern Harrier.** *Circus cyaneus* (Linnaeus, 1766). The northern harrier is a transient and a winter visitor to Cumberland Island. It breeds from Alaska south to Texas, Virginia, and occasionally in north Florida. This species winters south to the Bahamas, Cuba, and South America. Harriers have been recorded on Cumberland Island from September through April, with the earliest recent island observation 16 September and the latest 17 April. Pearson (1922) saw one here on 3 May in 1921, and Sprunt (1936) also reported them from the island. These birds are commonly observed foraging over salt marshes and over the interdune areas on Cumberland Island.

_____. Family Accipitridae. **Sharp-shinned Hawk.** *Accipiter striatus* (Vieillot, 1808). This small hawk is an autumn migrant and uncommon winter visitor. It breeds from Canada to Florida and winters south to Central America. Sprunt (1936) recorded it on Cumberland Island, and there are records from November and February, when one was found dead. Helme collected a specimen in December 1904.

_____. Family Accipitridae. **Cooper's Hawk.** *Accipiter cooperii* (Bonaparte, 1828). An uncommon permanent resident, this species was reported breeding on Cumberland Island in 1902 (Burleigh, 1958). Helme collected a specimen on 15 April 1903. Sprunt (1936) reported the species on Cumberland Island, and there are records from January 1992 and 1997. Cooper's hawks breed from Canada to Florida and winter south to Mexico and Central America.

_____. Family Accipitridae. **Northern Goshawk.** *Accipiter gentiles* (Linnaeus, 1758). A hawk of the north, the goshawk breeds from Alaska into the northern US states and winters from its breeding range south to Mexico and occasionally to Florida. There are few records for Georgia, but one bird that was thought to be ill was observed on Little Cumberland Island several years ago (1970s; G. Sciple, pers. comm.).

_____. Family Acctpitridae. **Red-shouldered Hawk.** *Buteo lineatus* (Gmelin, 1788). This Cumberland Island resident breeds from Canada south and winters to the Gulf Coast and Florida. Migrants may inflate winter numbers. Both Pearson (1922) and Sprunt (1936) reported this species on Cumberland Island. The red-shouldered hawk has been observed feeding on a butchered hog, a large beetle, and carrying a snake on Cumberland Island. Two have been found DOB.

_____. Family Accipitridae. **Broad-winged Hawk.** *Buteo platypterus* (Vieillot, 1823). A spring and autumn transient, this species breeds from Canada south to the Gulf Coast and Florida and winters from south Florida and southern Mexico through Central to South America. There are no specimens from Cumberland Island but there is an observation record (S. Willis, pers. comm.).

_____. Family Accipitridae. **Red-tailed Hawk.** *Buteo jamaicensis* (Gmelin, 1788). The red-tailed hawk is a permanent resident, but observations of this species on Cumberland Island are reduced during late spring and summer. They breed from Canada south to Florida and winter to the Gulf Coast. Burleigh (1958) said breeding had been reported on Cumberland Island. Helme took a specimen on 16 December 1904, and Pearson (1922) reported the species on the island. Food recorded here has been an egret, *Casmerodius* sp., a red-shouldered hawk, and a squirrel. One has been found dead on the road.

_____. Family Accipitridae. **Rough-legged Hawk.** *Buteo lagopus* (Pontoppidan, 1763). The rough-legged hawk is an irregular winter visitor to both Georgia and Florida. It breeds far to the north (Alaska, Canada) and winters south to the Gulf Coast and Florida. There are records from nearby Charlton County, but not Cumberland Island (S. Willis, pers. comm.).

_____. Family Accipitridae. **Golden Eagle.** *Aquila chrysaetos* (Linnaeus, 1758). An uncommon winter visitor and transient, the golden eagle breeds from northern Alaska to New England and south to North Carolina. The Georgia DNR introduced golden eagles in Georgia between 1984 and 1993 (Beaton et al., 2003). There are records from Camden County mainland (Sheila Willis, pers. comm.).

ORDER FALCONIFORMES. Family Falconidae. **American Kestrel.** *Falco sparvarius* Linnaeus, 1758. Two subsprecies of the American kestrel have been reported from Georgia, a large northern bird, and a small bird that breeds to the south and has been reported breeding on Cumberland Island (Burleigh, 1958). The larger form breeds from eastern Alaska and Newfoundland south to north Georgia and winters south to Central America. It is a regular transient and winter visitor on Cumberland Island, but the small form is no longer seen here. Pearson (1922) saw two on Cumberland Island but said "conditions...would appear not to be favorable for their presence, the forest growth being too heavy and open ranges too few to meet their requirements." At that time, much land formerly under agriculture was reverting to natural conditions. Ruckdeschel and Whitaker (2007) found suitable food, insects being prevalent in the interdune area, but acknowledged that the National Park Service's fire-suppression policy changed much inland community structure, reducing open habitat preferred by kestrels.

_____. Family Falconidae. **Merlin.** *Falco columbarius* Linnaeus, 1758. Helme first noted the merlin or pigeon hawk on Cumberland Island in 1902 (Burleigh, 1958) and collected specimens in 1903 and 1905. Sprunt (1936) recorded it on his visits in the early 1930s. It is a regular transient and winter visitor that breeds from Canada and Newfoundland south to northern Maine and winters from the Gulf states and West Indies to South America. It has been recorded on the island in all but the summer months, but it is most common in spring and autumn. One has been found DOR on Cumberland Island.

_____. Family Falconidae. **Peregrine Falcon.** *Falco peregrines* Tunstall, 1771. The peregrine falcon is a regular transient and common winter visitor. Records occur in all except summer months (June through August) and are most abundant in September and October. Pearson (1922) first recorded the species from Cumberland Island. Breeding takes place in northwest Alaska to Greenland and south to the mountains of North Carolina and Georgia. They winter south to the West Indies and South America. The species has been periodically banded on Cumberland Island.

ORDER GRUIFORMES. Family Rallidae. **Yellow Rail**. *Coturnicops noveboracensis* (Gmelin, 1789). Helme collected an undated museum specimen of this species on Cumberland Island, probably from the early 1900s. None have been found dead on the beach or collected here since, but one was seen on Little Cumberland Island (G. Sciple, pers. comm.). They breed in Canada and the northern US and winter along the Gulf states and Georgia and Florida. They are infrequently seen in Georgia and are considered rare transients and rare winter visitors only.

_____. Family Rallidae. **Black Rail**. *Laterallus jamaicensis* (Gmelin, 1789). This tiny rail is an irregular winter visitor and spring and autumn transient. It breeds in southern Canada and the northern US south to Florida and winters in South Georgia, Florida, Jamaica, and Central America. There are no confirmed records from Cumberland Island but it has been recorded on the adjacent mainland.

_____. Family Rallidae. **Clapper Rail**. *Rallus longirostris* Boddaert, 1783. The clapper rail is an abundant permanent resident breeding in the Cumberland Island salt marsh, where it nests in April and May. A bird was observed walking alone on 6 May carrying nest material to a mate who used it in a nest she occupied. Breeding extends along the Atlantic from the northeast to the West Indies and Brazil. Pearson (1922) reported it on Cumberland Island, and Helme collected thirty-three museum specimens from the island in March, April, December, and January of 1902 to 1905. This rail is considered a game bird and has been hunted on the island from the late 1880s to present time. The remains of several clapper rails have been found partially eaten. Eggs are sometimes stolen by crows. Eleven were found DOB from 1979 to 1998.

_____. Family Rallidae. **King Rail**. *Rallus elegans* Audubon, 1834. The king is the largest of the rails and was reported on Cumberland Island by Sprunt (1936). It breeds from Canada and the Northern states south to Texas, Louisiana, and Florida and winters in the Southern states. Cumberland Island records are from February and April. One was found DOB in April.

_____. Family Rallidae. **Virginia Rail**. *Rallus limicola* Vieillot, 1819. The Virginia rail is a transient and winter visitor on Cumberland Island. It breeds from Canada south to North Carolina and winters south to the Gulf Coast, Florida, and Central America. One was found DOB in April.

They have been observed on the island Audubon bird counts.

_____. Family Rallidae. **Sora**. *Porzana carolina* (Linnaeus, 1758). This small rail breeds from Canada south to Pennsylvania and Maryland and winters along the Gulf Coast, Florida, and the West Indies to South America. It is a spring and autumn migrant and winter visitor on Cumberland Island. Helme collected museum specimens in March and April of 1902 and April of 1903. Our records are February, March, April, August, and September, and three have been found DOB. One was identified in bobcat feces.

_____. Family Rallidae. **Purple Gallinule**. *Porphyrio martinica* (Linnaeus, 1766). This gorgeous species breeds from South Carolina to Mexico and South America and winters along the Gulf Coast and in south Florida, south through its breeding range. They are fairly common on Cumberland Island in the spring around freshwater. Island records are in April, May, and June. Both Pearson (1922) and Sprunt (1936) reported them, and Helme collected museum specimens on the island.

_____. Family Rallidae. **Common Moorhen**. *Gallinula chloropus* (Linnaeus, 1758). This widely distributed species breeds from Canada south and winters from North Carolina south to Panama. It was reported on Cumberland Island by both Pearson (1922) and Sprunt (1936), and Helme collected specimens in January 1905 and December 1909. Moorhens have been seen copulating in island freshwater areas in April, with chicks in May and June. Island numbers are reduced in autumn and winter.

_____. Family Rallidae. **American Coot**. *Fulica americana* (Gmelin, 1789). Sprunt (1936) reported American coots on Cumberland Island, and Helme collected scientific specimens in October 1903 and December 1904 and reported the species plentiful on the island 8 March to 12 April 1902 (Burleigh, 1958). They are regular winter visitors that breed from Canada south to New Jersey and sporadically in small numbers in south Georgia and Florida. Pairs have been seen on Cumberland Island in mid-April. An unusual number (fifteen) have been found DOB October through January.

_____. Family Gruidae. **Sandhill Crane**. *Grus canadensis* (Linnaeus, 1758). These large birds breed from Alaska to Michigan, with another group breeding from coastal Mississippi, the Okefenokee Swamp, and south Georgia to southern Florida, although there are no reports of their having bred or been present in large numbers on Cumberland Island. They winter from Texas and the Gulf Coast to south Florida and central Mexico. Burleigh (1958) reported they were hunted for food. Island records are from February and April and of two or three individuals at a time.

ORDER CHARADRIIFORMES. Family Charadriidae. **Black-bellied Plover**. *Pluvialis squatarola* (Linnaeus, 1758). The black-bellied plover is a winter visitor and transient that breeds to the far north along the Arctic Coast and islands, east to Baffin Island, and winters from southern Canada to the Gulf Coast and South America. Helme collected three museum specimens on Cumberland Island in April of 1902 and 1903, and Sprunt (1936) reported the species on the island. In Florida, nonbreeding birds are common year-round and they are fairly common on Cumberland Island, especially during spring and autumn.

_____. Family Charadridae. **American Golden Plover**. *Pluvialis dominica* (Müller, 1776). The American golden plover breeds in northern Canada and winters in South America. Its main migratory routes usually miss Georgia, making it an uncommon transient on Cumberland Island.

There is one report from Cumberland Island in the *Oriole* (58 [1–4]: 35).

_____. Family Charadridae. **Snowy Plover**. *Charadrius nivosus* (Cassin, 1858). This species, unusual to Cumberland Island and Georgia, breeds in the Western US, along the Gulf Coast, Mexico, and on Caribbean Islands, and it winters in the breeding range. It has been reported from Cumberland Island (S. Willis, P. Leary).

_____. Family Charadriidae. **Wilson's Plover**. *Charadrius wilsonia* Ord, 1814. A bird of the Southeast, Wilson's plover breeds from Virginia to Florida, along the Gulf Coast to Texas, and in the Bahamas. It winters from north Florida west and to Central America and the West Indies. It is a common summer resident on Cumberland Island, arriving as early as 19 February and departing in September. Pairs claim territory in the dunes near the beach soon after arrival, through March and April, and nesting occurs from April through May. Young have been recorded on Cumberland Island 11 May and as late as 25 July. Both Pearson (1922) and Sprunt (1936) recorded the species on the island, and there are twelve museum specimens from January, March, and April.

_____. Family Charadriidae. **Semipalmated Plover**. *Charadrius semipalmatus* Bonaparte, 1825. This abundant transient and winter visitor to Cumberland Island was recorded by both Pearson (1922) and Sprunt (1936), and there are seven museum specimens from 1902, 1903, and 1970. It breeds on the Arctic Coast from the Bering Sea to Greenland and south to Nova Scotia, and it winters from South Carolina and the Gulf Coast to South America. It may be found on Cumberland Island in all months, with large flocks frequently seen on the beach, but with reduced numbers during the late spring and early summer, when only nonbreeding birds remain.

_____. Family Charadriidae. **Piping Plover**. *Charadrius melodus* Ord, 1824. This bird of the ocean beach is a moderately common migrant and winter visitor to Cumberland Island. It was reported by Sprunt (1936) and there are two museum specimens collected by Helme, one January 1903, the other April 1903. Breeding occurs along the Atlantic Coast from Newfoundland south to North Carolina, and they winter from Georgia south along the Gulf Coast to northern Mexico.

Activity on Cumberland Island is greatest from August through April.

_____. Family Charadriidae. **Killdeer**. *Charadrius vociferous* Linnaeus, 1758. This plover may be found on Cumberland Island in all months, but numbers are highest from January through July and lowest in August and September. Pairs form from January through March, and nesting begins in early April and continues into late May. Young have been recorded as early as 13 April and as late as 13 July. Island nesting occurs in open fields, disturbed habitats, and in the interdune area. Groups of migrants are seen autumn and winter. Sprunt (1936) reported the killdeer from Cumberland Island, and the species has been noted on the island Christmas bird counts.

_____. Family Haematopoidae. **American Oystercatcher**. *Haematopus palliatus* Tenminck, 1820. An obvious shorebird, the oystercatcher was reported on Cumberland Island by both Pearson (1922) and Sprunt (1936), and a specimen was collected in May of 1905. It is a permanent resident, with about ten breeding pairs nesting along the beach each season. Courting begins in February and March and birds may be on eggs the first week in April. The nesting period is extended if a clutch is lost, and may continue into early June. Adults with young are seen from the second week in May through the end of July. Sabine et al. (2006) found the nesting success rate higher on the north end of Cumberland Island, with a total of fifteen young produced from thirty-two clutches over the two-year study. Causes of nest failure included predation by raccoons, bobcats, American crows, and ghost crabs as well as overwash, horse trampling, abandonment, and destruction by a visitor (child). Breeding occurs along the coast from Virginia to Texas and Mexico and into South America. The birds winter in the southern part of their range, including Georgia. Groups from five to over fifty assemble from August through February, then disperse. One has been found dead on the beach. The American oystercatcher is listed by the state as rare in Georgia.

_____. Family Recurvirostridae. **Black-necked Stilt.** *Himantopus mexicanus* (Müller, 1776). An uncommon transient on Cumberland Island, this slim bird breeds from Oregon and southern Colorado to New Mexico and the southern US, Bahamas, West Indies, Mexico, and South America. It winters from the Gulf Coast states to Brazil and Peru. Neither Pearson nor Sprunt reported it on the island, and there are no museum specimens from Cumberland Island. We have observations from April, May, and August.

_____. Family Recurvirostridae. **American Avocet.** *Recurvirostra americana* Gmelin, 1789. The avocet was missed by Pearson and Sprunt, and there are no specimens from Cumberland Island, but they have been recorded on the island (S. Willis, pers. comm.). A western breeder, this species nests from Canada south to southern Texas and Iowa and winters from there south to Central America. It is a rare transient and winter visitor to Cumberland Island.

_____. Family Scolopacidae. **Spotted Sandpiper.** *Actitis macularia* (Linnaeus, 1766). Neither Pearson nor Sprunt reported this regular, common migrant and occasional winter visitor to Cumberland Island, nor are there any museum specimens from the island. They have been recorded on the island Christmas bird counts. Spotted sandpipers breed from Alaska through Canada to the northern part of the Gulf states and winter from South Carolina to South America. Cumberland Island records are from October, December, January, and May. One was shot for food along with snipe in December 1974.

_____. Family Scolopacidae. **Solitary Sandpiper.** *Tringa solitaria* Wilson, 1813. A regular transient, this sandpiper was recorded on Cumberland Island by both Pearson (1922) and Sprunt (1936), but there are no museum specimens. The species breeds from Canada into the central US east to Pennsylvania and winters from Florida south to the West Indies, Mexico, and South America. They have been seen on Cumberland Island in May and one was found DOB on 14 May.

_____. Family Scolopacidae. **Greater Yellowlegs.** *Tringa melanoleuca* (Gmelin, 1789). The greater yellowlegs is a regular transient and winter visitor to Cumberland Island. This large shorebird prefers marshes, freshwater or salt-, to open beaches. It breeds from southern Alaska into Canada and winters from South Carolina and the Gulf Coast to South America. Helme collected two specimens on Cumberland Island in March and April 1902, and Sprunt (1936) reported it from the island. It is frequently seen on the Cumberland Christmas bird counts.

_____. Family Scolopacidae. **Willet.** *Tringa semipalmatus* (Gmelin, 1789). The willet breeds at Nova Scotia and Prince Edward Island and from New Jersey south along the East Coast and around the Gulf to Texas. It winters from South Carolina to the Bahamas and South America. Distribution in the Southeast has changed from the 1930s when Burleigh (1958) decided they must be considered summer residents only. The western subspecies augments winter numbers on Cumberland Island nevertheless, numbers from January to April now more than triple those other months, and the willet is accepted as a permanent resident. Nesting on Cumberland Island has been recorded in May, with young in June. The camouflage provided the eggs by feral horse droppings cannot be overlooked. There are a dozen museum specimens of this species taken by Helme and Greenway, and Pearson (1922) and Sprunt (1936) reported the Willet on Cumberland Island. Two have been found dead on the beach.

_____. Family Scolopacidae. **Lesser Yellowlegs.** *Tringa flavipes* (Gmelin, 1789). Five museum specimens of this species were collected by Helme in March and April in the early 1900s, and both Pearson (1922) and Sprunt (1936) reported the species on Cumberland Island. Pearson saw seventy birds on Cumberland Island on 3 and 4 May 1921. The lesser yellowlegs breed from Alaska into Canada and winters from Georgia south into South America and the Bahamas.

_____. Family Scolopacidae. **Upland Sandpiper.** *Bartramia longicauda* (Bechstein, 1812). This unusual migrant breeds from northwestern Alaska south to the midwestern prairie grasslands and east to Virginia. It winters in South America. Helme collected two specimens on Cumberland Island in April 1903.

_____. Family Scolopacidae. **Whimbrel.** *Numenius phaeopus* Linnaeus, 1758. The whimbrel is a migrant common in spring. It breeds from southern Alaska into Canada and winters from South Carolina to South America. Both Pearson (1922) and Sprunt (1936) reported it from Cumberland Island, and Helme collected three specimens in April 1903 and 1905. One bird was found DOB on 25 April, possibly the victim of a hailstorm.

_____. Family Scolopacidae. **Long-billed Curlew.** *Numenius americanus* (Bechstein, 1812). The longbilled curlew breeds in the midwestern states east to Illinois. This largest of our North American shorebirds is an uncommon migrant at Cumberland Island and winters from South Carolina to Mexico. It has been observed on the island (S. Willis, pers. comm.).

_____. Family Scolopacidae. **Marbled Godwit**. *Limosa fedoa* (Linnaeus, 1758). This large shorebird breeds from Canada south to South Dakota and winters from South Carolina and the Gulf Coast to South America. It is a bird of the mud flats rather than the open beach and an uncommon transient and winter visitor at Cumberland Island. The species is frequently seen on the Cumberland Christmas bird counts.

_____. Family Scolopacidae. **Ruddy Turnstone**. *Arenaria interpres* (Linnaeus, 1758). An Arctic nester, this handsome shorebird is a year-round, nonbreeding visitor and transient at Cumberland Island. It winters from North Carolina and the Gulf Coast to South America. Cumberland Island records are from all seasons. There are eight museum specimens and ruddy turnstones are observed on the Cumberland Christmas counts.

_____. Family Scolopacidae. **Red Knot**. *Calidris canutus* (Linnaeus, 1758). This regular migrant breeds from Alaska to north Greenland and winters from Georgia south into South America. The red knot was missed by early recorders, but there are specimens from November 1970 and May 1971. Our records are from November through February and May, and red knots are usually seen on the Cumberland Audubon Christmas Bird Counts

_____. Family Scolopacidae. **Sanderling**. *Calidris alba* (Pallas, 1764). Sanderlings breed from the Arctic coast of Alaska to Greenland and along the Atlantic Coast, and they winter along the Atlantic Coast from New England to South America. They are common to abundant regular transients on Cumberland Island and some nonbreeders may remain through the summer. There are seven museum specimens from Cumberland Island dating from June 1902 to May 1971, and Sprunt (1936) recorded them as well. Four have been found DOB, one killed by a vehicle.

_____. Family Scolopacidae. **Semipalmated Sandpiper**. *Caldris pusilla* (Linnaeus, 1766). The semipalmated sandpiper is a regular spring and autumn migrant from its breeding grounds along the Arctic Coast to northern Labrador and its winter retreats from South Carolina to the West Indies and South America. This sandpiper is an uncommon winter visitor to Cumberland Island. There are four museum specimens from the island (March 1902 and 1905). Pearson (1922) reported them in May of 1921, and Sprunt (1936) saw them on the island as well.

_____. Family Scolopacidae. **Western Sandpiper**. *Calidris mauri* (Cabanis, 1857). Western sandpipers breed along the Alaskan coast and winter along the Pacific coast and from North Carolina to Florida. Non-breeders may spend the summer around Cumberland Island. There are two museum specimens from Cumberland Island (September 1903 and November 1970) and Sprunt (1936) reported them on the island.

_____. Family Scolopacidae. **Least Sandpiper**. *Calidris minutilla* (Vieillot, 1819). Although nonbreeding birds may occur throughout the summer, breeding least sandpipers head for northwest Alaska east to Nova Scotia. They winter from North Carolina south through the West Indies to Central and South America. Least sandpipers are transients on Cumberland Island and regular winter visitors, least common midsummer. Museum specimens were collected on Cumberland Island (March 1902 and 1903, April 1903), and both Pearson (1922) and Sprunt (1936) recorded the species on the island.

_____. Family Scolopacidae. **White-rumped Sandpiper**. *Calidris fuscicollis* (Vieillot, 1819). The white-rumped sandpiper is a rare transient on Cumberland Island. It breeds on the Arctic Coast and in Canada and winters in South America. There is a record for the island in July (S. Willis, pers. comm.).

_____. Family Scolopacidae. **Pectoral Sandpiper**. *Calidris melanotos* (Vieillot, 1819). The pectoral sandpiper is a common, regular transient that breeds on the Arctic Coast and winters in South America. It is incidental in winter on Cumberland Island. There are seven museum specimens, all from April 1903, and the species has been observed on the island Audubon Christmas counts.

_____. Family Scolopacidae. **Purple Sandpiper**. *Calidris maritima* (Brunnich, 1764). A bird of northern latitudes, the purple sandpiper breeds from northern to southern Greenland and winters only casually south of New England. Its preferred habitat is rock jetties, and they have been observed near the jetty at the south end of Cumberland Island and on the Audubon Christmas counts.

_____. Family Scolopacidae. **Dunlin**. *Calidris alpina* (Linnaeus, 1758). The dunlin is a common winter visitor and transient at Cumberland Island. It breeds to the far north and winters from New Jersey south to Florida and the Gulf Coast. It is rare on Cumberland Island in summer. Thirteen museum specimens have been taken on the island, most in March, April, and May, with two in November and one in December. Sprunt

(1936) reported the species on the island and they are seen on the Audubon bird counts in December.

_____. Family Scolopacidae. **Stilt Sandpiper.** *Calidris himantopus* (Bonaparte, 1826). In 1905, Helme collected what Burleigh (1958) called the first state record of the stilt sandpiper on Cumberland Island. The species breeds in northern Canada and winters in South America and occasionally in Mexico and along the Gulf states, so is an uncommon transient on Cumberland Island.

_____. Family Scolopacidae. **Buff-breasted Sandpiper.** *Tryngites subruficollis* (Vieillot, 1819). Buff-breasted sandpipers breed along the Arctic coast of Alaska and Canada and winter in South America. They are only transients at Cumberland Island. There is a report of an observation on Cumberland Island in the *Oriole* (58 [1–4]: 35).

_____. Family Scolopacidae. **Short-billed Dowitcher.** *Limnodromus griseus* (Gmelin, 1789). The short-billed dowitcher breeds in Canada and winters from North Carolina to the West Indies and South America. This species is a common transient and winter visitor at Cumberland Island. There are two museum specimens from October 1903 and February 1905. Burleigh (1958) reported the species on Cumberland Island on 12 March 1903, and Sprunt (1936) saw them in April of 1932 or 1933. They have been recorded on the Cumberland Audubon Christmas counts.

_____. Family Scolopacidae. **Long-billed Dowitcher.** *Limnodromus scolopaceus* (Say, 1823). The long-billed dowitcher is less common than the short-billed, but there is a specimen from Cumberland Island from March 1903. This dowitcher breeds in Alaska and along the Arctic Coast and winters from South Carolina to Central America. It is considered a rare to uncommon transient and winter visitor at Cumberland Island.

_____. Family Scolopacidae. **Common Snipe.** *Gallinago gallinago* (Linnaeus, 1758). Sprunt (1936) observed common snipes on Cumberland Island, and they were shot for sport on the island at least from 1900 through 1974. They are regular transients and winter visitors to Cumberland Island. They breed from Alaska to Newfoundland and south into the northern US and winter from Virginia south through Central American and the West Indies into South America. A chewing louse has been identified on island snipe. See Appendix VI. B.

_____. Family Scolopacidae. **American Woodcock.** *Scolopax minor* Gmelin, 1789. The American woodcock is an uncommon Cumberland Island resident, which, unlike most shorebirds, prefers wooded wetlands to open marshes. Neither Pearson nor Sprunt recorded this species on the island, and there are no museum specimens and no reference to hunting of the species on the island. We have only three observations, one each in June, July, and October.

_____. Family Scolopacidae. **Wilson's Phalarope**. *Phalaropus tricolor* (Vieillot, 1819). This phalarope breeds from British Columbia east to Ontario and into the northwestern US and winters from south Texas to South America. It is considered rare to uncommon along the Georgia coast, but one was recorded on a Christmas bird count on the mainland adjacent to Cumberland Island.

_____. Family Scolopacidae. **Red-necked Phalarope**. *Phalaropus lobatus* (Linnaeus, 1758). The red-necked phalarope is a regular but uncommon offshore transient that breeds in the Arctic and winters off the coasts of South America and Africa. It is rare inshore along the Georgia coast. There have been observations offshore in the vicinity of Cumberland Island and it has been recorded on Jekyll Island (S. Willis, pers. comm.).

_____. Family Scolopacidae. **Red Phalarope**. *Phalaropus fulicaria* (Linnaeus, 1758). The red phalarope migrates off both US coasts between its breeding grounds in northern Alaska and Greenland south to Hudson Bay and its winter retreats on the open water and the northern Gulf of Mexico. They are transients sometimes seen offshore in the Georgia embayment, rarely inshore, and there are no Cumberland Island records.

_____. Family Laridae. **Black-legged Kittywake**. *Rissa tridactyla* (Linnaeus, 1758). The pelagic kittywake breeds in Arctic Canada, Greenland, and Labrador and winters on the northern Atlantic and Pacific oceans. It is mainly seen offshore and is a regular, rare to fairly common winter visitor to Florida. One was reported near Savannah, Georgia, (Burleigh, 1958) and the species has been observed from the pier at the north end of Amelia Island, Florida (S. Willis, pers. comm.). There are no Cumberland Island records.

_____. Family Laridae. **Sabine's Gull**. *Xema sabini* (Sabine, 1819). This attractive small gull breeds in Alaska, northern Canada, Greenland, and northern Siberia. It winters in the Pacific and is a rare autumn transient in the Atlantic. It spends its non-nesting time far at sea. There are no records for this species at Cumberland Island, but it has been recorded at Amelia Island, Florida (S. Willis, pers. comm.).

_____. Family Laridae. **Bonaparte's Gull.** *Chroicocephalus philadelphia* Ord, 1815. Bonaparte's gull is a winter visitor that Helme said was common on Cumberland Island in March of 1902 (Burleigh, 1958). It breeds from Alaska into Canada and winters along the East Coast to Florida and the Gulf of Mexico. Sprunt (1936) reported it on Cumberland Island, and there are museum specimens from January, March, and April. Our records, December through March, show thirteen have been recorded DOB.

_____. Family Laridae. **Laughing Gull.** *Leucophaeus atricilla* Linnaeus, 1758. The laughing gull breeds along the Atlantic and Gulf coasts from Nova Scotia to Mexico, including Georgia, but no breeding has been documented on Cumberland Island. Pearson (1922) and Sprunt (1936) recorded it on Cumberland Island and there are four museum specimens. Laughing gulls have been seen copulating on the island (27 May). Many were found dead on the beach throughout the year and represent months of general activity. Maximum numbers were in March through May and August through December; 62% were adults. There are seven banding records from 1979 to 1995, originating in New Jersey and Florida, with the oldest bird 11 years 10 months. Seven incidences of mortality from having a fish wedged/caught in the throat have been recorded. The species of fish varied and included two catfish, one croaker, two whiting, one hogchoker, and one tonguefish. These gulls have also been found caught with fishing lures and hooks.

_____. Family Laridae. **Franklin's Gull.** *Leucophaeus pipixcan* (Wagler, 1831). Franklin's gull is a rare migrant along the East Coast but one whose range is expanding. It breeds from central Canada south to Oregon and Ohio and winters primarily along the Pacific coast of South America and casually along the Gulf Coast to Florida. There are no records for Cumberland Island but the species has been recorded in St. Marys, Georgia (S. Willis, pers. comm.).

_____. Family Laridae. **Ring-billed Gull.** *Larus delawarensis* Ord, 1815. A common transient and winter visitor, the ring-billed gull breeds from Alaska east into the northern US to New York and winters south to Florida and the Gulf Coast, Cuba, and Mexico. An immature found dead on the beach had been banded near Charlesbourg, Quebec. Sprunt (1936) reported the species on Cumberland Island, and there are two museum specimens from November. Most activity on Cumberland Island occurs from November through May, with numbers only in single digits from June through August. Two birds have been found dead with a fish wedged in their mouth/throat, both in December. One fish was a whiting, the other a Florida pompano. Slightly over 50% of the strandings have been adults.

_____. Family Laridae. **Herring Gull.** *Larus argentatus* Pontoppidan, 1763. Herring gulls breed in Alaska, Canada, and the northern US and winter south to the Bahamas, Cuba, and Mexico, so they are transients and winter visitors to Cumberland Island. They were reported by Pearson (1922) and Sprunt (1936) and are regularly seen on the Christmas counts. Our records are from October through May, with less activity from June through September. Many have been recorded DOB, 16% of which were adults.

_____. Family Laridae. **Iceland Gull.** *Larus glaucoides* Meyer, 1822. As the name suggests, the Iceland gull is a bird of the far north, and it is considered incidental in Georgia. It breeds in Greenland and points north and usually winters south to New York and the Great Lakes, and occasionally farther south. It has been recorded on the Cumberland Island Audubon Christmas counts.

_____. Family Laridae. **Lesser Black-backed Gull.** *Larus fuscus* Linnaeus, 1758. Burleigh (1958) did not list this species for Georgia, but it is now increasing in numbers as a winter visitor. It breeds in Europe and Asia and generally winters south to the west coast of Africa. We have two records of it for Cumberland Island in April, and it has been recorded on the Cumberland Island Christmas Bird Counts.

_____. Family Laridae. **Glaucous Gull.** *Larus hyperboreus* Gunnerus, 1767. The glaucous gull is a large, rare spring and winter visitor to Cumberland Island. It breeds from Alaska east to Labrador and winters incidentally to Florida and Bermuda. It has been recorded on the Cumberland Audubon Counts.

_____. Family Laridae. **Great Black-backed Gull.** *Larus marinus* Linnaeus, 1758. The great black-backed gull is the largest of our gulls and has been increasing in numbers on Cumberland Island. The majority of observations occur from December through February. Breeding occurs in the far north from Greenland to Nova Scotia, and they winter along the Atlantic Coast to Florida. On the island, the species has been recorded on the Audubon Christmas counts, and five have been found DOB.

_____. Family Laridae. **Brown Noddy.** *Anous stolidus* (Linnaeus, 1758). The brown noddy is a tropical species that breeds in the Dry Tortugas, Bahamas, and West Indies to South America. It is an uncommon visitor to Cumberland Island and usually arrives in association with storms. Our records are from June, August, and October. There are two museum specimens from Cumberland Island.

_____. Family Laridae. **Sooty Tern**. *Onychoprion fuscatus* Linnaeus, 1766. This pelagic tern breeds from the Bahamas and West Indies to South America, then flocks may wander as far north as New England. Storms sometimes force them ashore, and fourteen have been recorded DOB on Cumberland Island from June through October, with one in April (1979 to 2008).

_____. Family Laridae. **Bridled Tern**. *Onychoprion anaethetus* Scopoli, 1786. The bridled tern breeds in the Bahamas, West Indies, Central America, and the northwest African coast and is closely associated with the Gulf Stream during the breeding season. It is sometimes found on shore following storms. It has been reported on Cumberland Island in August and October (Haney et al., 1986) and was found here in association with a tropical storm in 2008.

_____. Family Laridae. **Least Tern**. *Sternula antillarum* (Lesson, 1847). Pearson (1922) reported this smallest of our terns from Cumberland Island. The least tern is a summer breeder on Cumberland Island. Its breeding range extends from Massachusetts to Florida, along the Gulf Coast, the Bahamas, West Indies, and further south and it winters along the coasts of Central and South America. Cumberland Island records are from April through September, and nesting was documented in 1973, 1977, and most of the 1980s and 1990s, but has been irregular since. The earliest eggs on Cumberland Island were 12 May and the latest 14 August. Young were common in June and July. Eight have been recorded DOB, three of which were vehicle fatalities. Other island hazards include domestic dogs, coyotes, bobcats, and feral livestock.

_____. Family Laridae. **Gull-billed Tern**. *Gelochelidon nilotica* Gmelin, 1789. The gull-billed tern breeds along the East Coast from Virginia to Florida, the Bahamas, and Cuba and winters to South America. It has nested on Cumberland Island in association with least terns (Hillestad et al., 1975). There is one museum specimen from May 1971.

_____. Family Laridae. **Caspian Tern**. *Hydroprogne caspia* Pallas, 1770. This large, uncommon tern has not been reported breeding in Georgia. It is extremely widespread, breeding from Canada to Florida. The Caspian tern may be seen all year but its numbers are increased at Cumberland Island by migrants in autumn as it winters south to Mexico. It has been recorded on the Cumberland Audubon counts.

_____. Family Laridae. **Black Tern.** *Chlidonias niger* (Linnaeus, 1758). Black terns breed from Alaska south to Tennessee and winter from Mexico to South America. They are strictly migrants at Cumberland Island but are fairly regular visitors. Our sightings are from June through August.

_____. Family Laridae. **Common Tern.** *Sterna hirundo* Linnaeus, 1758. Pearson (1922, in May) and Sprunt (1936) both recorded this tern on Cumberland Island. It is a common transient on the island and breeds from Canada south to North Carolina and occasionally in Florida, Louisiana, and Texas, to South America. They may winter in Florida, Mexico, and South America. Our records are January, February, April, May, August, September, and October. Twenty-one have been found DOB on the island.

_____. Family Laridae. **Arctic Tern.** *Sterna paradisaea* Pontoppidan, 1763. A rare, irregular offshore migrant, the Arctic tern breeds in the Arctic and winters at the opposite pole, the Antarctic. The migration route is along the eastern Atlantic when they are heading south and along the western side when heading back north to breed. P. Leary (2009) recorded one on Cumberland Island on 24 May.

_____. Family Laridae. **Forster's Tern.** *Sterna fosteri* Nuttall, 1834. Although this species may be seen in any month, it is primarily a winter visitor and transient at Cumberland Island. It breeds from Canada into the US to Virginia and winters from South Carolina to Central America. Sprunt (1936) reported it from Cumberland Island and there are thirteen museum specimens from February, March, April, and November. Two birds have been found dead on the beach.

_____. Family Laridae. **Royal Tern.** *Thalasseus maximus* Boddaert, 1783. The royal tern is a common resident on Cumberland Island. They breed from Virginia through Florida and the Gulf Coast to the Bahamas and West Indies to South America. Numbers of this species are greatest on the island in spring (April and May) and autumn (August, September, October). They nest in Georgia, but no nesting has been reported on Cumberland Island. Sprunt (1936) reported them on the island and there are museum specimens from the island. Copulation has been noted here in April and May, and young have been observed begging food in early September. Many, 174, have been found dead on the beach (1974 to 2010); thirty-eight were banded in the following states: Maryland (one), Virginia (five), North Carolina (30), and South Carolina (two). Thirty-seven percent of the banded birds were less than 1 year old, less than 1% were between one and four years old, 58% were five or more years of age, and

29% were aged 10 years or older. The oldest bird found was 22 years one month of age; this is a long-lived species. Avian predation was one cause of mortality and two individuals were found with a shad (fish) stuck in their throats.

_____. Family Laridae. **Sandwich Tern.** *Thalasseus sandvicensis* Latham, 1787. Although the sandwich tern breeds from Virginia to Florida, the Bahamas, West Indies, and Central America, it is uncommon on Cumberland Island and no nesting has been reported on the island. The species winters from Florida south, so autumn transients may increase numbers. Helme collected three specimens in April (Burleigh, 1958), and our records are from May through November. It has been seen on the Cumberland Audubon Christmas Bird Counts

_____. Family Laridae. **Black Skimmer.** *Rynchops niger* Linnaeus, 1758. This distinctive bird is a year-round Georgia resident but numbers are reduced in the winter. Black skimmers breed along the coast from New England to Florida and the Gulf states and winter in the southern part of the range to South America. Pearson (1922) and Sprunt (1936) reported skimmers on Cumberland Island and there are five museum specimens from the island. The greatest numbers on Cumberland Island occur from May through August, which corresponds with the breeding season. Helme noted a large group (estimated 25,000 birds) on Cumberland Island in January (Burleigh, 1958). Nesting on Cumberland Island was recorded in 1973 (Hillestad et al., 1975) and from 1980 through 1991. The species has been found DOB throughout the year.

_____. Family Stercorariidae. **South Polar Skua.** *Stercorarius maccormicki* (Saunders, 1893). This species breeds around the Antarctic coast. South polar skuas begin nesting in late October and finish by the end of February after which the birds begin migrational wanderings. They are accidental off the Georgia coast but one was found DOB at Cumberland Island in September 2006 (Ruckdeschel, 2008). There are also accepted offshore sight records.

_____. Family Stercorariidae. **Pomarine Jaeger.** *Stercorarius pomarinus* (Temminick, 1815). The pomarine jaeger is an uncommon transient that has been recorded on the Cumberland Island Christmas counts. This species breeds in the Arctic and migrates at sea to tropical and southern Atlantic habitats. One was found DOB on the island in August.

_____. Family Stercorariidae. **Parasitic Jaeger.** *Stercorarius parasiticus* (Linnaeus, 1758). Jaegers are pelagic birds and this species is an uncommon offshore transient in the vicinity of Cumberland Island. It breeds on the tundra from northeast Alaska to Greenland and south well into Canada, and it winters at sea from a latitude of the southern US to Tierra dell Fuego. We have records from Cumberland Island: March, June, three in October, and one DOB in October.

_____. Family Stercorariidae. **Long-tailed Jaeger.** *Stercorarius longicaudus* Viellot, 1819. The smallest of the jaegers, the long-tailed also breeds in the Arctic regions and winters on the open ocean off South America. Identification is difficult for sight records, but the species has been recorded offshore from Cumberland Island, and one sighting was reported from the beach at Little Cumberland Island (G. Sciple, pers. comm.).

_____. Family Alcidae. **Dovekie.** *Alle alle* (Linnaeus, 1758). The dovekie is small species that has been recorded in the thousands during a few migrations but is considered an irregular winter visitor along the Atlantic Coast. They breed in Arctic Canada, Greenland, and Iceland and winter south along the East Coast, occasionally to Florida and Cuba. There is a specimen from St. Simons Island, Georgia, and from Jacksonville, Florida, (S. Willis, pers. comm.) but there are no Cumberland Island records

_____. Family Alcidae. **Razorbill.** *Alca torda* Linnaeus, 1758. The razorbill is considered an irregular, rare offshore winter visitor in the vicinity of Cumberland Island. They breed at the Bay of Fundy, Gulf of St. Lawrence, and south Greenland, and they winter offshore, occasionally to Florida. Groups containing from four to fifty birds have been sighted offshore in December and February, and there is one December specimen from inshore Cumberland Island.

ORDER COLUMBIFORMES. Family Columbidae. **Rock Dove.** *Columba livia* Gmelin, 1789. Officially known as the "rock dove," the pigeon is not native to this continent (Africa, Europe, Asia) but has many feral populations and is kept by hobbyists and raced for sport. Banded racing pigeons are the birds found most frequently on Cumberland Island. Fourteen have been found dead on the beach, thirteen of which were banded. Most mortality appeared to have been the result of avian predators, but a few local birds were shot on the island for sport in the early 1900s.

_____. Family Columbidae. **Eurasian Collared-dove.** *Streptopelia decaocto* (Frivaldszky, 1836). The Eurasian collared dove is native to India, Asia Minor, and the southeast Balkans. It was first recorded in Georgia in 1988 (Beaton et al., 2003). The first observation of this species on Cumberland Island was in May of 1997 (S. Willis, pers. comm.).

_____. Family Columbidae. **White-winged Dove.** *Zenaida asiatica* (Linnaeus, 1758). This visitor to Cumberland Island resides from southeast California into Texas and Central and South America, preferring hot coastal regions.

There is an introduced population in south Florida, and the species is a rare spring and autumn transient along the Gulf Coast. One bird recently spent several days in the Settlement (July 2014), and they have been noted on the adjacent mainland.

_____. Family Columbidae. **Mourning Dove.** *Zenaida macroura* (Linnaeus, 1758). Resident on Cumberland Island, the mourning dove breeds from Canada south through Florida and winters south to Mexico and Central America. Pearson (1922) and Sprunt (1936) reported the species on Cumberland Island. Numbers are greatest on the island from July through September and migrating groups are seen autumn and winter. They have been seen copulating on the island the end of March, and young have been seen with parents in May. Over 100 were shot for sport on Cumberland Island between 1885 and 1925, and five have been found DOB.

_____. Family Columbidae. **Common Ground-dove.** *Columbina passerina* (Linnaeus, 1758). An island resident, this small dove was reported by Pearson (1922) and Sprunt (1936) and is represented by ten museum specimens from Cumberland Island. It prefers open areas and uses the interdune and scrub habitats, especially the temporary ponds when they are dry. Parents with young have been observed in June. The species is reportedly declining in much of Florida and on the Georgia barrier islands. Fire suppression greatly alters their preferred habitats. Two have been found dead on the beach.

ORDER CUCULIFORMES. Family Cuculidae. **Yellow-billed Cuckoo.** *Coccyzus americanus* (Linnaeus, 1758). The yellow-billed cuckoo is a transient on Cumberland Island, which breeds from southern Canada to the Gulf Coast and Florida and winters from south Florida to northern South America. Both Pearson (1922) and Sprunt (1936) reported them on Cumberland Island. Twenty have been found DOB: April (six), May (eleven), June (one), September (one), and October (one).

_____. Family Cuculidae. **Black-billed Cuckoo.** *Coccyzus erythropthalmus* (Wilson, 1811). A transient at Cumberland Island, the black-billed cuckoo breeds from Canada to north Georgia and winters in South America. It has been reported in the vicinity of Cumberland Island (S. Willis, pers. comm.).

ORDER STRIGIFORMES. Family Tytonidae. **Barn Owl.** *Tyto alba* (Scopoli, 1769). The barn owl is a permanent resident and breeds on Cumberland Island. Its breeding range extends from the northern US to the Gulf Coast and into Mexico. It is secretive and uncommon. A nest on Cumberland Island had one young, which fledged 27 August. There are two museum specimens from the island from 1900 and 1904.

_____. Family Strigidae. **Eastern Screech Owl.** *Megascops asio* (Linnaeus, 1758). This diminutive permanent island resident may be seen and heard in any month. Sprunt (1936) reported them on Cumberland Island, and there is a museum specimen from January 1905. Two screech owls have been found dead and partially eaten, one a nestling (11 May). A live, apparently healthy nestling was found on the ground on 10 May. Both color phases occur on the island.

_____. Family Strigidae. **Great Horned Owl.** *Bubo virginianus* (Gmelin, 1788). The great horned owl is a large, fairly common Cumberland Island resident and was reported by both Pearson (1922) and Sprunt (1936). It has a wide distribution from Alaska to southern South America. Young have been reported on the island in the nest in March and April, and shrieking young have been noted on the island from May through July, September and November. One has been found dead on the Main Road.

_____. Family Strigidae. **Barred Owl.** *Strix varia* Barton, 1799. Pearson (1922) recorded the barred owl on Cumberland Island, where they are permanent residents. Barred owls are known to be "absent from most heavily settled sections" (Robertson and Woolfenden, 1992), and on the north end of Cumberland Island, their calls have been reduced in number since the 1990s as human use increased. A tick, and four chiggers have been identified on barred owls from the island. See Appendix VI. B.

_____. Family Strigidae. **Long-eared Owl.** *Asio otus* (Linnaeus, 1758). The long-eared owl is a transient and rare winter visitor to Cumberland Island. They breed from Canada south to Virginia and winter to Florida and central Mexico. Burleigh (1958) reported that Helme collected the first of this species known from Georgia on Cumberland Island on 22 December 1904.

_____. Family Strigidae. **Short-eared Owl.** *Asio flammeus* (Pontoppidan, 1763). This species breeds from Alaska to Greenland and south to Indiana and New Jersey, and it winters south to Cuba and Central America, so it is an uncommon transient or winter visitor on Cumberland Island. Helme collected several museum specimens on the island in the early 1900s.

ORDER CAPRIMULGIFORMES. Family Caprimulgidae. **Common Nighthawk.** *Chordeiles minor* (Forster, 1771). Both Pearson (1922) and Sprunt (1936) reported this common Cumberland Island resident. The nighthawk breeds from Canada to Florida and winters in South America.

Migrants arrive on Cumberland Island in April and depart at the end of the summer. The interdune area is a commonly used habitat.

_____. Family Caprmulgiformes. **Chuck-will's-widow.** *Caprimulgus carolinensis* Gmelin, 1789. The Chuck-will's-widow is a migrant and breeds in the Southeast quadrant of the US, including Cumberland Island, and winters from south Florida through the Greater Antilles to Central and South America. Cumberland Island records are from February through September, with greatest activity in March, April, and August. Both Pearson (1922) and Sprunt (1936) recorded the species on Cumberland Island. The earliest call on the island was noted on 27 February and the latest on 22 August. Nesting has been verified on Cumberland Island in May. Four Chuck-will's-widows have been found DOB in April and September; one died attempting to swallow a common yellowthroat (Ruckdeschel, 2003).

_____. Family Caprimulgidae. **Whip-poor-will.** *Caprimulgus vociferous* Wilson, 1812. The whip-poor-will breeds from Canada to north Georgia and winters from South Carolina and the Gulf Coast to Central America. It is a fairly regular transient on Cumberland Island. Its local presence, as determined by calls, is from February through April and August through October.

We have no record of calls between 1998 and 2004. The species has been recorded on the Cumberland Audubon Christmas Bird Counts.

ORDER APODIFORMES. Family Apodidae. **Chimney Swift.** *Chaetura pelagica* (Linnaeus, 1758). Chimney swifts winter in South America and breed from Canada south to Florida, including Cumberland Island. Activity on the island occurs from April into October and nesting has been noted in June and July. Pearson (1922) and Sprunt (1936) both found this species on Cumberland Island. Two have been found DOB and several in island buildings.

_____. Family Trochilidae. **Ruby-throated Hummingbird.** *Archilochus colubris* (Linnaeus, 1758). The ruby-throated hummingbird is a common summer resident on Cumberland Island, which both Pearson (1922) and Sprunt (1936) reported. The species breeds from Canada to Florida and winters south to Central America. The greatest activity on the island is from March through May and continues until November. The earliest arrival noted was 17 March (Burleigh, 1958). One island animal impaled its beak in a screen door and died.

_____. Family Trochilidae. **Rufous Hummingbird.** *Selasphorus rufus* (Gmelin, 1788). An uncommon transient on the island, the Rufous hummingbird migrates between its breeding grounds in Alaska and the western US into Mexico and winters in Mexico and occasionally along the Gulf Coast and north Florida. There is a Cumberland Island record for 10 September.

ORDER CORACIIFORMES. Family Alcedinidae. **Belted Kingfisher.** *Megaceryle alcyon* (Linnaeus, 1758). The belted kingfisher is a permanent resident on Cumberland Island and breeds from Canada south to Florida and winters to South America. It was recorded on Cumberland Island by Pearson (1922) and Sprunt (1936) and has been documented on the Cumberland Audubon Christmas counts. Months of greatest activity on Cumberland are January, March, April, and August through October. Nest burrows are dug in bluffs along the river beach.

ORDER PICIFORMES. Family Picidae. **Red-headed Woodpecker.** *Melanerpes erythrocephalus* (Linnaeus, 1758). An eye-catching species, the red-headed woodpecker is an uncommon resident on Cumberland Island. Pearson (1922) and Sprunt (1936) both encountered the species on the island and there are four museum specimens. Two birds have been found DOB.

_____. Family Picidae. **Red-bellied Woodpecker.** *Melanerpes carolinus* (Linnaeus, 1758). The red-bellied woodpecker is a common resident of Cumberland Island. It is found from Ontario south to Florida. Red-bellied woodpeckers were reported on the island by both Pearson (1922) and Sprunt (1936) and are represented by a museum specimen.

_____. Family Picidae. **Yellow-bellied Sapsucker.** *Sphyrapicus varius* (Linnaeus, 1766). The yellow-bellied sapsucker is a winter visitor to Cumberland Island with records from January through April and October. It breeds from Canada into north Georgia and winters to the West Indies and Mexico. It has been recorded on most Cumberland Christmas counts. The red bay is one of its favorite island trees.

_____. Family Picidae. **Downy Woodpecker.** *Picoides pubescens* (Linnaeus, 1766). Unlike the larger hairy woodpecker, the downy is considered a common resident of Cumberland Island. They are generally nonmigratory and range from Alaska to south Florida. Both Pearson (1922) and Sprunt (1936) saw them on Cumberland Island.

_____. Family Picidae. **Hairy Woodpecker.** *Picoides villosus* (Linnaeus, 1766). Hairy woodpeckers breed throughout the Eastern US, and northern birds move a bit south in winter. Sprunt (1936) noted this uncommon resident on Cumberland Island. The species is considered rare along the Georgia coast. It has been recorded on the Cumberland Island Audubon Christmas counts.

_____. Family Picidae. **Red-cockaded Woodpecker.** *Picoides borealis* (Vieillot, 1809). Sprunt (1936) reported this now rare species on Cumberland Island without special comment or details. His two trips to the island were in 1932 and 1933, which was prior to the Carnegie logging operations undertaken in the early 1940s. Some pines then were determined to be 100 to 200 years old, and thus fit the nesting requirements of this woodpecker. Without a natural fire regime, it is unlikely that pines suitable for this species will prevail.

_____. Family Picidae. **Northern Flicker.** *Colaptes auratus* Linnaeus, 1758. Sprunt (1936) noted the northern flicker on Cumberland Island, and there is one museum specimen of this island resident. Migrants from breeding grounds in Canada and Northern states may augment winter numbers on Cumberland Island. Most island activity has been recorded in February, April, and October and November. Groups have been seen in November. Four birds have been recorded DOB.

_____. Family Picidae. **Pileated Woodpecker.** *Dryocopus pileatus* (Linnaeus, 1758). This common Cumberland Island resident occurs from Canada to southern Florida. It was reported on Cumberland Island by both Pearson (1922) and Sprunt (1936). Pileated woodpeckers have been seen copulating in late March and feeding young the end of May on Cumberland Island. A mite and a biting louse have been found on island pileateds. See Appendix VI. B.

ORDER PASSIFORMES. Family Tyrannidae. **Eastern Wood Pewee.** *Contopus virens* (Linnaeus, 1766). The eastern wood pewee is a transient and summer resident on Cumberland Island. The species breeds from Canada across the Eastern US to Florida and winters in Central and South America. Sprunt (1936) recorded wood pewees on Cumberland Island, and there is a museum specimen from April 1905.

_____. Family Tyrannidae. **Acadian Flycatcher.** *Empidonax virescens* (Vieillot, 1818). The Acadian flycatcher is a summer resident and transient on Cumberland Island. It breeds from Canada across the US and south into Florida, including Cumberland Island. Sprunt (1936) noted it on the island. Young have been observed in May.

_____. Family Tyrannidae. **Least Flycatcher.** *Empidonax minimus* (Baird and Baird, 1843). The least flycatcher is a diminutive flycatcher that breeds from Canada into north Georgia and winters from Mexico to Central

America. It is a transient in the vicinity of Cumberland Island. There are no island records at this time (S. Willis, pers. comm.).

_____. Family Tyrannidae. **Vermilion Flycatcher**. *Pyrocephalus rubinus* (Boddaert, 1783). This bird is a rare visitor to Georgia, especially the coast. It breeds in the Southwest US and winters along the Gulf Coast to Florida. There is one coastal record from Sapelo Island in 1999 (Beaton et al., 2003) but no confirmed records from Cumberland Island.

_____. Family Tyrannidae. **Great Crested Flycatcher**. *Myiarchus crinitus* (Linnaeus, 1758). The great crested flycatcher is a common summer resident on Cumberland Island. It breeds from Canada through the Southeastern US and on Cumberland Island, and it winters south through Central to South America. Pearson (1922) and Sprunt (1936) recorded its presence on Cumberland Island and there are two museum specimens. A pair nested in June in a horizontal stovepipe on the north end of Cumberland Island, and at least once brought a ground skink to the nest as food. A tick has been collected on a great crested flycatcher on Cumberland Island. See Appendix VI. B.

_____. Family Tyrannidae. **Western Kingbird**. *Tyrannus verticalis* Say, 1823. The western kingbird breeds from Canada to Texas and Iowa and winters from Mexico to Central America, incidentally along the Southeast US coast. It is listed as a transient and rare winter visitor on Cumberland Island. There are December sight records from Cumberland Island (S. Willis, pers. comm.).

_____. Family Tyrannidae. **Eastern Kingbird**. *Tyrannus tyrannus* (Linnaeus, 1758). The eastern kingbird is a transient summer resident at Cumberland Island. It breeds from Canada to Florida, including Cumberland Island, and winters in southern Mexico and South America. The species was recorded on Cumberland Island by Pearson (1922), and a museum specimen was collected on the island in February of 1897. Island records are from April, May, and August. One has been found dead on the beach.

_____. Family Tyrannidae. **Gray Kingbird**. *Tyrannus dominicensis* (Gmelin, 1788). Georgia is at the northern limit of the gray kingbird's breeding range, which extends south through Florida, Cuba, and the Antilles. It winters from Jamaica and Haiti to South America and is considered a transient and possible local summer resident on Cumberland Island. There are no records of the species for Cumberland Island, but it has been recorded on the adjacent mainland and has nested on Jekyll Island, Georgia (S. Willis, pers. comm.).

_____. Family Tyrannidae. **Scissor-tailed Flycatcher**. *Tyrannus forficatus* (Gmelin, 1789). This spectacular bird is rare on Cumberland Island but frequently seen on the adjacent mainland. Scissor-tailed flycatchers breed in the southern mid-United States and casually to Georgia, and they winter in Mexico and Central America. There are records from Cumberland Island from March through May.

_____. Family Laniidae. **Loggerhead Shrike**. *Lanius ludovicianus* Linnaeus, 1766. The loggerhead shrike is a resident of Cumberland Island listed by Pearson (1922) and by Sprunt (1936) and there are museum specimens from the island. The species is widespread from Canada through the middle and eastern states to Mexico. It prefers open areas such as old fields and interdune habitats.

_____. Family Vireonidae. **White-eyed Vireo**. *Vireo griseus* (Boddaert, 1783). A common, vocal, summer island resident, the white-eyed vireo breeds throughout the Eastern US from Nebraska east and south to Florida. It winters from south Georgia to Mexico and Central America. Pearson (1922) and Sprunt (1936) both recorded it on the island, and there are eight museum specimens from March, April, and May. Nest construction has been noted in March and April and brooding in May.

_____. Family Vireonidae. **Yellow-throated Vireo**. *Vireo flavifrons* Vieillot, 1808. This vireo is a fairly common summer island resident and transient. The species breeds from Canada south to Florida and winters from Mexico to South America. Helme collected specimens on the island in April of 1902 and 1903.

_____. Family Vireonidae. **Solitary Vireo**. *Vireo solitarius* (Wilson, 1810). Sprunt (1936) recorded the blue-headed or solitary vireo on the island, and a specimen was collected in May 1897.

Breeding occurs from Canada south to the Northern states, and the species winters from South Carolina south through Mexico to Central America. It is an uncommon winter visitor on the island.

_____. Family Vireonidae. **Red-eyed Vireo**. *Vireo olivaceus* (Linnaeus, 1766). Breeding is widespread in this species, from Canada to the northwestern states and south to Texas and Florida. It winters in South America so is a common transient as well as a summer resident. Pearson (1922) and Sprunt (1936) recorded it, and there are two museum specimens.

_____. Family Corvidae. **Blue Jay**. *Cyanocitta cristata* (Linnaeus, 1758). The blue jay is a resident on Cumberland Island. It breeds from Canada to Florida and winters in the southern part of its range, so there are transients on the island in autumn. Pearson (1922) and Sprunt (1936) observed the blue jay on Cumberland Island. Good-sized young have been seen on the island in late May.

_____. Family Corvidae. **American Crow**. *Corvus brachyrhynchos* Brehm, 1822. There is one museum specimen of the American crow from Cumberland Island. The species is resident on the island with widespread distribution from Canada through the states to Florida. It has been observed harassing and scavenging ghost crabs on the beach.

_____. Family Corvidae. **Fish Crow**. *Corvus ossifragus* Wilson, 1812. The fish crow is a common Cumberland Island resident. It is a coastal species ranging from New England south, following the coast to Florida and the Gulf states to Texas. Both Pearson (1922) and Sprunt (1936) recorded it on Cumberland Island.

_____. Family Alaudidae. **Horned Lark**. *Eremophila alpestris* (Linnaeus, 1758). The horned lark is an irregular, rare winter visitor to Cumberland Island. It breeds from Alaska to Mexico and winters to the south and erratically along the Gulf Coastal Plain. It has been observed on Cumberland Island (S. Willis, pers. comm.).

_____. Family Hirundinidae. **Purple Martin**. *Progne subis* (Linnaeus, 1758). The purple martin breeds from Canada to Mexico and Florida and winters in South America. It is considered a common breeding summer resident across the Eastern US but no nesting activity has been reported on Cumberland Island. It has been reported nesting on the adjacent mainland and there are observations for Cumberland Island (S. Willis, pers. comm.).

_____. Family Hirundinidae. **Tree Swallow**. *Tachycineta bicolor* (Vieillot, 1808). The tree swallow is a fairly regular gregarious transient on Cumberland Island. It breeds from Alaska and Canada south to Louisiana and Virginia and winters south to Cuba and Central America. Both Pearson (1922) and Sprunt (1936) found them on Cumberland Island. Tree swallow activity is greatest on the island in October and November and February through April. Swarms of these birds gorge on wax myrtle fruit. One individual that had been hit by a vehicle on the beach contained sixty-seven berries from "stem to stern."

_____. Family Hirundinidae. **Northern Rough-winged Swallow**. *Stelgidopteryx serripennis* (Audubon, 1838). The rough-winged swallow is a relatively drab little swallow. It breeds from Canada to central Florida, including Cumberland Island, and winters south to Central America. There are two specimens from Cumberland Island from 1903 and 1905. Most island activity is April through June. Nesting burrows are in bluffs along the river.

_____. Family Hirundinidae. **Bank Swallow**. *Riparia riparia* (Linnaeus, 1758). The bank swallow has a wide distribution. It breeds from Alaska and Canada through the states to Alabama and Virginia and winters in South America. There are no island records. It would be an uncommon transient on Cumberland Island (S. Willis, pers. comm.).

_____. Family Hirundinidae. **Cliff Swallow**. *Pterochelidon pyrrhonota* Vieillot, 1817. The cliff swallow is considered an uncommon transient in the vicinity of Cumberland Island. It breeds from Alaska and Canada south to Alabama and Virginia and winters in South America. It is similar in appearance to the cave swallow. There are no verified records for Cumberland Island.

_____. Family Hirundinidae. **Cave Swallow**. *Petrochelidon fulva* (Vieillot, 1808). The cave swallow is a rare wanderer in the vicinity of Cumberland Island. It breeds from Texas into Mexico and winters to the south. There are no confirmed records for Cumberland Island (S. Willis, pers. comm.).

_____. Family Hirundinidae. **Barn Swallow**. *Hirundo rustica* Linnaeus, 1758. The barn swallow is an obvious transient and summer resident. It breeds from Alaska and Canada south to the Gulf states and occasionally along the Georgia coast. It was reported breeding on Wassaw Island, Georgia, in the early 1900s. Pearson (1922) and Sprunt (1936) reported it on Cumberland Island. Activity on the island has been recorded in nearly all months, with the greatest activity occurring in April, May, and July through September.

_____. Family Paridae. **Carolina Chickadee**. *Poecile carolinensis* Audubon, 1834. The Carolina chickadee ranges from Mississippi to North Carolina and south to Florida. It is an island resident and was recorded by Sprunt (1936). There are two museum specimens from the island. The species has been seen on the island carrying nest material in April and with chicks in May.

_____. Family Paridae. **Tufted Titmouse**. *Baeolophus bicolor* Linnaeus, 1766. A bird of the mixed and hardwood forests, the tufted titmouse was noted on Cumberland Island by Sprunt (1936) and is a common permanent resident. It has been observed collecting nest material in March and April.

_____. Family Sittidae. **Red-breasted Nuthatch**. *Sitta canadensis* Linnaeus, 1758. The red-breasted nuthatch breeds from Canada to North Carolina and winters south to Florida. It is a transient and winter visitor on Cumberland Island. There was an October observation, and one was heard at Dungeness in January (S. Willis, pers. comm.).

_____. Family Sittidae. **White-breasted Nuthatch**. *Sitta carolinensis* Latham, 1790. The white-breasted nuthatch is an uncommon transient on Cumberland Island. They range from the mid-US to the East Coast and south to Florida. There are two museum specimens from Cumberland Island taken in December, and they have been recorded on the Audubon Christmas counts.

_____. Family Sittidae. **Brown-headed Nuthatch**. *Sitta pusilla* Latham, 1790. The brown-headed nuthatch is a common permanent resident on Cumberland Island. It prefers pine woods habitats. The species was reported on Cumberland Island by both Pearson (1922) and Sprunt (1936) and has been noted nesting on the island in April.

_____. Family Certhiidae. **Brown Creeper**. *Certhia americana* Bonaparte, 1838. The brown creeper nests from Canada south to Indiana and New Jersey and winters to the Gulf Coast and Florida. It is an uncommon transient and uncommon winter visitor to Cumberland Island but has been documented on the Cumberland Audubon bird counts.

_____. Family Troglodytidae. **Carolina Wren**. *Thryothorus ludovicianus* (Latham, 1790). The Carolina wren is a cheerful, common resident on Cumberland Island. It was noted by Pearson (1922) and Sprunt (1936), and there is a museum specimen from 1902. Carolina wrens have been observed carrying nest material on Cumberland Island as early as February.

_____. Family Troglodytidae. **Bewick's Wren**. *Thryomanes bewickii* (Audubon, 1827). Bewick's wren breeds from Nebraska to Michigan and south to Texas and Tennessee and winters to Florida and the Gulf Coast. Populations in the east have been declining. It was previously considered a rare winter visitor on Cumberland Island but none have been recorded in Georgia since the early 1990s (Beaton et al., 2003).

_____. Family Troglodytidae. **House Wren**. *Troglodytes aedon* Vieillot, 1809. The house wren breeds from Canada south to Virginia and winters south to Florida and Mexico. Sprunt (1936) reported it on Cumberland Island and it has been recorded on the Cumberland Audubon counts.

_____. Family Troglodytidae. **Winter Wren**. *Troglodytes troglodytes* (Linnaeus, 1758). The smallest of the wrens, the winter wren breeds in Canada and the northern tier of states east to Rhode Island and winters south to

Florida. It has been recorded on Cumberland Island on the Audubon Christmas counts.

_____. Family Troglodytidae. **Sedge Wren**. *Cistothorus platensis* (Latham, 1790). This species breeds from Canada into the northern US and winters south to Florida. It is a transient and winter visitor on Cumberland Island. Burleigh (1985) reported that sedge wrens were noted on Cumberland Island in April of 1902.

_____. Family Troglodytidae. **Marsh Wren**. *Cistothorus palustris* (Wilson, 1810). The marsh wren is a common resident of the salt marshes around Cumberland Island. Both Pearson (1922) and Sprunt (1936) observed it, and there are also museum specimens from the island.

_____. Family Polioptillidae. **Blue-gray Gnatcatcher**. *Polioptila caerulea* (Linnaeus, 1766). The blue-gray gnatcatcher is a common summer resident whose presence on Cumberland Island was confirmed by both Pearson (1922) and Sprunt (1936), and there are four museum specimens. It breeds across the Eastern US from Wisconsin and New Jersey south to Florida and winters in the southern coastal states, Cuba, Mexico, and Central America.

_____. Family Regulidae. **Golden-crowned Kinglet**. *Regulus satrapa* Lichtenstein, 1823. The golden-crowned kinglet is a regular but uncommon winter visitor on Cumberland Island and was recorded on the island by Sprunt (1936). The species breeds in Canada and the northern US to North Carolina and winters south to Florida and Mexico.

_____. Family Regulidae. **Ruby-crowned Kinglet**. *Regulus calendula* (Linnaeus, 1766). The breeding grounds of the ruby-crowned kinglet, from Alaska to Newfoundland to northern New England, are clearly distinct from its wintering area, Virginia south to Mexico and Central America. It is a winter resident on Cumberland Island. Sprunt (1936) confirmed its island presence and it has been recorded on the Cumberland Christmas counts.

_____. Family Turdidae. **Eastern Bluebird**. *Siala sialis* (Linnaeus, 1758). Pearson (1922) recorded the bluebird on Cumberland Island, where it is considered a resident. The species breeds from Canada through the Eastern US to Florida and winters in the southern part of its range. Migrants may augment numbers in winter. The bluebird prefers open areas, which have been greatly reduced on Cumberland Island since the agricultural period and fire suppression.

_____. Family Turdidae. **Veery**. *Catharus fuscesens* (Stephens, 1817). The veery's breeding grounds in Canada and the northern US follow the mountains south to north Georgia, but the species winters in South America.

It is a transient on Cumberland Island. There are observations from the island (S. Willis, pers. comm.).

_____. Family Turdidae. **Gray-cheeked Thrush.** *Catharus mimimus* (Lafresnaye, 1848). The breeding grounds of the gray-cheeked thrush (Alaska and Canada) are quite separated from its wintering grounds in South America. It is an uncommon transient on Cumberland Island but has been observed here (S. Willis, pers. comm.).

_____. Family Turididae. **Bicknell's Thrush.** *Catharus bicknelli* (Ridgeway, 1882). Bicknell's thrush was originally recognized as a subspecies of the gray-cheeked thrush but is now a full species. It is a smaller version of the gray-cheeked and breeds in Nova Scotia, northern New England, and New York. It winters on Hispaniola and in South America. There is an observation from Cumberland Island (S. Willis, pers. comm.).

_____. Family Turdidae. **Swainson's Thrush.** *Catharus ustulatus* (Nutall, 1840). A regular spring and autumn transient, this thrush breeds from Canada to West Virginia and winters from Mexico to South America. There is one October record of a Swainson's thrush hitting a wire in the interdune area and being killed. There have been observations of the species on the island (S. Willis, pers. comm.) and one DOB.

_____. Family Turdidae. **Hermit Thrush.** *Catharus guttatus* (Pallas, 1811). Sprunt (1936) sighted the hermit thrush on Cumberland Island. It is a winter visitor and breeds from Canada to the northern US states south to Maryland and winters to Florida. A chigger has been found on an island hermit thrush. See Appendix VI. B.

_____. Family Turdidae. **Wood Thrush.** *Hylocichla mustelina* (Gmelin, 1789). Wood thrushes occur from Canada through the Eastern US into Florida but are considered transients on Cumberland Island. They winter from Mexico to Central America. One was found DOB in April and there are several unverified reports from Cumberland Island (S. Willis, pers. comm.).

_____. Family Turdidae. **American Robin.** *Turdus migratorius* Linnaeus, 1766. A common winter visitor to Cumberland Island, the American robin breeds from Alaska and Canada across the Eastern US incidentally into Florida. Pearson (1922) recorded them on Cumberland Island, and they are regularly seen on the Audubon counts. Local records are mainly from December through March. Three have been found dead on the beach and several killed by avian predators.

_____. Family Mimidae. **Gray Catbird**. *Dumetella carolinensis* (Linnaeus, 1766). The gray catbird breeds from Canada across the Eastern US to Georgia and winters in the south part of the range and to Cuba, Mexico, and Central America. Pearson (1922) and Sprunt (1936) both saw the gray catbird on Cumberland Island. Although catbirds are considered common transients and winter visitors to Cumberland Island, most of our observations are from April through June, with fewer in the autumn and winter. Gray catbirds have been observed eating fruit of the beautyberry on Cumberland Island. One species of tick and a feather mite have been found on island Catbirds. See Appendix VI. B.

_____. Family Mimidae. **Northern Mockingbird**. *Mimus polyglottos* (Linnaeus, 1758). This vocal mimic is a common resident on Cumberland Island. Mockingbirds are widely distributed across the US to Mexico and the Caribbean. Pearson (1922) and Sprunt (1936) recorded the species on Cumberland Island, and there are four museum specimens. Mockingbirds may have two to three clutches of eggs per year throughout the summer. One bird has been found DOB.

_____. Family Mimidae. **Brown Thrasher**. *Toxostoma rufum* (Linnaeus, 1758). The brown thrasher is the Georgia state bird and a common permanent resident of Cumberland Island. Pearson (1922) and Sprunt (1936) recorded them on the island, and they are regularly seen on the Cumberland Audubon Christmas Bird Counts. One specimen found dead had beetles and a mollusk in its stomach. They are abundant at times in the interdune area.

_____. Family Sturnidae. **European Starling**. *Sturnus vulgaris* Linnaeus, 1758. The European starling was introduced to the US in 1890 from Eurasia. It is now a resident of Cumberland, its presence confirmed by M. Hodges and S. Willis.

_____. Family Motacillidae. **American Pipit**. *Anthus spinoletta* (Linnaeus, 1758). The American or water pipit breeds from the Arctic through Canada and winters from Ohio south through Florida to Central America. It is a winter visitor on Cumberland Island. Burleigh (1958) reported a small flock on Cumberland Island but gave no specific date, and they have been seen on Little Cumberland Island (G. Sciple, pers. comm.). Open areas of high marsh or mud flats attract this species.

_____. Family Motacillidae. **Sprague's Pipit**. *Anthus spragueii* (Audubon, 1844). This rare winter visitor to Cumberland Island breeds from Canada into the northwest states to Minnesota and winters from the Gulf states into Mexico. Burleigh (1958) said Helme collected nine specimens from Cumberland Island in 1903; at least four were in March.

_____. Family Bombycillidae. **Cedar Waxwing.** *Bombycilla cedrorun* Vieillot, 1808. The cedar waxwing is an irregular or irruptive winter visitor on the island. It breeds from Canada into north Georgia and winters through the US to Cuba, Mexico, and Central America. It was recorded on the island by Sprunt (1936) and local records are from November through April.

_____. Family Calcariidae. **Snow Bunting.** *Plectrophenax nivalis* Linnaeus, 1758. An outstanding bird because of the amount of white on it, the snow bunting is an irregular, rare winter visitor to Cumberland Island. It breeds within the Arctic Circle, Alaska, and Canada, including Greenland, and usually winters in Canada and the northern US. Farther south migrations probably depend upon weather and food. They have been noted on the Cumberland Audubon bird counts, and our records are from November to January.

_____. Family Parulidae. **Ovenbird.** *Seiurus aurocapillus* (Linnaeus, 1766). The ovenbird breeds from Canada across the Eastern US to north Georgia and winters from the Georgia coast, Florida, the Bahamas, and West Indies to Mexico and South America. It is a common spring and autumn migrant on Cumberland Island. Pearson (1922) and Sprunt (1936) both confirmed its presence on the island. One specimen was found DOR in June and one DOB in April.

_____. Family Parulidae. **Worm-eating Warbler.** *Helmitheros vermivorus* (Gmelin, 1789). Helme collected three specimens from Cumberland Island in April 1903, and Burleigh (1958) reported that this warbler was seen on the island on 7 March 1902 and also that eight struck "the light on Cumberland Island" in April of 1902. The worm-eating warbler is a regular but uncommon transient on Cumberland Island. It breeds from Iowa east to New York and south to north Georgia and winters in Mexico, Central America, Cuba, and the Bahamas.

_____. Family Parulidae. **Louisiana Waterthrush.** *Parkesia motacilla* (Vieillot, 1809). Sprunt (1936) documented the Louisiana waterthrush on Cumberland Island. It is a fairly common migrant between its breeding grounds in Minnesota and New England to Texas and north Georgia and South Carolina and its winter habitat in the Bahamas, Greater Antilles, Mexico, and South America.

_____. Family Parulidae. **Northern Waterthrush.** *Parkesias noveboracensis* (Gmelin, 1789). An uncommon transient on Cumberland Island, the northern waterthrush migrates between its breeding grounds in Canada and the Northern states to its winter habitat in the Bahamas, West Indies, Mexico, South America, and casually in south Florida. It has been observed on Cumberland Island (S. Willis, pers. comm.).

_____. Family Parulidae. **Blue-winged Warbler.** *Vermivora cyanoptera* (Olson and Reveal, 2009). A regular rare to uncommon transient on Cumberland Island, the blue-winged warbler was recorded on the island by Sprunt (1936) in April. Breeding occurs from Minnesota to New England and south to north Georgia, and the species winters in Mexico and Central America.

_____. Family Parulidae. **Black-and-White Warbler.** *Mniotilta varia* (Linnaeus, 1766). A fairly common transient and winter visitor to Cumberland Island, the black-and-white warbler breeds from Canada to north Georgia and winters along the coast from South Carolina to Florida, the Bahamas, Mexico, and South America. Both Pearson (1922) and Sprunt (1936) recorded it on Cumberland Island, and it is seen on the Audubon Christmas counts. Island records are from May and September through November. One bird was found DOR.

_____. Family Parulidae. **Prothonotary Warbler.** *Protonotaria citrea* (Boddaert, 1783). This bird of the wooded swamps breeds from Nebraska east to Maryland and south to Florida and winters from Mexico to South America. It is a fairly common summer resident and transient at Cumberland Island. Pearson (1922) and Sprunt (1936) saw it on Cumberland Island, and Burleigh (1958) reported spring transients on the island in April.

_____. Family Parulidae. **Swainson's Warbler.** *Limnothlypis swainsonii* (Audubon, 1834). Swainson's warbler is a rare summer resident and transient on Cumberland Island, which Beaton et al. (2003) said is now absent from the Georgia coast and islands. Helme collected two specimens on Cumberland Island in March and April of 1902 and 1905. Swainson's warblers breed from Missouri to Maryland and south to Florida and winter in Jamaica. Burleigh (1958) said spring transients were reported on Cumberland Island in April 1902.

_____. Family Parulidae. **Tennessee Warbler.** *Oreothlypis peregrine* (Wilson, 1811). The Tennessee warbler breeds from Canada into Minnesota and New England and winters in Mexico and South America. It is a transient on Cumberland Island and more numerous in autumn than spring. There have been observations of it on the island (S. Willis, pers. comm.).

_____. Family Parulidae. **Orange-crowned Warbler.** *Oreothlypis celata* (Say, 1823). A northern breeder, the orange-crowned warbler breeds from

Alaska across Canada and winters in the coastal states from North Carolina to Texas and Mexico. It has been recorded on a Cumberland Audubon Christmas count.

_____. Family Parulidae. **Nashville Warbler**. *Oreothelypis ruficapilla* (Wilson, 1811). This rare transient to Georgia breeds in Canada and the northern US and winters in Mexico and South America, and incidentally to Florida. There are no specific Cumberland Island records, but it has been documented in the vicinity of the island (S. Willis, pers. comm.).

_____. Family Parulidae. **Connecticut Warbler**. *Oporornis agilia* (Wilson, 1812). The Connecticut warbler breeds from Canada into Minnesota and Michigan and winters in South America. It is rare on Cumberland Island. One observation on Cumberland Island was provided by S. Willis (pers. comm.)

_____. Family Parulidae. **Kentucky Warbler**. *Oporornis formosus* (Wilson, 1811). The Kentucky warbler is a spring and autumn transient on Cumberland Island and breeds from Nebraska and Texas east, stopping short of extreme south Georgia and southern South Carolina. It winters from Mexico to South America. There are observations of this species on Cumberland Island (S. Willis, pers. comm.).

_____. Family Parulidae. **Common Yellowthroat**. *Geothlypis trichas* (Linnaeus, 1766). A common Cumberland Island resident, the yellowthroat's numbers may be augmented in autumn by migrants. Breeding occurs from Alaska through Canada to Florida and Mexico, and they winter from North Carolina south to Central America and Puerto Rico. Helme collected four specimens on Cumberland Island in April and December, and the species is seen on the Cumberland Christmas bird counts. One individual died wedged in the throat of a Chuck-will's-widow (Ruckdeschel, 2003).

_____. Family Parulidae. **Hooded Warbler**. *Setophaga citrine* (Boddaert, 1783). The hooded warbler must have been common on Cumberland Island in spring during the early 1900s when Helme collected nineteen specimens. Pearson (1922) recorded the species on Cumberland Island, but today they are uncommon summer residents and transients. Hooded warblers breed from Nebraska to southern New England and to the Gulf states and north Florida, and they winter in Mexico and Central America.

_____. Family Parulidae. **American Redstart**. *Setophaga ruticilla* (Linnaeus, 1758). The American redstart is a regular and common spring and autumn transient at Cumberland Island. It is usually obvious on the island in

May and August through October, and we have one February record. Redstarts breed from Canada through most of the Eastern US to Louisiana, southwest Georgia, and the mountains of South Carolina, and they winter in the West Indies and Mexico to South America. Sprunt (1936) recorded the species on Cumberland Island, and they have been seen congregating at the island dumpster to catch flies.

_____. Family Parulidae. **Kirtland's Warbler**. *Setophaga kirtlandii* (Baird, 1852). The first Kirtland's warbler reported in Georgia was collected on Cumberland Island by Helme in 1902. The small population breeds only in north central Michigan and winters in the Bahamas, so it is indeed a very rare transient at Cumberland Island. Population numbers are thought to have been greater during the early 1900s.

_____. Family Parulidae. **Cape May Warbler**. *Setophaga tigrina* (Gmelin, 1789). The Cape May warbler is a transient on Cumberland Island. It breeds in Canada and the northern US and winters in the Bahamas and West Indies. Helme collected a specimen on the island in April 1903 and there is a local record from October.

_____. Family Parulidae. **Northern Parula**. *Setophaga americana* (Linnaeus, 1758). The northern parula is a summer breeder and transient at Cumberland Island documented by Pearson (1922) and Sprunt (1936) and thirteen voucher specimens. The parula's wide breeding range includes Canada to the mid-Northern states and east to Cape Breton and south to the Gulf states and Florida, and they winter in Florida, the Bahamas, West Indies, and Mexico to South America. Young have been observed on the island in May and June. Two parulas have been found DOB.

_____. Family Parulidae. **Magnolia Warbler**. *Setophaga magnolia* (Wilson, 1811). The magnolia warbler breeds from Canada and the northern US to Virginia and winters in Mexico and Central America. It is a regular transient on Cumberland Island. Pearson (1922) recorded it on the island. Numbers are more numerous in the autumn and one bird was found DOB in October.

_____. Family Parulidae. **Bay-breasted Warbler**. *Setophaga castanea* (Wilson, 1810). This warbler migrates through south Georgia between its breeding grounds in Canada, the Adirondacks, and New England and its wintering areas in Central and South America. The bay-breasted warbler is considered uncommon on Cumberland Island but there have been island observations (S. Willis, pers. comm.).

_____. Family Parulidae. **Blackburnian Warbler**. *Setophaga fusca* (Müller, 1766). A rare transient in the vicinity of Cumberland Island, the Blackburnian warbler breeds from Canada and the northern US south to north Georgia and winters in South America. There are several unverified records for Cumberland Island and verified ones for the adjacent mainland (S. Willis, pers. comm.).

_____. Family Parulidae. **Yellow Warbler.** *Setophaga petechia* (Linnaeus, 1766). Pearson (1922) caught sight of this transient on Cumberland Island, and there are two museum specimens. The yellow warbler breeds across Canada and the US south to central Georgia and winters from Mexico to South America.

_____. Family Parulidae. **Chestnut-sided Warbler.** *Setophaga pensylvanica* (Linnaeus, 1766). The chestnut-sided warbler is a rare transient on Cumberland Island. It breeds in Canada and the northern US states to Pennsylvania and in the mountains south to north Georgia, and it winters in Central America. They have been observed on Cumberland Island (S. Willis, pers. comm.).

_____. Family Parulidae. **Blackpoll Warbler.** *Setophaga striata* (Forster, 1772). The blackpoll warbler is a regular common transient on Cumberland Island, most frequently in spring. It breeds in Alaska, Canada, and the Northeast US and winters in South America. There is a specimen taken in April and there are local records from May.

_____. Family Parulidae. **Black-throated Blue Warbler.** *Setophaga caerulescens* (Gmelin, 1789). The black-throated blue warbler is a regular transient on Cumberland Island between its breeding grounds in Canada and the northern US to its wintering grounds in the Bahamas and West Indies, and casually to Central and South America. Sprunt (1936) saw the species on Cumberland Island and Helme collected six specimens in April and September. Our records are in September and October.

_____. Family Parulidae. **Palm Warbler.** *Setophaga palmarum* (Gmelin, 1789). The palm warbler is a common winter visitor and transient and both Pearson (1922) and Sprunt (1936) recorded them and sixteen specimens have been taken (four in winter, twelve spring). The species breeds from Canada into the northern US and winters from South Carolina to Florida, the Bahamas, Greater Antilles, and Mexico. Groups have been seen on the island in October, and one individual was seen being eaten by a merlin on 2 October.

_____. Family Parulidae. **Pine Warbler.** *Setophaga pinus* (Wilson, 1811). The pine warbler is a common permanent resident of Cumberland Island and pinelands in Georgia in general. They breed from Canada across the

Eastern US to Florida and winter along the coast and into Mexico, so there are transients also. Pearson (1922) and Sprunt (1936) recorded them on Cumberland Island, and there are museum specimens from April and March.

_____. Family Parulidae. **Yellow-rumped Warbler**. *Setophaga coronata* (Linnaeus, 1766). The yellow-rumped or myrtle warbler breeds from Canada into the northern US and winters in the Southern states, Greater Antilles, Mexico, and Central America. It is a regular common transient on Cumberland Island. Sprunt (1936) recorded the species and they are seen on the Audubon bird counts. Our records are between November and March. One was found DOB.

_____. Family Parulidae. **Yellow-throated Warbler**. *Setophaga dominica* (Linnaeus, 1766). The yellow-throated warbler is a common summer resident on Cumberland Island. It breeds across the Eastern US and winters casually from South Carolina through Georgia but primarily in south Florida, the Bahamas, and Greater Antilles. Sprunt (1936) recorded it on Cumberland Island. This warbler has been seen carrying nest material on the island as early as 18 March and feeding young in May. It is occasionally the victim of cowbird nest parasitism on Cumberland Island.

_____. Family Parulidae. **Prairie Warbler**. *Setophaga discolor* (Vieillot, 1809). The prairie warbler is a fairly common summer resident and transient on Cumberland Island. Sprunt (1936) confirmed the presence of this species on the island and there are six museum specimens (five in April, one May). Breeding occurs from Canada and New England to the Southeast US and they winter in the Bahamas and West Indies.

_____. Family Parulidae. **Black-throated Green Warbler**. *Setophaga virens* (Gmelin, 1789). Sprunt (1936) saw this warbler on Cumberland Island in April of 1932. It is a transient on the island between its breeding area in Canada, the northern US states to north Georgia and its wintering area in Mexico and Central America. It was seen on the 2001 Cumberland Christmas count.

_____. Family Parulidae. **Wilson's Warbler**. *Cardellina pusilla* (Wilson, 1811). Wilson's warbler is a rare transient between its breeding grounds in north Alaska, Canada, and northern New England and its wintering grounds in Mexico and Texas and occasionally into the Gulf states and Georgia. There is one observation for Cumberland Island in September 1999 (A. Mahoney, pers. comm.).

_____. Family Parulidae. **Yellow-breasted Chat**. *Icteria virens* (Linnaeus, 1758). Pearson (1922) recorded this uncommon summer resident on Cumberland Island. It breeds from Minnesota and southern New England south to the Gulf Coast and Florida and winters in Mexico and Central America, rarely in Florida. One was found DOB here in May and there are several island observations (S. Willis, pers. comm.).

_____. Family Emberizidae. **Eastern Towhee.** *Pipilo erythrophthalmus* (Linnaeus, 1758). Both Pearson (1922) and Sprunt (1936) recorded this common Cumberland Island resident and there are seven museum specimens. Their breeding range includes Canada and from across the US south to Central America. They winter from southern New England south, so there may also be migrants. These towhees are common in thick vegetation in the interdune and scrub.

_____. Family Emberizidae. **Bachman's Sparrow.** *Peucaea aestivalis* (Lichtenstein, 1823). Bachman's sparrow is an uncommon resident of open pinewoods, which are usually reliant on fire to maintain their character. Bachman's breeds across the Southeast US from Ohio and Pennsylvania to Florida and winters from North Carolina to Florida, so there may be migrants. Sprunt (1936) recorded the species on Cumberland Island.

_____. Family Emberizidae. **Chipping Sparrow.** *Spizella passerina* (Bechstein, 1798). Although this sparrow breeds from Alaska through Canada and the US states to Georgia, it is only a winter visitor on Cumberland Island. There is one museum specimen from February, and Burleigh (1958) said it was on Cumberland Island as late as 17 April. I have a record of a flock in March.

_____. Family Emberizidae. **Clay-colored Sparrow.** *Spizella pallida* (Swainson, 1832). An elusive, casual transient and winter visitor to Cumberland Island, the clay-colored sparrow breeds from Canada into the US to Colorado and Texas and winters in Mexico and wanders to the Southeastern states. Sprunt (1936) reported it on Cumberland Island but failed to secure a specimen, so Burleigh (1958) refused to accept the record. It has been observed on Cumberland Island by S. Willis (pers. comm.).

_____. Family Emberizidae. **Field Sparrow.** *Spizella pusilla* (Wilson, 1810). Sprunt (1936) recorded the field sparrow on Cumberland Island on his visits in April, when the species is said to be accidental on the island. Breeding occurs from Canada and the northern US states south to Texas and north Georgia, and the species winters in the southern US, including on Cumberland Island.

_____. Family Emberizidae. **Vesper Sparrow.** *Pooecetes gramineus* (Gmelin, 1789). The breeding grounds of the vesper sparrow are from Canada to North Carolina in the eastern states, and these birds winter south to Florida and Mexico. A few may use Cumberland Island as a winter resort, but they are not common. Helme collected one museum specimen here in January 1905.

_____. Family Emberizidae. **Lark Sparrow**. *Chondestes grammacus* (Say, 1823). The lark sparrow is a rare, irregular transient on Cumberland Island that breeds from Canada south to Mexico and east to Alabama. It winters from Texas to Florida and south into Mexico. It has been observed on the island by S. Willis.

_____. Family Emberizidae. **Savannah Sparrow**. *Passerculus sandwichensis* (Gmelin, 1789). The Savannah sparrow or "Ipswich sparrow" was collected on Cumberland Island by Helme in January, March, and April and is a transient and winter visitor. It breeds in Alaska, Canada, and the northern US states and winters south to Cuba, the Bahamas, and Central America.

_____. Family Emberizidae. **Grasshopper Sparrow**. *Ammodramus savannarum* (Gmelin, 1789). The grasshopper sparrow is a rare to uncommon winter resident and transient along the Georgia coast. This is a grassland, open-field species, which spends its time on the ground, and not in woodlands. Along the East Coast, this sparrow's winter range extends from Tennessee and North Carolina to Yucatan and Guatemala, and includes the Bahamas and Cuba. It breeds from southern Canada and New England south to Ecuador and the Greater Antilles, with the highest US breeding occurring from North Dakota south through South Dakota, Nebraska, Kansas, and Oklahoma to north Texas. An active grasshopper sparrow was observed on the north end of Cumberland Island for three consecutive days, 28 to 30 April (A. Mahoney and C. Ruckdeschel).

_____. Family Emberizidae. **Nelson's Sparrow**. *Ammodramus nelsoni* Allen, 1875. Helme collected a Nelson's sparrow on Cumberland Island in January, where they are winter visitors. Breeding occurs in Canada and the northern US states south to North Carolina, and they winter in salt marshes from New York to Texas.

_____. Family Emberizidae. **Saltmarsh Sparrow**. *Ammodramus caudacutus* (Gmelin, 1788). The irregular breeding distribution of the saltmarsh sparrow is from Canada to the New England coast and south to North Carolina. It winters from New Jersey to Florida, so it is a winter visitor on Cumberland Island, which Helme said was common (Burleigh, 1958). There are two specimens from the island, oddly from April and May, and Burleigh (1958) said there was one from January.

_____. Family Emberizidae. **Seaside Sparrow.** *Ammodramus maritimus* (Wilson, 1811). The seaside sparrow is a common permanent resident on Cumberland Island, which Helme found numerous (Burleigh, 1958) and Sprunt (1936) recorded. There are also sixteen museum specimens. This species breeds along the Atlantic Coast from New England to Florida and around the Gulf Coast and winters from Virginia south.

_____. Family Emberizidae. **Fox Sparrow.** *Passerella iliaca* (Merrem, 1786). The fox sparrow is a more western species and a rare winter visitor to Cumberland Island. It breeds in Canada and winters in the US from Ohio to Texas and incidentally along the Gulf Coast into Georgia and Florida. Heavy snow may push it farther south. It has been documented on the Cumberland Audubon Christmas Bird Counts.

_____. Family Emberizidae. **Song Sparrow.** *Melospiza melodia* (Wilson, 1810). The song sparrow breeds in Canada and Newfoundland and south to north Georgia and winters to Florida, so it is a regular winter visitor on Cumberland Island. Sprunt (1936) recorded it, and it is frequently seen on the Cumberland Audubon bird counts.

_____. Family Emberizidae. **Swamp Sparrow.** *Melospiza georgiana* (Latham, 1790). Common on Cumberland Island as a winter visitor, the swamp sparrow breeds from Canada south to Nebraska and West Virginia and winters south to Florida and Mexico. Both Pearson (1922) and Sprunt (1936) recorded the species on Cumberland Island, and it has been seen on Christmas bird counts.

_____. Family Emberizidae. **White-throated Sparrow.** *Zonotrichia albicollis* (Gmelin, 1789). The white-throated sparrow is a common winter visitor on Cumberland Island. It breeds in Canada and the northern US states including New England to Pennsylvania and spends the winter in the southern US and Mexico. Sprunt (1936) recorded it on Cumberland Island, and there was a museum specimen taken in April. Island records are from November through March.

_____. Family Emberizidae. **Dark-eyed Junco.** *Junco hyemalis* (Linnaeus, 1758). The dark-eyed junco is a winter visitor that breeds from Alaska and Canada into the northern US and winters south to Florida. Its abundance in this area relates to the severity of the winter. Island records are from December, February and March. Its presence on Cumberland Island has been confirmed by M. Hodges.

_____. Family Cardinalidae. **Summer Tanager**. *Piranga rubra* (Linnaeus, 1758). The summer tanager is a common summer resident on Cumberland Island and uncommon transient. They breed from Iowa east and south across the Eastern US and winter in Mexico and South America. Pearson (1922) and Sprunt (1936) recorded them on Cumberland Island, and there are nineteen museum specimens from the island taken in April, May, and August. Our records add March and July.

_____. Family Cardinalidae. **Scarlet Tanager**. *Piranga olivacea* (Gmelin, 1789). The striking scarlet tanager breeds from Canada across the Eastern US to north Georgia and winters in South America. It is a transient on Cumberland Island. Pearson (1922) recorded it on the island and one was found DOB in April.

_____. Family Cardinalidae. **Northern Cardinal**. *Cardinalis cardinalis* (Linnaeus, 1758). The northern cardinal is a very common permanent resident on Cumberland Island, and there are also autumn migrations. Its range extends across all but the northernmost eastern US. They may have three broods a year, and nesting has been noted on Cumberland Island in May, with young May through August. One bird was observed killing and eating a newly emerged cicada, but sandspurs and seeds are more common fare. An adult was killed by a rattlesnake in a domestic situation (Mitchell and Ruckdeschel, 2008). Ticks, a biting louse, and feather mites have been found on cardinals on Cumberland Island. See Appendix VI. B.

_____. Family Cardinalidae. **Rose-breasted Grosbeak**. *Pheucticus ludovicianus* (Linnaeus, 1766). The rose-breasted grosbeak is a rare migrant on Cumberland Island between its breeding grounds across Canada and the Northeastern US and its wintering areas in Mexico to South America. They follow the mountains south into north Georgia for breeding and occasionally winter along the Gulf Coast but are mostly transient in this area. There is one unverified observation of this species on Cumberland Island (S. Willis, pers. comm.).

_____. Family Cardinalidae. **Blue Grosbeak**. *Passerina caerulea* (Linnaeus, 1758). Breeding in this species occurs in Southeastern states from Missouri to Maryland and south to Florida, and they winter in Mexico and Central America. Blue grosbeaks are uncommon summer residents and transients on Cumberland Island. Island records are from April and May, one was found DOB, and there are other unconfirmed observations on Cumberland Island (S. Willis, pers. comm.).

_____. Family Cardinalidae. **Indigo Bunting**. *Passerina cyanea* (Linnaeus, 1766). The indigo bunting is not as common along the coast as it is farther inland, and it is considered an uncommon summer resident and regular transient on Cumberland Island. Their breeding range includes south Canada and across the Eastern US from North Dakota to Maine and south into Florida, generally avoiding the coast from Georgia around the Gulf states. They winter in Cuba, Mexico, and Central America. Helme collected two specimens from Cumberland Island in April, and local records are from April through July.

_____. Family Cardinalidae. **Painted Bunting**. *Passerina circis* (Linnaeus, 1758). This colorful beauty is a common summer resident on Cumberland Island, although it is becoming less common. Its range includes the south central states and the fringe of coast from Virginia to Florida. They winter in the Bahamas, Cuba, Florida, and Mexico to Central America so may be transients on Cumberland Island also. Pearson (1922) and Sprunt (1936) verified their presence on the island, and twenty-two museum specimens were collected on the island. Painted buntings arrive in April, the 8th being my earliest date, they mate in May, and young have been seen June through September. The latest island records island are mid-November.

_____. Family Icteridae. **Bobolink**. *Dolichonyx oryzivorus* (Linnaeus, 1758). The bobolink or rice bird is a common spring transient at Cumberland Island, between its wintering grounds in South America and its breeding locales in Canada and the northern part of the US. It is uncommon in the autumn. Pearson (1922) recorded it on Cumberland Island and there are four museum specimens. Island records are in April and May. One was DOB and one DOR.

_____. Family Icteridae. **Red-winged Blackbird**. *Agelaius phoeniceus* (Linnaeus, 1766). The red-winged blackbird is a common permanent resident of Cumberland Island. Both Pearson (1922) and Sprunt (1936) recorded it. The red-winged blackbird's breeding range includes Canada and the Eastern US to Georgia and Florida. Nest construction begins in April on Cumberland Island and nesting occurs primarily in May. A male was seen luring a blacksnake away from a nest by feigning a broken wing. Following nesting, groups are frequently seen on the beach feeding on sea oats. One has been found DOR.

_____. Family Icteridae. **Eastern Meadowlark**. *Sturnella magna* (Linnaeus, 1758). Both Pearson (1922) and Sprunt (1936) recorded the eastern meadowlark on Cumberland Island, and eleven museum specimens have been collected. It is an island resident and breeds over most of the state, but Beaton et al. (2003) said it was uncommon along the coast. Numbers in autumn are increased by migrants from Canada and the Northern states. Local island records are from October through December and February.

_____. Family Icteridae. **Yellow-headed Blackbird**. *Xanthocephalus xanthocephalus* (Bonaparte, 1826). This large blackbird breeds from British Columbia through the western and central US and winters from the Gulf Coast and Florida to central Mexico. Its range has been changing in recent times and it is becoming more common in Florida. There are no records for Cumberland Island but the species has been recorded in St. Marys, Georgia (S. Willis, pers. comm.).

_____. Family Icteridae. **Rusty Blackbird**. *Euphagus carolinus* (Müller, 1776). An uncommon winter resident on Cumberland Island, the rusty blackbird breeds from Alaska to the Northeastern states and winters in the Southeast US to Florida. Sprunt (1936) saw rusty blackbirds on Cumberland Island, and I have a record from March.

_____. Family Icteridae. **Common Grackle**. *Quiscalus quiscula* (Linnaeus, 1758). The common grackle is more obvious on Cumberland Island than the boat-tailed, especially when flocks of winter migrants appear. They breed from Canada south to Florida and winter in the Southern states. Pearson (1922) and Sprunt (1936) recorded them and there are two museum specimens from Cumberland Island. Island nesting has been documented in April. One was seen flying carrying a dead green snake, and a juvenile was found DOB

_____. Family Icteridae. **Boat-tailed Grackle**. *Quiscalus major* Vieillot, 1819. This distinctive long-tailed grackle is associated with the coast from New Jersey to Florida and is a common resident on Cumberland Island. Pearson (1922) and Sprunt (1936) both recorded it on the island, and there are four museum specimens.

Family Icteridae. **Shiny Cowbird**. *Molothrus bonariensis* (Gmelin, 1789). The first Georgia observation of the shiny cowbird was on Cumberland Island in 1989 (Ruckdeschel et al., 1996). The species distribution includes the Antilles and South America. A natural colonization northward put them in Florida in 1985, from where they have continued spreading. Local observations were in May and June of 1989, 1996, and 1998.

_____. Family Icteridae. **Brown-headed Cowbird**. *Molothrus ater* (Boddaert, 1783). The brown-headed cowbird is a fairly common summer resident on Cumberland Island and also a transient and winter resident, all of which resulted from range expansion beginning in the late 1950s. Neither Pearson nor Sprunt reported them on Cumberland Island, and there are no museum specimens from the island. Their breeding distribution is from Canada across the Southeast US to Florida and they winter in the Southern states. Island records are mainly February through June, with one in October. They have been observed mating in May and parasitizing yellow-throated warbler nests here.

_____. Family Icteridae. **Orchard Oriole**. *Icterus spurious* (Linnaeus, 1766). This oriole is a common summer resident on Cumberland Island and also a spring and autumn migrant. The species breeds from the Northern states south to Florida and Mexico and winters from South Mexico to South America. Sprunt (1936) recorded it on Cumberland Island, and there are six museum specimens from April.

_____. Family Icteridae. **Baltimore Oriole**. *Icterus galbula* (Linnaeus, 1758). The Baltimore oriole is a regular, uncommon transient on Cumberland Island between its breeding area in Canada south to north Georgia and its wintering grounds in southern Mexico and South America. Island records are from April, August, and September. Baltimore orioles were noted eating mulberries in April, and one was found DOB in April.

_____. Family Fringillidae. **Purple Finch**. *Carpodacus purpureus* (Gmelin, 1789). The purple finch is an irregular, uncommon winter visitor on Cumberland Island and has been recorded on the island (M. Hodges). It breeds across Canada and into the Northeastern US and winters south to the Gulf Coast and Florida.

_____. Family Fringillidae. **House Finch**. *Carpodacus mexicanus* (Müller, 1776). The house finch is an exotic species, fairly recently established in Georgia. In the 1940s to 1950s, finches being sold illegally in New York were released to dispose of evidence, and house finches spread across the Eastern US. They are native to the Western US and Mexico. One was observed in the Settlement on Cumberland Island in April.

_____. Family Fringillidae. **Pine Siskin**. *Spinus pinus* (Wilson, 1810). This small finch is an unusual, irregular, and sometimes irruptive winter visitor. It breeds from Alaska and Canada into the Northern states and south along the mountains to North Carolina and winters from Florida to Texas and Mexico. It has been confirmed on the island by M. Hodges.

_____. Family Fringillidae. **American Goldfinch.** *Spinus tristis* (Linnaeus, 1758). The goldfinch is primarily a winter visitor to the island, which breeds from Canada through the US to Georgia and winters in much of the range and south into Florida and Mexico. Sprunt (1936) noted them on Cumberland Island, and my records are from January and April.

_____. Family Fringillidae. **Evening Grosbeak.** *Coccothraustes vespertinus* (Cooper, 1825). Breeding in this species is confined to Canada and the northern US states, and they winter mid-continent, east of the Rocky Mountains. They were first reported in Georgia in 1955 and in Florida in 1968 or 1969 and were not noted by early naturalists. They are unpredictable in their travels, so while listed as an uncommon winter visitor, they may skip years on the island. Our records are from October and February.

Mammals

Introduction

The number of mammal species on Cumberland Island is about half the number occurring on the adjacent mainland (Table 5), and is ever changing. First came the armadillo in the early 1970s, expanding its range northward. It was soon reported on most of the barrier islands. In 1976, there was an active beaver dam on Cumberland Island, which was maintained until the end of 1978. Scattered through the 1990s were reports of beavers dead and alive on the island, but no permanent residence was established. In the 1980s, the National Park Service released thirty-two bobcats on the island where there had been no mammalian "cruising" predator. All vertebrates were taken by surprise and many suffered great losses before they could "learn" to be wary. The coyote first showed up in the late 1980s, with records of sign and sightings for several months, followed by a gap of about a year before sign was again seen. Coyotes are now an acknowledged component of the Cumberland Island fauna. In 1993, someone from the mainland released Virginia opossums on the island. No reason was given other than that they were not here. Given the generalist behavior of opossums, the released animals multiplied.

The standard way to present tooth arrangement is with the capital initial I for incisor, C for canine, PM premolar, and M molar, each followed by the number of teeth in the species on one side, upper / lower, so the number must be doubled for the total number of teeth. I 1/1, C 0/0, PM 1/1, M 3/3

= 20 teeth total. Teeth are usually involved in species identification. Total length (TL) is a key measurement, and tail (T), hind foot (HF), and ear (E) are also standard measurements.

Below is a summary of changes to the list of mammals occurring in recent times (1900 to 2010) on Cumberland Island.

1. Colonizers or introduced species.

Virginia opossum. The opossum did not recently occur on the island until it was introduced in 1993. See Ruckdeschel and Shoop (1986) for details.

Nine-banded armadillo. The armadillo may have been on the island as early as 1972, but its presence was not confirmed until 1974. It presumably arrived under its own power, that is, colonized the island.

Feral horse. Feral horses were introduced in the 1920s by the Carnegies.

Beaver. A dam in a wooded swamp was maintained for some time, and several individuals made it to the island at various times, but none survived.

Coyote. Coyotes have been resident since the late 1980s.

Bobcat. Between 1972 and 1989, thirty-seven bobcats from Georgia and Florida were released on Cumberland Island.

2. Species listed based on circumstantial evidence only and should be omitted.

Least shrew. While common on the adjacent mainland and on one Georgia barrier island, this small shrew has not been verified on Cumberland Island, despite much trapping effort. The one reference to it is from an owl pellet.

Eastern harvest mouse. Along with the least shrew, the harvest mouse is frequent on the mainland but has not been verified from the island. One individual came from an owl pellet. Contents of owl pellets reflect a wide foraging area, perhaps beyond the island. See the discussion under roof rat.

3. Errors in identification.

Eastern fox squirrel. The basis for including the fox squirrel in the island fauna was a specimen in the Carnegie Museum collected on Cumberland Island. Close scrutiny showed this species to be a young eastern gray squirrel, and their museum records now indicate this.

Beach or oldfield deermouse. A.H. Wright's listing of a beach/oldfield mouse on Cumberland Island in his Okefenokee publication is described as "a lapsus on the part of Wright" by D. Wilson, Department of Vertebrate

Zoology, US National Museum, Smithsonian Institution (email 8 June 2010). Wilson found no reference to the species on Cumberland Island.

Eastern Cottontail rabbit. A specimen of this purported species was collected on the island and curated in the Carnegie museum, but close scrutiny of the young and less-than-perfect specimen revealed it to be a marsh rabbit, which the museum catalogue now shows.

Until more information can be collected on the black or roof rat on Cumberland Island, it will have to be listed as status unknown.

Note that nomenclature below follows Wilson, D.E., and D. M. Reeder. 2005. *Mammal Species of the World, a Taxonomic and Geographic Reference* 3rd Edition (Baltimore, MD: Johns Hopkins University Press).

Species Accounts

ORDER MARSUPIALIA. Family Didelphidae. **Virginia Opossum.** *Didelphis virginiana* Kerr, 1792. The Virginia opossum is a medium, almost raccoon-sized animal with a long pointed snout, large canines that are visible in its defense posture with mouth open, leathery round ears, and a long, rat-like, prehensile tail, nearly naked except at the base. The color ranges between light gray to very dark gray, almost black, with a white face. The hair is of two different types, a seasonally thick, short, soft underfur, with longer, coarser, white-tipped guard hairs, which give the animal a full, plump appearance. The head of adult males is disproportionately large for the body, and most of it is facial area, with the cranial cavity being relatively small. The number of teeth exceeds that of other Cumberland Island mammals; incisors are numerous, with 5/5 upper and 4/4 lower. Dentition is I 5/4, C 1/1, PM 3/3, M 4/4, which equals 50 total.

Total length measurements of thirty-nine males from Cumberland Island averaged 806 millimeters (range 597 to 900), fifteen females 749 millimeters (range 596 to 840), and sexes combined averaged 790 millimeters. Other measurements are available.

Opossums occur throughout Georgia and from southern Canada into South America. Before they were introduced on Cumberland Island in 1993, the only other barrier islands on which they resided were Sapelo, where they were probably also introduced, and Little St. Simons Island, which is at the mouth of the Altamaha River, a possible source of transport.

Tracks of the opossum may be found on the Cumberland Island ocean beach, wandering along the wrack line or in the dunes, in woodlands, and along stream corridors, and they are comfortable around human habitations.

They are sensitive to drought either because of its impact on their food resources or their physiology or both.

The description "omnivorous" truly fits the opossum. It is an opportunist of the first order, not hesitating to eat carrion, even if a member of its own species. On Cumberland Island (Table 6), vegetation/fruit was a common item identified in opossum digestive tracts, but much vegetation appeared to have been incidentally ingested. Hair observed in the digestive tract appeared to have been from the animal itself rather than prey items. Identifiable prey items in order of importance were insects, birds (as represented by feathers), reptiles, and mammals. Of the ten reptiles, six were lizards (two fence lizards and four anoles) and four were small snakes (one a southern ring-necked snake). One mammal was identified as a mole. Mollusks occurred in low volume and frequency.

Opossums swim well and scull with their tails. They have been described as strong swimmers with the ability to float, which enables them to rest during long periods in the water. As a defense, they can submerge and swim underwater (Doutt, 1954).

Cumberland Island females with young have been reported on 12 April, 16 April, 27 June, and 25 July, and litter size was six (one) and seven (three). Life expectancy is short, thus population turnover is rapid. The maximum life expectancy suggested is seven years (McManus, 1974) but more likely less than two (Petrides, 1949).

On Cumberland Island, three species of ticks, one species of flea, five species of mites, and one chigger have been identified on the Virginia opossum. See Appendix VI. C. *Besnoitia* sp., a protozoan parasite, was first noticed in mice and opossums on Cumberland Island the summer of 2003 and winter of 2004. Yabsley et al. (2015) reported the first incidence of the Virginia opossum as an intermediate host for a pentastome on the island.

Few mammalian predators regularly take adult opossums, but birds and reptiles, including alligators, may have an impact on young animals. Vultures are wary of a fresh opossum carcass, possibly because of the opossum's habit of "playing dead," but they ultimately feed on it. Humans find the meat flavorful and the fat mild and savory.

F. Harper (1927) concluded that the absence of opossums on Cumberland Island implied that the species did not arrive in the coastal area until a later period. While opossum remains have been found in island aboriginal middens, limited numbers of individuals could have been brought to the island for food as special gifts, as was the case in the 1970s (Ruckdeschel and Shoop, 1986).

Since opossums use a variety of habitats, are good swimmers, and willingly share human-modified environments, their sensitivity to lack of freshwater may be the important factor regarding distribution on the Georgia barrier islands. Critical dependence on available freshwater coupled with a short life expectancy are traits incompatible with long-term residency on the barrier islands. A two- or three-year drought eliminates most island freshwater sources, and the remainder would be dangerously alive with alligators. Once eliminated, it is unlikely that numbers of opossums necessary for re-population would have been able to successfully traverse the miles of salt marsh that, before Europeans, also supported extensive numbers of alligators.

Discussion. On the local barrier islands, opossum remains have been found in middens on Amelia Island, Florida, and on Sapelo, St. Catherines, and Cumberland islands in Georgia. Remains on Cumberland Island dated from 500 BC to at least AD 200, but no sign was found during excavations of slave cabins at Stafford, indicating their absence during the mid-1800s. Confusing the issue are erroneous literature reports from 1849 to 1981 (White, 1849; Ober, 1880; Schemmel, 1975; NPS General Management Plan-Wilderness Study, 1977; Bullard, 1982; and Wood, 1981), the details of which were discussed by Ruckdeschel and Shoop (1986).

Opossums were introduced on Cumberland Island in the latter part of 1993 and have since spread over the entire island. The first report to reach me was in December 1993, when a park ranger mentioned seeing one in Davisville, where he lived. During the first six months, the reported sightings were less than a half a mile apart. By autumn of 1995, a year and a half later, the animals had been seen over a half a mile north of the original sighting. By autumn of 1996, they were regularly seen three to four miles north and south of Davisville, and the first seen on the north end was in September 1997, three years and nine months after the first report. By spring of 1999 (five years, four months) they were common and had become a nuisance in the yard at the north end of the island.

ORDER CINGULATA. Family Dasypodidae. **Nine-banded Armadillo.** *Dasypus novemcinctus* Lineaus, 1758. The appearance of this animal is unusual. Its reptilian-like, scale-covered bony armor is not meant to camouflage but to protect the animal, especially from above. The anterior and posterior shields offer little flexibility but the lower edges are moveable enough to accommodate locomotion. The belly, limbs, and neck are covered with scantily haired, tough skin. Hair is everywhere sparse although in some areas quite long. The front feet are covered with scales and have four strong toes with large nails for digging. The rear feet also have relatively large nails on all five toes. The ears are erect, noticeable, and hearing is good. Eyes are small and seem to be relatively inefficient. Their sense of smell is keen.

Members of the order Cingulata are found only in the New World and include sloths, anteaters, and armadillos. They have no incisors or canines, and the peg-like premolars and molars are similar in shape. Dentition of the nine-banded armadillo averages 8/8 for a total of about 32 teeth. The teeth are widely spaced so mastication is limited, but the teeth continue growing throughout life.

The earliest US occurrence of the nine-banded armadillo was in extreme southern Texas (Audubon and Bachman, 1854). Since then, there has been a steady range expansion eastward in the US. It was reported in Louisiana by 1925, had crossed the Mississippi River by 1943, and reached Western Florida and south Georgia by 1972. The species presently occurs up the East Coast into South Carolina.

There was a tentative sighting of an armadillo on Cumberland Island in September of 1972, and they were strongly suspected to be on the island in 1973, but their presence was not verified until May 1974. They were reported on Little St. Simons Island in 1979, on Sapelo Island in August of 1991, and although there was a stranding in 1994 on St. Catherines Island, there were reportedly no residents.

Any area that is not too dry or too wet and accommodates burrowing and foraging is acceptable habitat. Armadillos may succumb to heat if daylight catches them in the island interdune area or out on the open beach.

Between 1975 and 2006, 134 armadillo stomachs were collected on Cumberland Island (Whitaker et al., 2012a). The most important foods eaten were a variety of beetles and ants. Plant material made up 11.8% of the volume and vertebrates only 1.9%. Two species in the armadillo diet diminished in importance over time: the fiery searcher beetle, *Calosoma scrutator*, and the millipede, *Narceus* sp. The reason for the apparent changes in abundance of these two species is not clear, but since the armadillo is a new island colonizer, it might be expected to have an impact on the ecology.

On Cumberland Island, burrows, above-ground nests, and trees with open, hollow bases all serve as refugia. During cold weather, burrows and open bases of trees may be tightly stuffed with nest material. The animal gathers a double armful of litter with its front limbs and then takes little hops backward, dragging the material to the nest site. One island animal dragged material more than 20 feet, even though litter was undisturbed closer to the site. On Cumberland Island, nest material consists of pine needles, oak leaves, grasses, and Spanish moss. Burrows are located in all forested habitats and even though some may appear to be in unsuitable places, such as the edges of ponds, fluctuating water level determines their use.

Armadillos can swim. They dog-paddle in the typical fashion, but their legs are short and their feet are not efficient paddles. To overcome their high specific gravity, which causes their body to submerge, they swallow air and inflate their stomach and intestines (Layne, 2003) until they become more buoyant. Nevertheless, an individual has been recorded swimming across a 450-foot wide Florida river, and they occur on islands in the marine environment. To cross shallow areas, they may walk under water. Whether for hygiene or physiological reasons, they frequently roll and wallow in shallow water or muck.

Another surprising behavior of this compact animal is its ability to climb. It can go up hog wire fences until it can squeeze through a larger opening, and under a perceived threat, has been observed climbing the inside of a hollow tree on Cumberland Island to above four feet.

Although the integument is sparsely haired and much of the surface is scaled, there is adequate area, especially between the flexible bands of the "carapace," that appears suitable for external parasites, yet few occur. Ticks are the only external parasites that have been found on armadillos on Cumberland Island, and they are scarce. See Appendix VI C.

Armadillos on Cumberland Island are infected with cystacanths, a juvenile internal parasite that is infective to the raccoon, its popular definitive host. Cystacanths form when the infective stage is eaten by an unsuitable host. The internal flagellate parasite, *Trypanosoma cruzi*, has little host specificity, and through Polymerase Chain Reaction (PCR) five mammal species, besides the armadillo, have been shown to be infected with *T. cruzi* on Cumberland Island (C. Hall, pers. comm.).

On Cumberland Island, the ocean beach presents a hostile environment for armadillos, especially during summer. Coupled with the intense heat of the sun, from which no refuge can be found, the cooling but eventually lethal saltwater takes its toll. Some animals may wash in from elsewhere, but most armadillo strandings are presumed to be island animals that became disoriented and fell victim to the harsh conditions. Some individuals that were cooled and provided fresh water recovered. While armadillos have stranded in all months, May through July are the months of highest numbers, supporting the environmental stress theory. Since 1979, there have been 120 recorded armadillo strandings, between thirty and fifty a decade.

Not only on the mainland, with its blanket of paved roads, but also on Cumberland Island, vehicles are a major source of mortality for armadillos. While strandings or beach mortality has a seasonal peak based on environmental conditions, road fatalities now average over twelve per month, with no outstanding temporal peak. From 1979 to 1988, twenty-four animals were found DOR; from 1989 to 1998, seventeen; and from 1999 to 2008, 145. Traffic on the island has increased during that time, but armadillo population numbers are unknown.

On Cumberland Island in 1990, slightly over 10% of alligator fecal samples examined contained armadillo, and the alligator might be expected to be a regular predator on armadillos.

Discussion. Reasons for the entrance of the armadillo into the US and its phenomenal spread across the Southeast have never been explained. Armadillos are tropical animals, and the nine-banded species is the only armadillo that occurs as far north as the United States. In 1854, it had not begun its range-expansion odyssey, and the northern limit of its range was the Mexico-US border. The species has a physiological thermal limit to its distribution because of its low metabolic rate and high thermal conductance (McNab, 1980). The design of the animal is to function in a tropical setting, and because of its poor insulation it is unable to reduce its energy demand. If the ground freezes, food becomes unavailable. Food is not stored, and the animal has limited fat reserves with which to wait out the cold spell so may starve. Speculation on distribution of the species has reached the "perplexing question" (Humphry, 1974) of why the armadillo waited so long to enter the US, since the climate has not dramatically changed in recent times. All agree that arid conditions are avoided by this armadillo and that bottomland and riparian habitat are heavily utilized. What about predators? Can it be only a coincidence that the southern range of the American alligator stopped at the Mexico-US border, and that in the 1800s the alligator population in the Southeast was being decimated? Alligators occupied every aquatic system in the Southeast US prior to their near extinction and could have been a limiting factor in armadillo distribution. Millions of alligators were slaughtered for hides and probably an equal number were shot for sport. Those populations never recovered and are not likely to, given our use of the land and fear of large predators. Remaining potential predators include bobcats and coyotes. Bobcats ignore armadillos as food even though they may be abundant (Wassmer et al., 1988), although young ones have been taken on Cumberland Island.

Armadillos on Cumberland are not considered an important prey item in the diet of coyotes.

ORDER SORICOMORPHA. Family Talpidae. **Eastern Mole.** *Scalopus aquaticus* (Linnaeus, 1758). The greatly enlarged front feet and limbs of the eastern mole are obvious adaptations to its fossorial, digging life and distinguish it immediately from shrews and mice. The front feet, with broad, straight nails, are wider than long, fixed in an open-palm position, and held out from the body with naked palms toward the rear, most of the time. The hind feet are more in proportion and shape to the size of the animal, and both front and hind feet are webbed. The animal is a powerful digger with a muscular neck and shoulder region tapering off to a narrow waist and pelvic area. So reduced is the pelvic region to facilitate maneuvering within the tunnel that the urogenital and alimentary tracts cannot pass through it, as is usually the case. Instead, they lie ventral to the pubic symphysis (Slonaker, 1920). The nostrils are on top of the tip of a fairly long, pointed, flexible proboscis equipped with a specialized bone, the purpose of which is unknown other than to help support the nostrils (Slonaker, 1920). The proboscis is mostly free of hair and is a very sensitive tactile organ.

The thick pelage is generally silvery gray to brownish and soft like velvet. No unusually colored animals have been found on Cumberland Island, but here they vary in color from light to dark, rich brown to slate gray. Depending upon the season, they may have a wash of light orange-brown on their face and a brownish area on their chest/belly. The tail is short and nearly naked, the eyes and their infrastructure are greatly reduced and separated from the outside by a thin, translucent membrane. Eyes are probably limited to differentiating light from dark.

General size changes with latitude, decreasing to the south. The average total length of Cumberland Island animals is 133.5 millimeters, with males averaging 135.0 millimeters and females 131.5 millimeters. Average tail length is 18.2 millimeters, and the hind foot average is 17.0 millimeters. Skull measurements of Cumberland Island animals varied only slightly between the sexes. Averages for adults were: length 32.0, width 16.5, depth 9.4, inter-orbital 7.2, and palate 13.5 millimeters.

Eastern moles are found throughout Georgia and on both the Pleistocene core and Holocene barrier islands, where they are quite common. The species is also common on Amelia Island, Florida.

All island habitats except standing water and salt marsh are used by moles. Interdune areas appear inhospitable, but the water table is close and moles are frequent. Their tunnels occasionally even occur out onto the firm beach below the recent tide line (Fig. 29), suggesting that the animals do not have a strict aversion to the salty environment.

Moles can swim quite well, but they are not considered aquatic. These terrestrial moles do not voluntarily enter water in search of food, but the ability to swim could be an advantage when foraging in and along wetlands subject to flood. A swimming mole could easily climb on floating debris and thereby increase its chances of survival and dispersal.

On Cumberland Island, eighteen food items were identified from stomach contents of sixteen eastern moles (Whitaker and Ruckdeschel, 2013). Beetles ranked highest, earthworms second, and ants were found with significant frequency. Four species of mites and one tick have been identified on Cumberland Island moles. See Appendix VI C.

Eastern moles have one litter per year, and the timing of the breeding season may vary geographically. Young have been collected on the island between March and November.

A new predator for the eastern mole on Cumberland Island is the nine-banded armadillo. Three separate local observations indicate that the armadillo may regularly take moles for food. On Cumberland Island an armadillo was seen pouncing on a mole with its front feet until the mole was dead, but observations ended there (F. Whitehead, pers. comm.). On Little Cumberland Island, an armadillo was seen with a mole that it repeatedly shook, but the observer did not see the mole eaten (D. Makemson, pers. comm.), and a visitor to Cumberland Island watched an armadillo catch a mole, tear it in two with its feet, and eat the pieces whole (F. Whitehead, pers. comm.).

Discussion. The range of one other species of mole, the star-nosed mole, *Condylura cristata*, extends south along the Georgia coast and perhaps includes Amelia Island, Florida. Anecdotal accounts of this mole with a strange frilly nose are common on Amelia, but there are no voucher specimens. Likewise, R. Hayes, the long-time caretaker of St. Catherines Island to the north, said in 2007 that he had not seen a star-nosed mole there in twenty years and that there were no preserved specimens from the island. Specimens do exist from the Okefenokee Swamp, where a disjunct population still exists. Presently, the majority of the range of this species is in the Northeast US and eastern Canada, with a finger following the coasts south from Virginia barely into Florida. Widely separated or disjunct populations occur from the Dismal Swamp in Virginia south to the Okefenokee population.

Family Soricidae. **Southern Short-tailed Shrew.** *Blarina carolinensis* (Bachman, 1837). The southern short-tailed shrew is slate gray to dark brown, and the belly is only slightly lighter than the back. The hair is fine and silky, of a fairly uniform length, and reflects their use of underground runways by being quite reversible in direction. The ears are not obvious except on close inspection, and the tiny eyes may be obscured by fur. These characteristics instantly separate shrews from mice.

The total length of island animals averages 90.5 millimeters. Weight averages 8.6 grams, tail length 16.5 millimeters, hind foot 11.25. Its snout is long and pointed and extends well beyond the mouth. The animal has 32 teeth, with paired prominent incisors, which protrude forward from the skull. The tips of the incisors, premolars, and molars are reddish brown, with the darkest coloration on the incisors. No sexual dimorphism is apparent in skull measurements.

The southern short-tailed shrew is one of the most common animals on Cumberland Island and the other older barrier islands, but does not occur on Little Cumberland or the other Holocene islands at this time.

This shrew occupies many different habitats. On the island it is found in disturbed and developed areas, around all freshwater wetlands, in forested uplands, mature scrub, and in relatively open areas of Holocene sand, but it seems to be most abundant in lowland hardwood forests. Tolerance of poorly drained sites may be partially seasonal and depend upon the availability of underground runways. There are no island records from the beach-dune area, which lacks ground cover and is not conducive to shallow burrows. But these shrews may enter water without hesitation when threatened (Engles, 1933).

Shrews feed on invertebrates. On Cumberland Island, one of the main foods of this shrew in at least one location was the introduced terrestrial amphipod *Talitroides topitotum* (Whitaker and Ruckdeschel, 2006). Other important items in the island diet include larval beetles, centipedes, and earthworms.

Shrews were collected on Cumberland Island with equal trapping effort in every month except July and September, with only low numbers occurring in August and October. The highest activity was in February and March (peak reproductive activity), and 80% of the overall activity occurred during cool months between December and April. There was moderate activity in May, June, and November (16%), and a period of low activity, as reflected by availability of specimens, from July through October. Perceived changes in population numbers likely reflect behavioral changes more than a change in numbers of individuals present. However, annual changes in abundance have been reported from South Carolina and attributed to drought (Smith et al. 1974).

From 105 Cumberland Island animals from which sex could be determined, sixty-one were males and forty-four females. There were two clear peaks in reproductive activity for males, a tightly defined one in late winter to early spring (February and March) and a more loosely defined one in November and December. One island female with three embryos was found in May, lactating females were found in February and April, and those with the uterus and horns enlarged or with scars were collected in February, March, and December. Two females provided information on litter size, one with three embryos (March) and another with five placental scars (December).

Many species of ectoparasites have been collected on Cumberland Island shrews. See Appendix VI. C. Yabsley et al. (2015) reported the first incidence of the southern short-tailed shrew as an intermediate host of a pentastome on the island.

Most natural mortality of short-tailed shrews on the island and mainland is probably due to owls. A barn owl used to live in what is now the NPS "Ice House Museum," and shrews, including this species, were identified in its regurgitated pellets. A large pellet (8 by 4 millimeters) from the open yard at Greyfield also contained a short-tailed shrew. A southern short-tailed shrew was also recovered from the stomach of an island cottonmouth.

Family Soricidae. **Least Shrew.** *Cryptotis parva* (Say, 1823). This is a very small, short-tailed shrew, more brown in color than the larger southern short-tailed shrew, although the shades of color vary; the belly is lighter and the tail is slightly bicolored. Teeth provide the best diagnostic character, there being only a total of thirty. Behind the large bicuspid incisor are four unicusped teeth on both the upper and lower jaws. This is the only North American shrew with four unicuspeds.

An unknown number of individuals from Cumberland Island were collected from an owl pellet found on the island. No other specimens or data have been collected from this species on Cumberland Island. The least shrew is present on Sapelo Island, Georgia.

Discussion. O. Bangs (1898) reported the least shrew on Skidaway Island after having collected on many of the Georgia barrier islands. F. Golley (1962) stated that the least shrew was "probably not found on the Sea Islands," and J. Layne (1971) found no least shrews on Amelia Island, Florida. Neuhauser and Baker (1974) surveyed the coastal region of Georgia and reported least shrews from Blackbeard, Sapelo, and Cumberland islands. A query to the authors in 2006 regarding the specimen from Blackbeard Island revealed some confusion and no specimen. It is unclear how many individuals were collected from owl pellets on Cumberland Island, but Hillestad et al. (1975) referred to "specimens," plural.

National Park Service inventory projects on the island were not specifically focused on the appropriate available habitat for least shrews, so it may yet turn up. The species is frequent on the adjacent mainland in Camden County.

ORDER CHIROPTERA. Family Vespertilionidae. **Eastern Pipistrelle**. *Perimyotis subflavus* (Cuvier, 1832). Although there is considerable variation in overall pelage color of this species, the hair is distinctly tricolored, dark at the base with light brown in the middle and a dark tip. The anterior third of the interfemoral membrane is furred. Females are usually heavier than males. Dentition is I 2/3, C 1/1, PM 2/2, and M 3/3 = 36.

The eastern pipistrelle has been recorded from the Georgia barrier islands of St. Catherines, Sapelo, and Cumberland. It is abundant in wooded areas, especially ones with streams and ponds over which they can forage.

Although they may remain active through most of the year in Georgia, this species is an obligate hibernator in Florida and undergoes long periods of torpor. Animals usually hibernate singly rather than in clusters. On Cumberland Island, a female containing two large embryos was recorded on 18 May. An adult male pipistrelle was found on the island, on the ground, barely alive, in early July. Sticky strands of a tough spider web (*Nephila* sp.) were stuck on one wing.

_____. Family Vespertilionidae. **Big Brown Bat.** *Eptesicus fuscus* (Beauvois, 1796). The big brown bat is a medium- to large-sized bat with rather short wings and rounded ears. Its soft hair is a variable shade of brown, and the wings are blackish and darker than the interfemoral membrane. The tip of the tail extends a short way beyond the interfemoral membrane, which is thinly haired on about a quarter of the proximal edge; the remainder is naked. Dentition is I 2/3, C 1/1, PM 1/2, M 3/3 for a total count of 32 teeth.

Big brown bats are common in Georgia from the mountains to the coast and have been collected on Sapelo and Cumberland islands. They prefer deciduous forests, although their winter and summer roosts are usually in buildings. Foraging habitat is fairly general but usually over land.

There was a maternity colony of big brown bats in the carriage house at Dungeness in 1975. In February of 1976, the National Park Service covered and fumigated the building (Fig. 30), eliminating all bats.

_____. Family Vespertilionidae. **Eastern Red Bat.** *Lasiurus borealis* (Müller, 1776). This is a moderate-sized bat with an outstandingly beautiful bright brick to rusty reddish coat and a pale belly. The hair is thick and soft and frequently tipped with white, giving it a frosted appearance. The interfemoral membrane is heavily haired and there is a patch of white hair on each shoulder and extremely contrasting ones at each wrist, which may distract as eye spots. Dentition is I 1/3, C 1/1, PM 2/2, M 3/3 for a total of 32 teeth. The first upper premolar is inside the tooth row and may be lacking.

They occur statewide in Georgia and have been recorded on Ossabaw, Sapelo, and Cumberland islands. Their roosting habitat is primarily in hardwoods, such as deciduous sweet gum and oaks, but they have also been recorded close to the ground in leaf litter and dense grass (Mager and Nelson, 2001). In the South, they frequently make use of Spanish moss as a roosting site.

_____. Family Vespertilionidae. **Northern Yellow Bat.** *Lasiurus intermedius* Allen, 1862. This relatively large bat has long, silky, yellowish hair in contrast to the usual grayish or reddish-brown of other *Lasiurus* spp. The hair of the mid-central back is especially long. There is no hair on the distal half of the interfemoral membrane. White areas at the wrist or shoulder are lacking. The sexes are alike in color, but females may average larger than males. Dentition is I 1/3, C 1/1, PM 1/2, M 3/3, which totals 30 teeth.

In Georgia, it occurs only south of the fall line and is most common in the lower Coastal Plain. Yellow bats have been collected on Sapelo and

Cumberland islands. Spanish moss is a favored roosting habitat for the northern yellow bat, and the bat's distribution nearly coincides with that of the moss.

Yellow bats are considered permanent residents of Cumberland Island. They become torpid during cold spells. On 24 February 1978, an individual was found floating dead in the small runoff water from an old artesian well on the north end of Cumberland Island. It was too rotten to sex or to determine the cause of death.

_____. Family Vespertilionidae. **Seminole Bat**. *Lasiurus seminolus* (Rhoades, 1895). The Seminole bat is medium-sized and very similar to the eastern red bat except in pelage color. Seminoles are a dark mahogany color, but the hairs may also be tipped with white or silver, giving them a frosted appearance. There are whitish patches on the shoulders, and males and females are colored the same. The shades of color between Seminoles and red bats do not overlap, they are distinctive. Dentition is I 1/3, C 1/1, PM 2/2, M 3/3 for a total of 32 teeth.

This is a bat of the Southeastern US. It is rarely found north of the fall line in Georgia, and its distribution roughly corresponds with that of Spanish moss. The species has been documented on Sapelo and Cumberland islands. Spanish moss is important as a roosting site to this solitary species. It uses the interior of large festoons of moss, as well as clumps of thick foliage and loose bark.

One individual on Cumberland Island was found dehydrated on 28 June but refused food and water and finally died. Three captured over an island swimming pool on 24 June were all females and were released.

_____. Family Vespertilionidae. **Evening Bat**. *Nycticeius humeralis* (Rafinesque, 1818). This small to medium-sized bat is a dark umber brown on the dorsal surface and slightly paler below. The rather long hair, darker at the base, covers the body only, not the ears, the short, narrow wings, or interfemoral membrane. The young are black for the first month. Dentition is I 1/3, C 1/1, PM 1/2, M 3/3 for a total of 30 teeth. The single upper incisor on each side is a good character to distinguish the evening bat from confusing species.

It is reported from Sapelo and Cumberland islands in Georgia and probably occurs statewide, except for perhaps the mountains. Evening bats become torpid in cold weather. They usually migrate, arriving in north Georgia around the second week of April and leaving by early October. They fatten up prior to migration, but the location of winter roosts is not known.

Northern populations likely migrate southward.

In June of 1994, forty-four evening bats were collected from the big house at Plum Orchard on Cumberland Island. The bats apparently went down the chimneys and could not get back out, or perhaps the top of the chimneys had been covered. Occasional individuals were found through 1997.

ORDER CARNIVORA. Family Canidae. **Coyote**. *Canis latrans* Say, 1823. The coyote is roughly the shape of a small, lithe German shepherd, with a full bushy tail. The color may vary geographically, but it is usually mostly gray with a yellowish or reddish cast and darker along the middorsal line of the back. The back of the ears are rust-colored and the belly and throat light to whitish. The coarse hair is differentiated from that of dogs by the number, order, and color of the bands on it (Feldhamer et al., 2003). There are five webbed toes on the front feet, the middle two of which are enlarged, and only four on the hind feet. Males are usually larger than females.

Dentition is I 3/3, C 1/1, PM 4/4, M 2/3 for a total of 42 teeth.

Coyotes are presently found throughout the continental US and Canada, although pre-European distribution is thought to have been only in the western half of this country. They were first reported in Georgia in the 1950s and now occur throughout the state. They have been reported on Ossabaw, Blackbeard, Sapelo, Little St. Simons, Little Cumberland, and Cumberland islands.

The most important foods of the coyote on Cumberland Island are nearly equally divided between animal and vegetable, mammals 43.7% and plant material 46.7% (Table 7). Insects ranked third, followed by other invertebrates.

Pups are subject to mortality from predation by large carnivores and starvation due to environmental conditions, but humans with rifles, traps, and poison, operating under the justification of predator control, far outdo nature in having an adverse impact on coyotes. Even in national parks, coyotes have been poisoned, trapped, and shot. Between 1907 and 1935, more than 4,000 coyotes were killed in Yellowstone National Park; they are killed on Cumberland Island as well.

Discussion. In 1989, tracks suspected to be those of a coyote were first seen on Cumberland Island. A clearly written episode of a canid catching a deer was printed in the wet sand of the beach in July of that year. The chase, the lunge, the stagger, the splash of blood, and then the chase continued, but unfortunately the track went into vegetation and was lost. Then came other deer kills, howls, and even two sightings, but after 1990, nothing. For several years canid tracks were occasionally seen, but people have dogs on the island so there was always a question. In January of 2007, a deer hunter reported seeing a coyote, in April howls were heard, and again the correct size tracks were seen in remote places. In November of 2008, a pair was finally confirmed on the island by a photograph, and the species has remained since that time.

_____. Family Canidae. **Gray Fox.** *Urocyon cinereoargenteus* (Schreber, 1775). The gray fox is a medium-sized canid with a bushy tail. Its coarse hair is grizzled and tipped with black along the center of the back; the base of the hair is tan. The tail has very coarse black guard hairs on the dorsal surface and a black tip. The belly, inside of the legs, throat, and bORDER of the upper jaw are white. Reddish brown hair covers the back of the ears, side of the neck, and lower throat. The sexes are similarly colored. The young are blackish. These foxes have sharp claws that facilitate tree climbing. Dentition is I 3/3, C 1/1, PM 4/4, M 2/3 for a total of 42 teeth. The skull is distinguishable by the prominent temporal ridges, which form a U-shape on the braincase.

The gray fox is found statewide in Georgia, but has only been reported from two of the local barrier islands, Cumberland Island and Amelia Island, Florida. It does not occur on Cumberland Island at this time.

Discussion. The occurrence of the gray fox on Cumberland Island has been accepted by some authors based on an account of the Chuck-will's-widow written by A. Sprunt Jr. and published in A. C. Bent's "Life History Series" in 1940. Four years earlier, Sprunt reported a similarly worded account of his visit to Cumberland Island but omitted seeing a fox. E. B. Chamberlain of the Charleston Museum, who accompanied Sprunt to Cumberland, did not recall seeing a fox. There is no zooarchaeological evidence to support its presence on the island. Neither Bangs (1898) nor early local records mention the animal. Ruckdeschel and Shoop (1986) suggested that Sprunt took literary license in his recollection well after the trip.

The only record from Amelia Island is a sight record, but the species has not been recorded from the state park there. A bridge connects Amelia to the mainland.

In 1990, a single specimen was collected from Drum Point Island, which is between Cumberland Island and the mainland. This supports the potential for colonization. However, because the gray fox is not found on any of the Georgia barrier islands, its permanent residence on Cumberland Island seems unlikely. Describing it as "extirpated" suggests it was deliberately eliminated.

More evidence is needed to evaluate its status as a temporary or occasional island resident.

_____. Family Ursidae. **American Black Bear**. *Ursus americanus* Pallas, 1780. This relatively small, robust, and stocky bear has small ears and eyes and a short tail. The pelage is long and heavy and generally black with a lighter muzzle and sometimes a light chest patch. The feet have five digits with nonretractible, long, strong claws and are plantigrade. Smell and hearing are keen but eyesight is poor. The dentition increases from 28 deciduous teeth to I 3/3, C 1/1, PM 4/4, M 2/3 for a total of 42 permanent teeth.

Both Bangs (1898) and Harper (1927) found the local south Georgia name for the American black bear to be "hog bear." On Cumberland Island, George Merrow said his father used to say, "There is no bad bear here, just hog bear."

Bartram, in the late 1700s, said Cumberland Island was an excellent haunt for bears (Harper, 1958) but did not mention seeing one. In the late 1800s, Bangs (1898) said they occurred on Cumberland Island. Harper (1927) reported that there were none along the St. Marys River in the vicinity of St. George for several years prior to 1921, but in the 1930s, Sprunt (1936) said bears were still present in small numbers on Cumberland Island. Two or three individuals had been released on the island fifteen to twenty years earlier. In 1948, the Carnegies acknowledged that there were no bears on the island (letter to H. B. Sherman, Carnegie collection, GDAH). There was a report of an escaped cub in 1985.

Bears have been reported between some Georgia barrier islands and the mainland (Johnson et al., 1974) and periodically on St. Catherines Island (Anderson, 1972), but none apparently resided there in recent times. J. Bailey (pers. comm.) reported one released on Sapelo Island, but it had been a pet of R. J. Reynolds and was soon shot (V. J. Henry, pers. comm.).

In the Southeast US, the black bear chooses flatwoods, hardwood swamps, bays, and gum ponds, all areas usually with thick understory and plenty of food, such as berries and mast. Seasonal food drives habitat use, but reproduction has the special requirements of isolation and security, which are significant for a large animal.

On Cumberland Island prior to 1919, J. Merrow (pers. comm.) described how a bear would steal a hog from his father's pen on the north end of the island. "The old man would get lightwood splinters and hold 'em up and try and find the bear, but [laugh] da bear just about as wise as da old man, cause he got the hog 'n gone."

Most mortality today is human related. Killing a bear has always been considered a manly feat and even in 1820 was worthy of a newspaper article. The bear killed on Cumberland Island was "a monster beyond all description" and estimated to have weighed 500 pounds (*Daily Georgian*, 28 December). In 1898, O. Bangs reported that bear on Cumberland Island were protected by the owners of the island. But the owners were hunters, and six bears were apparently killed on Cumberland between 1885 and 1911. The Carnegies released two or three after that, and three were reported killed between 1911 and 1930.

Discussion. Despite its productivity, Cumberland Island is too small to support many bears or other large predators, and it is likely that in the past, most individuals visited in appropriate seasons but did not reside on the island. Bears are known to congregate when food is plentiful, and their ability to swim and move great distances would enable them to take advantage of seasonal island resources. Food in the form of turtle eggs, alligator eggs, and fruit, such as grapes, persimmons, bay, acorns, and of course, palmetto, was seasonal.

_____. Family Procyonidae. **Raccoon**. *Procyon lotor* (Linnaeus, 1758). Most everyone is familiar with the black mask and ringed tail of the "coon," as it is locally called. It is a medium-sized, usually dark-colored animal with a thick, durable coat, especially in the winter, and a noticeably bushy tail. The overall color is variable and sometimes a light brown or almost reddish-blond individual is seen. A black "mask" camouflages the eyes by running horizontally from just above them. The belly is a light tan, which color extends down the legs and feet. Footpads are black, and there are five toes on all feet. The front paws are slender and the digits remarkably thin, finger-like, and dexterous. The gait is plantigrade, so the large hind foot makes a clear track quite distinctive. Tracks register a two-two-two pattern, with a print of the hind foot close or adjacent to the alternate front track. Raccoons are color-blind but have good night vision and good hearing. Dentition is I 3/3, C 1/1, PM 4/4, M 2/2 for a total of 40 teeth. No other carnivore has that number. On Cumberland Island it is not rare to see molars of old animals worn past the crown to pegs of the roots.

Measurements of 112 adults from Cumberland Island averaged total length 744 millimeters, tail 251, hind foot 113, and ear 57. Males averaged 13 millimeters longer in total length and 8 grams heavier in weight than females.

Raccoons occur on all the Georgia barrier islands and large marsh islands. Wooded bottomlands and hardwood swamps are preferred habitat but forested uplands and fresh and salt marshes are also used. To support a resident raccoon population, islands in the salt marsh must be large enough to have a reliable source of freshwater (groundwater) for drinking.

The catholic diet of the raccoon is well known, and coupled with the cleverness of the animal, ignores no available food resource, from farmer's fields to urban trash cans to camper's packs. Items that are commonly recorded from natural sources are crayfish, insects, and fruit, such as blackberries, persimmons, and acorns. A detailed list is lengthy. Samples of feces, stomach, and gut contents from raccoons on Cumberland Island were collected and examined beginning in 1981 and continuing through 2008. Collections were opportunistic, but because of the time scale, may present a truer picture of diet than if all were collected at one time. Environmental factors can affect availability of some items in some years. Differential digestibility is always a bias when using fecal material and should be acknowledged. On Cumberland Island, vegetable material was consumed twice as frequently as animals (Table 8). Items most important in the diet by frequency of occurrence varied by season, but the top five were: fiddler crabs, crayfish, acorns, tough bully fruit, and fruit of the greenbrier. One snake, the scarlet snake, was recorded from island raccoon stomach contents. Only fiddler crabs were eaten in all seasons. Fiddler crabs and gifts from the sea are resources not available inland on the mainland, so diets along the coast are specialized and show the adaptability of the animal.

On Cumberland Island, four seems to be the average litter size. Females accompanied by young on Cumberland Island have been noted only May through September, with the majority in July. Gestation takes sixty-three days (two months), and the altricial young remain in the den for three months.

External parasites on Cumberland Island raccoons include ticks, which at times may be numerous, a biting louse, which is extremely abundant and has been found on 95% of the island raccoons examined, a chigger, and two species of fleas. See Appendix VI. C. The individuals not supporting lice or their obvious egg cases were postpartum females. Chiggers occur infrequently.

Internal parasites of the gut are common in island raccoons and include the nematodes *Physatoptera rara* and *Gnathostoma procyonis* and the acanthocephalan *Macracanthorhynchus ingens*. The latter use the millipede, *Narceus americanus*, as an intermediate host (Crites, 1964). Adults of the cestode, *Spirometra mansoides*, live in the intestine, but the larval stages occur subcutaneously and are fairly common in island raccoons. A subcutaneous nematode also occurs, *Dranunculus insignis*, which concentrates in the lower portion of the limbs and sometimes springs out when the area is cut with a knife.

The protozoan parasite responsible for Chagas disease has been verified to occur in the local species of kissing bug, *Triatoma sanguisuga*. A test of antibodies in raccoons on St. Catherines Island revealed that 66% were seropositive for the parasite (Yabsley et al., 2001). Raccoons on Cumberland Island have also tested positive for the parasite (C. Hall, pers. comm.).

On Cumberland Island, recorded sport hunting took only forty-three from 1885 to 1923. Trapping for hides from 1924 to 1927 garnered an average of 189 per season, and the 1942 season produced 450. Presumably much more trapping occurred than what is documented, and it continued into the 1980s. There are very few ways for a caretaker to augment his income on the island, and trapping was a tradition. In 2002, a mainland resident got sixteen raccoons in one night on Cumberland Island. In the state, an average of just over 6,000 raccoons per year were taken for hides during the 2004 through 2007 season.

Young raccoons have been found in bobcat scat on the island, but they seem to be a minor part of the cat's diet. F. Whitehead (pers. comm.) saw a bobcat carrying a raccoon on the island one morning in December 1993. Another first-hand account of predation on raccoons came from Little

Cumberland Island in April of 1987. M. Kingsley said he had seen an alligator catch a raccoon in the pond adjacent to his house. The alligator's head was toward and maybe on the bank as the coon followed the edge of the pond. Raccoon carcasses have been observed floating in alligator holes, and 69% of alligator fecal samples examined from Cumberland Island contained raccoon hair.

Disease appears to be the most commonly recorded cause of natural mortality of raccoons. Canine distemper is acknowledged to be an important factor and is suspected to periodically reduce the Cumberland Island population. Confirmation of the disease, a viral infection, requires laboratory procedures, so it is not regularly verified. The symptoms, which include neurological problems, may resemble those of rabies, so care must be taken to avoid sick animals.

It is likely that alligators were/are an important factor for raccoons, not only on Cumberland Island, but throughout the Southeast US, since they will take unwary adults as well as naive youngsters. The fact that raccoons are loath to enter deep water in warm weather suggests a long association with aquatic predators.

Raccoon mortality on Cumberland Island, with all categories combined, is not constant. It peaks, then drops, and probably reflects population density. Interestingly, it was extremely low for the years 1975 to 1978 and again in 1990 to 1998. There was a population low on St. Catherines Island in 1974 to 1975, which followed a mast failure in 1974 (Lotze, 1979), but it was ultimately believed to be the result of canine distemper, which could explain the fluctuation of Cumberland Island numbers.

_____. Family Mustelidae. **Mink**. *Neovison vison* Schreber, 1777. Mink are surprisingly small animals, about the size of a large eastern gray squirrel, with females smaller and more lightweight than males. Long guard hairs overlay dense, soft underfur, which is water-repellent. Along the south Georgia coast, mink are mahogany in color when dry and darker when wet. The color naturally darkens on the head and toward the rear and blends into black on the tip of the tail. The chin is white, and the white may extend down the throat to a blotch on the chest. In typical weasel style, the body is long and further exaggerated by a long, stout neck of similar diameter. The legs and ears are short, the tail heavily furred and bushy. Their vision is better above water than below, and their hearing is acute. They can also hear ultrasonic frequencies produced by rodents. The terrestrial gait produces a slightly offset version of paired prints, and when running, repeated groups of four separate prints are clear.

Dentition is I 3/3, C 1/1, PM 3/3, M 1/2, for a total of 34 teeth, with molars lacking in the deciduous set of 28 teeth. The rear upper molars appear perpendicular to the preceding teeth, and the palate extends beyond the last molars.

In Georgia the mink is found statewide. A population decline began in the 1960s from North Carolina through Georgia, and Coastal Plain populations plummeted. Environmental contaminants, especially mercury and PCBs, were identified as the most likely causes (Osowski, 1992). Johnson et al. (1974) found specimens, literature references, or sight records for most of the Georgia Pleistocene and Holocene barrier islands, but Layne (1971) was unable to verify the occurrence of mink on Amelia Island, Florida.

Mink spend most of their time in proximity of water. Forested bottomland swamps, cattail marshes, thickets along streams, and standing water are all good habitat, as is the salt marsh of the Georgia coast. The majority of Cumberland Island sightings have been in salt or brackish water, or in the vicinity thereof, and even on the ocean beach. In dry areas of the country, populations are known to decline during droughts.

On Cumberland Island, two partial skeletons have been found away from water in a hardwood forest, suggestive of capture and consumption by an avian predator. A nine-foot, six-inch alligator found dead on the north ocean beach in March of 1987 had consumed three male mink, all of which were in different stages of digestion. At that time of year, the mink were possibly under the influence of sex hormones and less cautious than usual. Between 1885 and 1911 only six were estimated killed on the island as "game." Five have been found dead on the beach on Cumberland Island 1983 to 2001.

_____. Family Mustelidae. **North American River Otter**. *Lontra canadensis* (Schreber, 1776). This husky, short-legged, long-tailed mustelid, which may weigh up to 20 pounds, has a hydrodynamic shape, water-repellent, dense fur, ears and nostrils that can be closed in water, and fully webbed toes. It is a master swimmer. Its flattened head, with small eyes and ears near the top, allow breathing and surveillance with minimum exposure. The head blends almost imperceptibly into the unusually long neck, and it into the heavy body, with no angles or disruptive contours. The thick, short under pelage overlaid with sleek guard hairs appears to be a coat size too large for the animal, but it allows maximum contortions with minimal restraint and ultimate streamlining. These otters have been described as agile as an eel in water and as a puddle of fur on land. Their color is rich, dark brown above, which appears even darker when wet, with a lighter, more gray color on the lips and throat as high up as the eyes and ears and well down into the neck. The nose and footpads are black. All five toes on each foot are webbed and the tracks are circular and wide. Dentition is I 3/3, C 1/1, PM 4/3, M 1/2 for a total of 36 teeth. When walking on land, an alternate gait is used, but bounding and sliding are usually interspersed, so the tracks are typically in pairs. Otters rarely just stand. When forward motion stops, they usually drop to their belly.

Otters are common on the Coastal Plain and on and around all the Georgia barrier islands. Bangs (1898) said they were more common along the coast than inland. On Cumberland Island, their habitat preferences seem to change seasonally. In cooler months, when alligator activity is reduced, otters take advantage of the open freshwater of ponds and lakes and deep tidal streams, while during warm months, they are more likely to be seen in shallow water areas and high salt marshes.

Island freshwater habitats contain few fish of any size and few species; consequently, judging by feces, crayfish are the most common food taken in freshwater areas on Cumberland Island (Table 9). However, otters are not confined to inland areas so may feed in the surrounding tidal areas as well, augmenting their diet with fish and small marine crabs.

There has been sporadic trapping on Cumberland Island, but not specifically for otters. In 1974, when casting in Christmas Creek for mullet, J. Bailey (pers. comm.) had an otter dive toward him just as he threw his net. He pulled the otter in the boat and tried to kill it with a paddle, but it tore a hole in the net and escaped. "Why did you try and kill it?" I asked. He gave me a sideways glance and said, "Shoo, dat ting wort $50!"

_____. Family Felidae. **Bobcat**. *Lynx rufus* (Schreber, 1777). The bobcat is the only native mammal in the Southeast US that is spotted. The dark to black spots are most clearly defined on the white belly but occur throughout the reddish-brown coat, the general color of which may change slightly seasonally. These cats are larger than a typical house cat but smaller than an average large dog. Their four-inch tails are relatively short, sometimes banded, and the dorsal surface of the tip is black. The ears are of moderate size, usually have a noticeable extension of hair at the tip, a tuft, and the backside of each is black with an outstanding large white "eyespot." The nose is brick-reddish brown. Lengthened hair on the cheeks enlarges the appearance of the face as "burnsides." Dentition is I 3/3, C 1/1, PM 2/2, M 1/1, for a total of 28 teeth. Their track is told from that of a canid by a lack of nail impressions and from a domestic cat by size.

They are found statewide in Georgia but are not known to be resident on any of the barrier islands without bridges at this time other than Cumberland, where they have been introduced. In the past, bobcats have been recorded on Ossabaw Island (up to the mid-1950s), St. Simons Island (only after 1865), Amelia Island, Florida (tracks in the early 1970s), and on Cumberland Island in 1887, 1889, and 1893. In his study of the fauna of the Okefenokee Swamp, F. Harper (1927) included the St. Marys River water basin, which included Cumberland Island, and he consulted with a local naturalist, I. Arnow of St. Marys. Arnow told him that "the species was common on Cumberland Island up to about 1907, when some disease exterminated it there." Ten years prior, in 1897, O. Bangs, who became a curator at the Museum of Comparative Zoology at Harvard, had a field collector in the St. Marys area and on Cumberland Island who reported that he was unable to get a bobcat on Cumberland Island. He said that his conscience was clear for he had worked hard for it in all the places he visited. He even "had the crackers trapping for it..., as I offered $5.00 for it, which is a big sum to a cracker and more money than some of them ever saw. Some of the crackers took their hen coops into the woods to entice the wild cats to their traps." He collected over 100 other specimens in two weeks on the island so was indeed diligent in his efforts. The cats were apparently scarce at that time both on the island and the mainland.

In 1953, the Georgia Game and Fish Commission (Jenkins) reported that bobcat populations were common to abundant over most of the lower Coastal Plain. Between 1972 and 1989, a total of thirty-seven bobcats were released on Cumberland Island. Their origins and histories varied greatly, but all were from Georgia and Florida and most came from the lower Coastal Plain. There were eighteen males and nineteen females. As of 2012, the population seems to be doing well, and sightings of tracks, adults, and kittens are not uncommon. On Cumberland Island, tracks may be found in every habitat from the edge of the salt marsh to interior wetlands to the interdune and even out on the open beach.

On Cumberland Island, food items were identified from 128 fecal samples collected between 1989 and 2012 (Table 10). Marsh rabbits ranked highest, followed by hispid cotton rats, gray squirrels, and feral hogs. Species of birds were not identified except for one in March, a sora rail, and a "wren" in November (Feather Identification Lab, Smithsonian Institution). A broad-leafed grass occurred with 18% frequency. Vegetation is commonly ingested, some of which may be incidental to other feeding, but some, such as coarse grass, is thought to be deliberately taken as a cathartic. There are public hunts on the island for white-tailed deer and feral hogs, providing the potential for bias by scavenging cats. Hunters have seen cats attempting to steal or eat their deer carcasses awaiting pickup. The National Park Service has an ongoing program to reduce the feral hog population, and that shooting may occur at any time of year. Baker et al. (2001) found rabbit, deer, and cotton rats the principal dietary species of the cats released in 1988 and 1989, with lesser use of gray squirrels, raccoons, birds, cotton mouse, and feral hog.

Following the release of fourteen adult bobcats on Cumberland Island in 1988, four dens containing ten kittens were located in April 1989 with an average litter size of two and one-half. By December 1989, a total of thirty-two adult cats had been recently released on the island, and only one den with two kittens was located the following April. Several of the adults suffered misfortune or escaped the island, so the minimum number of adults known at that time was twenty-six, the actual number unknown. One cat from the Cumberland Island 1980s introductions was examined and it had ticks and listrophorid mites on it, cestodes and a nematode, *Trichostrongylus wilsoni*, in it.

On Cumberland Island between 1885 and January 1911 three cats were reported killed. In February of 1903, people from Cumberland Island went to Cabin Bluff on the adjacent mainland to hunt cats, suggesting very low island numbers, if any.

Discussion. The fact that bobcats are absent from most of the Georgia barrier islands at this time is interesting since it seems likely they would have occurred there or have been able to easily colonize the islands in the past. Human influence could certainly restrict distribution, but considering the low number of individuals likely to successfully inhabit each island at any one time, other possibilities are also plausible. On islands, not only is the likelihood of oscillations in the numbers of prey greater than on the mainland, but dispersal to more productive environs is not possible without leaving the island.

Another possibility is that because there would be relatively low numbers of these top-level predators naturally occurring on any island at any one time, they would be susceptible to elimination by disease. Feline panleukopenia or feline distemper is a highly contagious viral disease that is widespread in Florida and also infects mink and raccoons.

_____. Family Phocidae. **Hooded Seal.** *Cystophora cristata* (Erxleben, 1777). These large seals, with males reaching 2.7 meters (9 feet) in length and females 2 meters (6.6 feet), have baggy elastic skin on the top of their heads, which hangs limp when not inflated. Only males are able to inflate their "hoods," and do so during aggressive behavior or excitement. True seals all lack ear pinnae, have short front flippers, and the hind flippers cannot be turned forward, so locomotion out of the water is an ungainly humping. All digits possess strong claws.

These are animals of the Atlantic Arctic from Newfoundland, Baffin Island, and Greenland to Iceland. The young are recognized wanderers and have showed up as far south as Florida, Puerto Rico, and the Virgin Islands. A single animal from Bull Head Bluff on the Satilla River in Camden County was tentatively identified in the 1940s.

On 28 January 1945, a Charlton County, Georgia, judge, A. S. McQueen, wrote Dr. Francis Harper "about a seal that had been killed about three years ago...by one Damon Manning at Bull Head Bluff" on the Satilla River. He mentioned that there was an article in the *Charlton County Herald* telling of the episode (17 May 1940), which placed the killing on 5 May. On 29 December 1961, Ivan Tomkins met Mr. Manning, who reported that he had shot the seal in May about 1938 to 1940. The animal was five and one-half feet long, estimated to weigh 250 pounds, and its head was "all slicked back," which Mr. Tomkins interpreted to mean without ears. The skull was collected but ultimately lost. Colonel McQueen sent a piece of the hide to Dr. Remmington Kellogg at the United States National Museum, who tentatively identified it as a hooded seal.

_____. Family Phocidae. **Caribbean Monk Seal**. *Monachus tropicalis* (Gray, 1850). Adult Caribbean monk seals were from 2 to 2.5 meters (6.6 to 6.8 feet) in total length, and females were perhaps slightly smaller. The short hair was brownish dorsally with yellowish-white along the lower sides and on the belly. The lips were bordered with white. Pups were born with a wooly, black coat.

As the specific name suggests, these seals were tropical in distribution and ranged through the Caribbean Sea and the Gulf of Mexico. They were at the Bahamas and the Florida Keys. Remains of two individuals were found on Cumberland Island in association with aboriginal occupation estimated from 500 BC to at least AD 200. The Cumberland Island occurrence extended their known range northward. Bones found as far north as Charleston, South Carolina, are thought to have been from strays and not part of a breeding population (Timm et al., 1997).

Although these seals were historically abundant, they were easily caught and killed for their hides and oil, even by native hunting. With European exploitation came added pressure, and by the mid-nineteenth century the species was scarce. The last one recorded in the US was killed in 1922 off Key West. They are now considered extirpated.

The monk seal bones from Cumberland Island include part of a humerus and a scapula (I. R. Quitmyer, pers. comm.). Allen (1878) described the skeleton of the Caribbean monk seal as having "striking peculiarities," with the scapula very short and very broad, and the humerus short and "peculiarly formed." Curtiss Peterson, a graduate student of Dr. E. Wing, was also Florida State Archaeologist in the mid-1970s and positively identified the bones from Cumberland Island (Cumbaa, 1980). Evidence suggests that Caribbean monk seals were found along the entire Southeast US coast during the Quaternary (Ray, 1961).

_____. Family Phocidae. **Harbor Seal**. *Phoca vitulina* Linnaeus, 1758. Small, with short limbs, harbor seals have hind limbs modified for swimming and permanently turned to the rear so they cannot be brought under the animal, making movement on land awkward. They scoot themselves along inch-worm fashion and roll when convenient. Both sexes have highly variable color from yellowish-gray with dark brown spots or markings to dark with yellowish markings. They have excellent hearing and sense of smell on land and in the water. The valvular nostrils are V-shaped, and the animals lack external ear pinnae; a fold of skin covers the ear canal.

They are found worldwide, but in the western North Atlantic range from Greenland and Hudson Bay south to Long Island. The few animals to show up south of New York along the East Coast are considered strays. Caldwell and Caldwell (1969) reported the southernmost record for the species, the stranding of a young, injured animal south of Daytona Beach, Florida. One harbor seal stranded on Cumberland Island on 18 February 1984, and another young seal of unknown species was reported to have gone back in the sea on 22 February 2003.

ORDER CETACEA. Family Delphinidae. **Rough-toothed Dolphin.** *Steno bredanensis* (Cuvier, 1828). Rough-toothed dolphins may reach 2.78 meters (9 feet) total length and have a long, narrow snout or beak that is laterally compressed. The forehead slopes directly to the rostrum with no separation by a transverse groove, as in the bottlenose dolphin. The color is gray or black on the dorsal surface with spots or splotches of white along the lower sides and a white belly. The eyes and flippers are relatively large. A confirming specific characteristic is the sandpaper-like fine vertical wrinkles on the lateral surfaces of the teeth, from which the common name is derived.

In the western North Atlantic, rough-toothed dolphins occur from Virginia south to the West Indies, northeast South America, and the Gulf of Mexico. This species prefers deep waters, staying well offshore, usually beyond the outer continental shelf. They often frequent deep water near islands. Two decomposing carcasses were found on Little Cumberland Island in March 1971 (Richardson, 1973), and in July 2003 seventeen animals stranded on Jekyll Island to the north.

_____. Family Delphinidae. **Pygmy Killer Whale.** *Feresa attenuata* Gray 1874. This small, fairly rare member of the dolphin family reaches a total length of 2.4 to 2.7 meters (8 to 9 feet). It has a rounded forehead (melon) with no beak. The dorsal fin, located midway on the back, is large, usually 20.3 to 30.1 centimeters (8 to 12 inches) tall or greater. Dark gray or black, this species also has irregular but sharply contrasting white areas on the lips, chin, and lower abdomen to the anal region. A groove runs from mid-body to the anus on the ventral surface. They have ten to thirteen relatively large, conical teeth per side in the upper and lower jaws.

In the western North Atlantic, pygmy killer whales range from North Carolina south to the Lesser Antilles and the Gulf of Mexico. A gregarious species, they usually travel in groups of five to ten, but at times hundreds have been seen together.

Two stranded on Cumberland Island and eleven along the entire Georgia coast between 1977 and 2006. The two island specimens were both adult males with empty gastrointestinal tracts, and their teeth were worn and broken. One had flattened parasitic worms associated with the hyoid connection, likely a sinus fluke.

_____. Family Delphinidae. **Short-finned Pilot Whale.** *Globicephala macrorhynchus* Gray 1846. Male short-finned pilot whales are slightly larger than females and may reach a total length of 6 meters (20 feet), females 5.2 meters (17 feet). Mostly black, they have gray on the throat and a variable patch on the belly. The forehead or melon in females is rounded and full but streamlined. In older adult males, prominent bulges on either side of the melon may give the forehead a squared or flattened appearance from the front. The front of the mouth protrudes a bit but not enough to be called a beak. Stout teeth number seven to nine per row in the upper and lower jaws. The falcate dorsal fin is situated anterior to the middle of the back. The common name derives from their tendency to follow a leader, which is usually an old bull.

In the western North Atlantic they range from about New Jersey and Bermuda south to Venezuela, the Gulf of Mexico, the Caribbean, and the West Indies, with long-finned pilot whales distributed farther north. These whales prefer deep water, usually seaward of the continental slope. Their intelligence and agreeability inspired the navy to train some animals.

Cumberland Island experienced one mass stranding of fifteen individuals in February of 1977. Records of mass strandings (more than one or two animals) go back to Aristotle, yet the primary cause remains unknown. Animals stranded on Cumberland Island had parasites in their sinuses. Infections by nematodes and trematodes in the air sinuses and brain causing degeneration of the eighth cranial nerve, neuropathy, have been suggested as possible causes, as have anomalies in the local geomagnetic field, storms, and echolocation problems.

_____. Family Delphinidae. **Spinner Dolphin**. *Stenella longirostris* Gray 1828. This slender, streamlined animal reaches a maximum length of 2.1 meters (7 feet). Its dorsal surface is dark gray to black, which transitions abruptly to tan or yellowish brown on the sides, which in turn sharply changes to white on the belly. The dorsal surface of the long snout, including the tip and the lips, is black, the throat light. The snout length is relatively long but variable. A noticeable black stripe runs from the eye to the flipper. The triangular dorsal fin is situated mid-body and is a lighter color in the center than on the edges. This species has more teeth than any of its congeners, 46 to 65 per row.

Spinner dolphins are infrequent in warm temperate waters, preferring deep tropical to subtropical water far out to sea or areas close to oceanic islands. In the western Atlantic, they occur from Virginia south into the Caribbean and Gulf of Mexico. Their common name derives from the habit of leaping above the water and spinning on their longitudinal axis. They may make two full revolutions before splashing back into the sea.

There were four strandings on Cumberland Island in 1997 and 1998. Spinner dolphins infrequently strand, and the four Cumberland Island records all occurred within two months, from 18 December 1997 through 19 February 1998. All carcasses were badly decomposed and may have washed in from a great distance. The grouping of the incidents could suggest a common problem.

_____. Family Delphinidae. **Atlantic Spotted Dolphin**. *Stenella frontalis* (Cuvier, 1829). Atlantic spotted dolphins reach an adult total length of about 1.7 to 2.3 meters (5.6 to 7.5 feet), with a tall falcate dorsal fin and a long, relatively thin beak. The dorsal surface of the Atlantic spotted dolphin is dark with light grayish or white spots. The pattern reverses on the light belly and the spots become dark. Spots on the light gray sides are intermediate; the degree of spotting is variable. Calves are unspotted at birth. The eye is ringed with black, which extends to the melon and rostrum. A broad, dark stripe runs from the gape of the mouth to the flipper, with a dark "cape" on the top of the head. The upper and lower lips are white or light. There are 32 to 42 teeth per row in the upper jaw and 30 to 40 in the lower.

Atlantic spotted dolphins are best known from the West Indies but are endemic to the warm, temperate, and tropical waters of both the North and South Atlantic. These gregarious, deep-water animals usually travel in small groups of five to thirty, sometimes up to 100 individuals, but most often one to fifteen, along the continental shelf within 155 to 217 miles of the coast.

They generally occur in water 65 to 164 feet deep. Five strandings have occurred on Cumberland Island between 1993 and 2007.

_____. Family Delphinidae. **Atlantic White-sided Dolphin.** *Lagenorhynchos acutus* (Gray, 1828). This robust dolphin has a tall, broad-based, pointed dorsal fin, a short but distinct beak, and a bold color pattern. The dorsal surface is black, including the upper beak and flippers, the sides are streaked with zones of gray, tan, and white, and the lower jaw and belly are white. Atlantic white-sided dolphins may reach a total length of 2.8 meters (9 feet). The conical teeth number 29 to 40 in the upper jaw and 31 to 38 in the lower.

This species occurs only in the North Atlantic Ocean. The southern limit of their range along the East Coast is usually considered North Carolina. These fast-swimming animals typically occur in groups of fifty to sixty, which mostly remain offshore in temperate to subarctic waters. Some mortality occurs as bycatch from commercial fishing activities using gill nets and trawls.

There has been one stranding on Cumberland Island. A juvenile, male Atlantic white-sided dolphin, total length 165 centimeters, stranded alive on Cumberland Island on 26 February 2011. Attempts were made to put it back in the water but the animal was unable to swim, so was euthanized by DNR.

_____. Family Delphinidae. **Bottlenose Dolphin.** *Tursiops truncatus* (Montague, 1821). Adult bottlenose dolphins may reach a robust 3.7 meters (12 feet) total length and have a clearly defined snout. The snout is relatively short compared to other delphinids and has a groove around the base. The intensity of the gray-black color is variable, shading from dark on the dorsal surface to light on the sides and white on the belly. The dorsal fin is prominent, rather pointed at the tip, and located in the middle of the back, and the flukes have a clear median notch. There are 20 to 28 teeth in each upper and lower row. The sexes may be differentiated externally by the number of abdominal openings. Males have two openings, the anterior one into which the penis retracts and behind it the anal opening. Females have a single opening which serves the urinary, vaginal, and anal apertures. On each side is a short crease that conceals a teat.

Bottlenose Dolphins occur in two morphological types, a small, shallow-water, coastal form and a large offshore form with a proportionately shorter snout and pectoral flippers (Hersh, 1987). The offshore form may be

15% larger than its coastal counterpart and differ in distribution, skull morphology, food habits, parasites (Mead and Potter, 1995), and nuclear and mitochondrial genetic markers (Hoelzel et al., 1998). The common inshore populations use estuaries and shallow bays and are usually less than three to six miles from land. They may ascend freshwater rivers. The larger, offshore animals frequent pelagic waters to the edge of the continental shelf and beyond.

In the Southeast US, the bottlenose dolphin is referred to as a "porpoise." The names are used interchangeably in the vernacular although scientifically there are classification distinctions.

Bottlenose dolphins are distributed worldwide in tropical and temperate waters, roughly between latitudes 45°N to 45°S. This is the most common species of marine mammal in the vicinity of Cumberland Island. The larger offshore form may range to Newfoundland and Greenland.

Some bottlenose groups are resident and some transient (Gubbins, 2002).

Whether out of playfulness or for protection of young, these porpoises have been known to chase a large American alligator to the bank of a river and toss him ashore (Lyell, 1849). Because of their intelligence and strength, bottlenose dolphins are trained by the US Navy to work in underwater security and have been employed at the Kings Bay facility opposite Cumberland Island on the mainland.

A total of twenty nursing young stranded on Cumberland Island between 1974 and 1991. December was the month with the greatest number (seven) of stranded young and winter the season with the most (ten), followed by spring and autumn. No nursing young have come ashore during the summer months, June through August.

The large tapeworm *Diphyllobothrium* sp. was identified in a Cumberland Island stranding. The barnacle *Xenobalanus* sp. is frequently attached to the trailing edge of the flukes in stranded animals, and amphipods in the family Cyamidae, whale lice, have been recovered on Cumberland Island.

There are several references to shooting porpoises in a diary kept on Sapelo Island, Georgia, in the 1870s, and mention of greasing a new sailboat mast with porpoise oil (Humphries, 1991). Another more recent report said residents on Sapelo Island shot these dolphins when they came up in the shallow creeks and rendered their oil to use on cattle (J. Bailey, pers. comm.). The primary threats in US waters today are from interactions with commercial fishing gear, such as trawl nets and gill nets, and pollution. Bottlenose dolphins are the marine mammals that most frequently strand on Cumberland Island. From 1974 through 2008, 192 carcasses were documented.

_____. Family Physeteridae. **Pygmy Sperm Whale.** *Kogia breviceps* (Blainville, 1838). Prior to 1966, this relatively small whale, total length 2.7 to 3.4 meters (9 to 12 feet), was not distinguished from the dwarf sperm whale, *K. sima*, which confuses early data. Nursing *K. breviceps* calves may be almost as large as adult *K. sima*. Pygmy sperm whales have a short, blunt head with an inferior mouth located back from the tip of the snout. The jaw is narrow with 12 to 16 teeth that resemble large dog canines on each side of the lower jaw; teeth in the upper jaw are lacking. Much of the bone of the mandible is almost paper thin.

The dorsal surface of the animal is dark gray and the belly light to white. A key characteristic separating the pygmy from the dwarf sperm whale is the position and size of the dorsal fin. The dorsal fin of the pygmy sperm whale is small and set to the rear of the body's midpoint. Dwarf sperm whales have a relatively large and more centered dorsal fin. Pygmy sperm whales feed on cephalopods, the beaks of which are common in the stomachs of stranded animals on Cumberland Island.

Pygmy sperm whales occur in all tropical and temperate seas of the world. Strandings show no seasonal pattern in Florida or Georgia. The only month with no strandings on Cumberland Island was February (1974 to 2009). Four cow/calf pairs have stranded on Cumberland Island. In March 1978, the calf measured 193.5 centimeters total length; in June 1978 the length was about 120 centimeters with a weight estimated at 23 to 34 kilograms (50 to 75 pounds); in August 1998, 119.8 centimeters; and in December 1997, the calf had a total length of 140 centimeters. The teeth had not erupted on animals ≤140 centimeters total length.

A parasite encysted in the blubber has been common in Cumberland Island strandings, and most adults have nematodes in the stomach. Long nematodes are fairly common in the neck musculature, and one animal on Cumberland Island had flukes in the liver.

Several individuals stranded on Cumberland Island have had broken lower jaws, the cause of which has been attributed to intraspecific fighting. One female pygmy sperm whale had fatally extruded her reproductive tract, which also could have attracted sharks. None stranded on Cumberland Island have had plastic in their stomachs, but that seems to be a continuing problem for this species throughout its range.

_____. Family Physeteridae. **Dwarf Sperm Whale.** *Kogia sima* (Owen, 1866). Taxonomy. Handley (1966) separated the two species of *Kogia* into the dwarf sperm whale, *K. simus*, and the pygmy, *K. breviceps*. Rice (1998) corrected the grammatical gender agreement of the genus and species of the dwarf, leaving the proper scientific name *K. sima*.

The dwarf sperm whale resembles a miniature pygmy sperm whale. Adult dwarf sperm whales attain a maximum total length of 2.7 meters (8.8 feet), slightly overlapping the minimum length for an adult pygmy sperm whale. The dorsal fin of the dwarf is situated near the middle of the back and is tall and curved, much like that of a porpoise. Visible teeth, sharp and numbering eight to eleven on each side, occur in the lower jaw only, and all resemble canines of a shepherd-sized puppy. One author described them as reminiscent of python teeth.

The range of the two *Kogia* species overlaps, with worldwide distribution in temperate and tropical seas. On Cumberland Island, this species strands throughout the year (1973 to 2008), offering no pattern. Stomach contents of animals stranded on Cumberland Island consist mostly of squid beaks, with some pelagic crabs and few fish. As with pygmy sperm whales, the dwarf basks at the surface and also ejects a cloud of specialized waste material when threatened, presumably to act as camouflage for escape. Cardiomyopathy has been diagnosed in Florida strandings of the dwarf sperm whale as well as the pygmy.

One pregnant female was recorded on Cumberland Island on 14 March 1991. Her total length was 2.4 meters and the well-formed fetus measured 38 centimeters total length.

The two species of *Kogia* share habitat and their ranges overlap. Handley (1966) stated that the two species had never been taken at the same time or from the same net yet they occurred along the same coasts. In March of 1991, amid a spate of marine mammal strandings on Cumberland Island, two dwarf sperm whales, a pregnant female and a juvenile male, came ashore the same day as a pygmy sperm whale. The cause of the strandings was not determined.

_____. Family Ziphiidae. **Blainville's Beaked Whale.** *Mesoplodon densirostris* (Blainville, 1817). Blainville's beaked whale, or the dense-beaked whale, may reach a total length of 5.2 meters (17 feet). The color on the dorsal surface is black, which fades to a light gray on the abdomen, and they may be blotched with lighter areas. The flukes are dark above and light below. There are two V-shaped grooves on the throat, with perhaps a slight indentation in the middle of the trailing edge of the flukes, but no real notch, and the rather small dorsal fin is situated behind the midpoint of the back. The flippers are small and located low on the side. The most distinguishing feature of this species is its perpetual "grin" when viewed from the side. The location of the teeth in the jaw is a key characteristic for species identification. At the rear of the mouth, just before the gape, the lower jaw makes a graceful arch upward in the female, and in the male it continues up to a disproportionately large prominence bearing a single tooth. In this species it is the only pair of teeth that become well developed, and only do so in the male. The teeth are exposed when the jaw is closed and are used only for defense. In the female, they never erupt. With no teeth effective for feeding, this species uses suction to capture squid and other cephalopods.

Blainville's beaked whale occurs worldwide in warm temperate and tropical seas. In the Western Atlantic they have stranded from Nova Scotia south to Florida and along the Gulf of Mexico. One female, who had never given birth, stranded on Cumberland Island in March 1978 and is the only record of this species for the state.

The most significant mortality recorded has been the mass strandings that occurred coincidental with navy use of mid-frequency sonar and airgun arrays, both of which are apparently used worldwide respectively for defense and subbottom profiling. The difficulty in locating and observing this species hinders determining the actual impact of these techniques.

_____. Family Ziphiidae. **Gervais' Beaked Whale.** *Mesoplodon europaeus* (Gervais, 1855). Female Gervais' beaked whales reach a length of 4.5 to 4.8 meters (14.8 to 5.7 feet) and males may attain 5.2 meters (17 feet). The small dorsal fin sits well behind the midpoint of the back in the midlumbar region. Small pectoral flippers fit in depressions on either side of the thorax, perhaps enhancing swimming. Overall, the animal appears slightly laterally compressed. The dark gray to black back, sides, and flanks become lighter on the belly. The wide flippers and wide, pointed flukes are dark above and light below. Females are light around their genital slit and mammary folds.

There are two long grooves on the throat between the mandibles. The single pair of laterally compressed teeth, exposed only on males and only in the lower jaw, erupt a third of the way from the tip to the gape. The exposed teeth have reciprocal grooves in the upper jaw into which they fit. No teeth erupt in the female. The location of the teeth in the mandible is a key characteristic for the species.

In the western North Atlantic, Gervais' beaked whales range from New York and New Jersey south to Florida, the Gulf of Mexico, and the Caribbean. This species inhabits deep water in the tropical and warm temperate waters of the Atlantic Ocean. They may frequent areas closer to shore during calving season.

Two females have stranded on Cumberland Island, both in 1982, with just three recorded along the Georgia coast 1977 to 2006. Only one of the specimens that stranded on Cumberland Island was fresh enough for a thorough necropsy. The young female, total length 2.5 meters (8.2 feet), appeared in good health but had an empty gut. A six-by-four-inch plug of vegetation was lodged in the esophagus about half way to the stomach. The surrounding tissue was necrotic. With no teeth effective for feeding, they use suction to capture their prey.

Family Ziphiidae. **Cuvier's Beaked Whale.** *Ziphius cavirostris* Cuvier, 1823. The robust goosebeaked or Cuvier's whale may reach 6.7 meters (22 feet) total length, with females slightly larger than males. The short beak blends smoothly into the sloping forehead with no bulging melon. This species has a single pair of grooves on the throat and a single blowhole. The two teeth, located at the tip of the beak in the lower jaw only, usually occur only in males. The 15-inch-high dorsal fin sits to the rear, well behind midback. The color varies from rust brown and slate gray to fawn-colored, with frequent white or off-white splotches, especially toward the rear. Adult males usually have white on the head and upper back and are frequently scarred, apparently from intraspecific fighting.

Cuvier's beaked whales range worldwide in temperate and tropical seas. This is a decidedly deep-water species, with poorly known habits. Most data have come from strandings. One specimen was collected from Cumberland Island about 1961, and one from Little Cumberland Island in January 1968 (Neuhauser and Ruckdeschel, 1978).

_____. Family Balaenopteridae. **Humpback Whale**. *Megaptera novaeangliae* (Borowski, 1781). Humpbacks are large baleen whales reaching more than 15.2 meters (50 feet) in length, colored black above with white bellies. The flippers, the largest of any cetacean, extend nearly one-third of the body length, white below with a varying degree of white on the leading edge and upper surface, and sometimes all white. The leading edge of the flipper is knobby and irregular. The underside of the flukes is white. The small dorsal fin is variably shaped and sits well behind the center of the back, frequently situated atop a "hump" especially noticeable when the animal dives. It is from this feature the common name is derived.

Humpbacks occur worldwide in all oceans. In the North Atlantic they range from Iceland and Greenland to the Caribbean, West Indies, and Venezuela.

A floating carcass, found off Cumberland Island and towed ashore on 31 January 2000 by the University of Georgia to collect the skeleton, was a juvenile with a total length of 884 centimeters (29 feet). The flipper measured 8.8 feet long with a maximum width of 1.8 feet. Another juvenile (TL 895 centimeters) stranded on 3 March 2011. No island strandings have been necropsied.

The species is now listed as endangered. With direct harvest controlled, they remain vulnerable to entanglement in commercial fishing gear.

_____. Family Balaenidae. **Northern Right Whale**. *Eubalaena glacialis* (Borowski, 1781). These robust large whales average 12 to 16 meters (40 to 55 feet) total length with the head composing from a quarter to a third of that length. The dorsal surface is black and there may be gray areas on the belly and throat. Cornified patches of light-colored skin called callosities occur on the head, even on newborns. They are located above the eyes, behind the blowhole, and along the lower jaw. Their arrangement varies, allowing individual identification. The upper jaw is highly arched to accommodate the long baleen, which is slightly over seven feet and extremely fine. The lower lip is large and fleshy. As with all baleen whales, the blowhole is divided into two separate channels, making the right whale's "blow" a distinctive "V." There are no throat grooves. The flippers are short and broad, and a dorsal fin is lacking. The angular flukes have pointed tips and a deep notch.

In the western North Atlantic, the northern right whale seasonally ranges from eastern Canada to the Southeast US. Specialized habitat use has been recognized for feeding and breeding and as a nursery for calving. The most important feeding habitats are in the Northeast US and southeast Canadian waters along the continental shelf. Coastal Georgia and northeast Florida waters, from the Altamaha River, Georgia, south to Sebastian Inlet, Florida, are considered critical nursery habitat, with most use occurring within five to fifteen miles of shore. Pregnant females head south each winter to the warmer waters of coastal Georgia and northeast Florida where they have their young. In the past it is likely that naturally protected sounds and bays of the area were used. The precise wintering ground of males and off-season females is unknown.

One newborn right whale stranded alive on Cumberland Island on 3 January 1989 with no mother in sight the entire time. The calf was 407 centimeters (13 feet) total length and had a freshly torn umbilicus. Because of its rarity, the carcass was transported to the New England Aquarium in Boston where a through necropsy was performed. On 2 December 2000, a right tympanic bulla of a juvenile right whale was found at the wrack line on the island. It was sand-worn and not a fresh specimen.

Discussion. According to early Spanish accounts, natives hunted whales along the US Southeast coast during the winter. They went out in canoes, lassoed the animal, climbed aboard its back and drove wooden stakes into its nostrils to suffocate it. Besides butchering the animal for food, they removed two bones from the head, presumably auditory bullae, which were implicated with their burials and worship (Larson, 1980). The capture was done in shallow water to reduce chances for escape, and calves were mentioned. While it is likely that northern right whales ventured into relatively shallow, protected sounds along the coast to calve and nurse young, especially with supporting evidence like the Spanish name for St. Andrews Sound being the Bay of Whales, getting a rope over the "neck" of a right whale and remaining "astride" it while it dove, however shallow the water, requires a stretch of imagination. Allen (1916) described one Spanish account as "an absurd relation...of a supposed method of capturing whales by the Indians of Florida," and Swanton (1946) agreed, rejecting the idea. Elliott (1943) related an identical capture method used by the Timucuan people for manatees. And Baughman (1946) quoted a 1525 Spanish account that described a "certain stone or rather bone in the head [of the manatee] within the brain, which is of a quality greatly appropriate against the disease of the stone."

When asked if he ever saw whales, Josie Merrow, born on Cumberland Island in 1902, replied that in the early 1950s he trawled for shrimp off St. Augustine beach.

> seen 'em out there when I was fishing. One come as close to me as from here to that house over there [about 15 meters; 50 feet.]. Oh boy, when he put that tail up...water from it rocked the boat and I was scared. If he'd a got up in my cables, he would have sunk my boat. So I just swung right hard around and wind up all my net. Look like he's determined to follow the boat. After we got the net up, he went straight out, and as far as I could see him, he's blowin that water up 'n flashing that tail. I guess his tail must have been as wide as this house [about 12 meters; 40 feet]. Oh, that's the biggest thing I most ever seen. Every once in a while we see 'em out there.

While the species Josie saw is unknown, it could have been a northern right whale.

ORDER SIRENIA. Family Trichechidae. **West Indian Manatee.** *Trichechus manatus* Linnaeus, 1758. The West Indian manatee is a large, rotund, bloated-looking, fully aquatic, herbivorous mammal with front limbs adapted as flippers and rear limbs absent. The eyes are small with a nictitating membrane, and ear pinnae are lacking. The front of the snout is flattened, with the upper lip cleft and studded with stiff, worn vibrissae. The two valvular nostrils are separated. The continually replaced series of cheek teeth number from three to ten in each jaw. As the worn anterior ones are lost, they are replaced with new ones at the posterior end of the row as they move forward. Only five to seven are functional at any one time. The dorsoventrally compressed, broad, spatulate tail is used for propulsion and as a rudder. The color is gray in the adults and darker in infants. The total length of adults is from 250 to 450 centimeters (8.2 to 14.8 feet), with females slightly heavier and longer than males. Their bones are extremely dense and no marrow cavities are formed in the ribs or long bones. This increases specific gravity and makes them neutrally buoyant. The otic bullae are large and dense, contributing to exceptional hearing. Females accompanied by young have been seen around Cumberland Island in summer and early autumn.

During warm weather and at their maximum distributional range, West Indian manatees may be found from Virginia south along the coast. The northern limit of their winter range is north Florida and extreme south Georgia.

Water temperature has a great influence on range and habitat use. During warm weather, manatees inhabit the coastal zone, including rivers, lagoons, estuaries, bays, and open water east of the barrier islands. They prefer water at least six to seven feet in depth and move freely between marine and freshwater habitats. They do not drink saltwater, so freshwater habitats are important, especially to nursing calves (Oritz and Worthy, 2006). As water temperature seasonally drops, manatees move to warm-water areas, which were historically provided by naturally warm springs, such as the Crystal River in Florida. Power plants have since augmented warm water options, allowing some animals to overwinter farther north. During warm months, manatees may be seen in many of the tidal creeks on the west side of Cumberland Island and are frequently seen at Dungeness dock. Local sightings have occurred in all seasons, with most during the summer.

Manatees are herbivorous and eat a variety of freshwater and marine plant species. Georgia water is too turbid for sea grass, so here they make use of benthic algae, such as *Ulva* sp., which they have been observed grazing off floating docks (Zoodsma, 1991), and marsh grass. As opportunists, they make use of bank vegetation as well as submerged, emergent, and floating species.

Southeastern aboriginals hunted manatees for food, hides, and oil. The Seminole called them "big beaver," no doubt for the shape of their tails as well as the taste of the meat. Today, the most frequent cause of manatee death is an encounter with a powerboat, which usually kills from impact trauma rather than propeller wounds. A greater percentage of adults are killed by human-related actions than by natural threats, and because of their low reproductive potential, high adult survivorship is essential. Strandings on Cumberland Island (1978 to 2007) have occurred in every season, with the most during the spring and summer, March through August.

Discussion. An exhaustive presentation of accounts of early explorers describing "whale hunting" by Southeastern Indians was made by Larson (1980). The "whale" Larson proposed was the northern right whale, which comes south to the Georgia-Florida area in the winter to calve and breed. Preponderant evidence, however, supports the West Indian manatee as a much more likely candidate. Manatees have a more discrete head over which to throw a lasso and a more "rideable" back, plus the manatee species in Brazil was still hunted in the 1970s in the same manner described for the "whale" by the early explorers. Capturing manatees during the winter while they were congregated at a warm water spring makes sense. It was not until the first half of the 1800s that manatees were scientifically separated from whales, meaning that manatees were called "whales" in the early accounts.

ORDER ARTIODACTYLA. Family Cervidae. **White-tailed Deer.** *Odocoileus virginianus* (Zimmerman, 1780). Deer are large mammals, the size of which varies geographically, with long slim legs, two narrow, pointed hooves on each foot, and the males have antlers during breeding season. They are the only remaining representative of the order in the state and are not likely to be confused with any other native animal.

Color aberrations are usually white, but true albinos are rare. More common are white patches, piebald, or entirely white animals with brown eyes and black noses and hooves. Many white and piebald deer have been documented on Cumberland Island (Fig. 31).

During breeding season usually only the males have antlers. Antlers differ from "horns" in being branched, shed annually, and have no epidermal covering except during development, which is called "velvet." In their final form, antlers are extensions of the frontal bones of the skull and consist of solid bone. At the conclusion of each annual breeding season, known as "rutting," as the level of testosterone diminishes, a separation layer develops between the pedicel on the skull and the antler and the antler soon drops off. Size of the antler is determined somewhat by age but more by nutrition; the number of points do not necessarily reveal age. On Cumberland Island, bucks are in velvet June through early August, the antlers are ready for use in September, and begin to drop off in January. White-tail dentition is I 0/3, C 0/0, PM 3/0, M 3/3 for a total of 32 teeth.

White-tails occur on all of the Georgia barrier islands except Little St. Simons Island. Although deer are adaptable, they prefer edge or early successional stage habitats rather than undisturbed forest. Open land, swamps, thickets, and especially bottomland hardwoods offer the highest quality forage for them. On Cumberland Island, deer may be found in all habitats.

Deer evolved to be able to take advantage of select woody browse, but they also graze herbaceous species. Acorns, where they are available, are a concentrated energy source and are the food most often selected in autumn. On Cumberland Island, deer must compete for resources with two species of feral livestock as well as native species. What impact that has on their overall diet is unknown. Usually acorns and other fruit replace tender spring browse in the latter part of the year, but competition is stiff for those resources. Other island foods include several wetland species, rushes, arrowhead or duck potato, frogbit, mallow, and pickerelweed, and on higher ground, Hercules club and palmetto and persimmon fruit. Mushrooms, some species of lichen, and fallen mistletoe are also eaten. The latter is said to be especially relished. On the beach in summer, railroad vine is sometimes eaten, along with many herbaceous interdune species.

They are excellent swimmers and may be seen in Georgia tidal creeks swimming between marsh islands. A local person said in 1981 that "old timers used to see 12 to 15 at a time swimming the river at Plum Orchard towards the mainland" (J. B. Peeples, pers. comm.).

The peak of breeding season on Cumberland Island, based on gonad production (Miller, 1988), is from mid-September through early December. The earliest observation date for a fawn is late March, and the latest date for a tiny spotted fawn is 11 September, and a spotted fawn with no size given, 22 January. Twins are unusual on Cumberland Island.

Parasites found on white-tailed deer on Cumberland Island include ticks, a mite, a chigger, several species of biting lice, a ked (louse fly), and a head maggot. See Appendix VI C. The most infectious disease they experience in the Southeast is hemorrhagic disease. It is caused by a virus transmitted by the bite of a midge of the genus *Culicoides*, and cases have been reported from the Georgia barrier islands.

The most important arthropod parasite affecting white-tailed deer on the barrier islands prior to the 1960s was the screwworm. It was said to reduce populations by as much as 75% in some years. The female fly deposits eggs near an open wound, such as a scratch or tick bite, and the larvae, which cannot penetrate intact skin, feed on the raw tissue, enlarging the wound and causing secondary infection. Umbilical cords of newborns are popular sites for infestation and cause considerable mortality. The larvae pupate on the ground and the cycle is complete.

The screwworm fly is tropical to subtropical and endemic to Mexico and Central America. It is killed by freezing or near freezing temperatures and can survive winters in south Florida and spread north seasonally. The species is thought to have been restricted to the Southwest US and accidently introduced to the Southeast by importation of animals in 1933. If that is the case, it had little effect on the natural history of Southeastern mammals, except during the brief period following its introduction until its eradication in 1959. Deer on the coastal islands were said to have had serious infestations (Osborne et al., 1992) and on Cumberland it was mentioned as being "active" in November of 1936 and "very bad" in August of 1949.

One female white-tailed deer on Cumberland Island, estimated to be six years old, was determined to have invasive meningioma. Meningiomas are rarely diagnosed in deer and appear to be an individual problem.

Anthropogenic manipulations have greatly altered mortality factors for deer on Cumberland Island and the mainland. Of the present mortality factors, hunting is primary, but the occurrence of coyotes may eventually change that. Less than forty deer a year were killed on Carnegie land on Cumberland Island during the period 1885 to 1950. The number taken annually on the north end is unknown, but presumably equaled that of the south end for a total of about eighty deer a year for the entire island. The National Park Service public deer hunts began in 1980, and during the following ten years, an average of 112 per year were killed. That number dropped to less than forty per year during the next decade. All numbers are minimal and only provided to give a rough measure of hunting pressure on the island. On the mainland, collisions with automobiles are an important factor, but on Cumberland Island only four deaths between 1978 and 2008 can be positively attributed to autos.

Deer have few natural predators now, which on the island include alligators, coyotes, and introduced bobcats. Since the coyotes have become established only recently, judging their impact on the island deer population must be delayed. Elsewhere, coyotes are considered the primary cause of mortality of fawns less than seven months of age and are judged significant deer predators. Bobcats are considered a minor factor in deer predation. Alligators have long been overlooked as major predators in the Southeast, but on Cumberland Island, before the introduction of bobcats and the colonization by coyotes, they were the primary predators on deer, other than humans. In a study of Cumberland Island alligator diets, deer were found to compose 10% of the species identified (Shoop and Ruckdeschel, 1990). The alligator population has been reduced for many years, not only on Cumberland Island, but also in the entire Southeast, so in the recent past, deer have escaped much predation pressure.

Discussion. Authors repeatedly suggest that there is limited nutritious food for deer on the barrier islands (Allen, 1948; Osborne et al., 1992;

LaGory et al., 1991), but how many islands are free of feral competitors to give a true picture of the diet available to deer? Even horses eat acorns.

The size of deer varies with latitude, with smaller animals occurring nearest the equator. On Cumberland Island, the deer are noticeably smaller than those from New York state or New England, where the Carnegies were familiar with them. It is not surprising then that "a number of deer from the North" were released on the island in 1898, probably with the intent of increasing the size of island animals (newspaper article [private collection], 1898). In 1993, an island caretaker released a fawn from Jekyll, but its survival is unknown. State restocking programs in the Southeast released more than 32,000 deer between 1890 and 1971 to reestablish populations mostly north of the Coastal Plain. This genetic scrambling, coupled with the swimming inclination and ability of deer, makes it highly unlikely that the original genetic composition of coastal island populations has remained intact.

On Cumberland Island, observations on deer density, fawn success, age structure of the population, diet, and general natural history cannot be put in true perspective because of the modified conditions existing there. Human-modified habitat, be it by agriculture, fire manipulation, or feral livestock, confounds typical environmental perturbations, and hunting changes the age structure of the population, all of which alter "natural conditions." On islands, where environmental conditions are exaggerated, deer and other mammal populations naturally fluctuate, which filters the gene pool to produce individuals best fit for their particular situation. Where population fluctuations are eliminated or greatly dampened, the species affected are at a disadvantage and may suffer in the long run.

ORDER RODENTIA. Family Sciuridae. **Eastern Gray Squirrel.** *Sciurus carolinensis* Gmelin, 1788. This is a small to medium-sized animal with the dorsal surface an almost uniform grizzled brown-gray, although color in the group as a whole is variable. O. Bangs (1898) commented that the squirrels on Cumberland Island were "peculiar" and unlike those taken elsewhere along the Georgia coast, based on color and some measurements. There is a bright tan to reddish brown ring around the eye and the same color on the dorsal surface of the feet. The throat and belly are white, frequently with parallel longitudinal streaks of gray, brown, or reddish brown extending from mid-chest to groin between the two rows of four mammae each. Another longitudinal line of reddish color may occur along the grizzled brown-gray at the junction with the white ventral surface. A noticeable patch of cottony, white fur sometimes occurs at the base of the ears, and the long hair tipped in light color on the tail extends laterally, producing a flattened appearance that equals or surpasses the width of the body. It is not uncommon to see an individual on Cumberland Island whose tail appears carrot red when backlit by the sun. The tail is often held over the body when the animal is feeding and inspired the generic name which in Greek means "shade tail." A type of vascular heat-exchange system has been identified at the base of the tail so it may be used anatomically as well as physically for thermoregulation (Koprowski, 1994).

Average measurements for island animals, sexes combined, were: total length 418.3 millimeters, tail 179.7, hind foot 57.1, ear 27.3. Skull measurements: average length 57.4 millimeters, average width 32.1. The number of animals available for measurements was influenced by the method of collection, which was "salvage" and many times roadkills. Dentition is I 1/1, C 0/0, PM 2/1, M 3/3, which equals a total of 22 teeth. The average length of the maxillary tooth row was 15.1 millimeters. Sixteen species of external parasites have been identified on island gray squirrels. See Appendix VI. C.

The eastern gray squirrel is found throughout the state of Georgia, and occurs naturally on some of the Pleistocene core (older) barrier islands, including Cumberland Island. Tomkins (1965) reported that it was not native on Tybee, Wassaw, Ossabaw, Blackbeard, Sapelo, or Little Cumberland islands, but it has been introduced on all but Little Cumberland. The first report of a gray squirrel on Little Cumberland Island was in January 1989, and they have since been found in bobcat scat from that island. Gray squirrels are also presently on Amelia Island, Florida.

Distribution of this species correlates closely with that of deciduous forests, including bottomlands with thick ground cover and a diverse woody understory. Nuts of deciduous trees, especially acorns and hickory nuts, and seeds of various species of pines are seasonally important foods on the island. From the end of July well into autumn, neat piles of brightly colored, stripped pinecones catch the eye throughout the island, and a rain of debris falls under the hickory trees. Squirrels have devised a clever technique to deal with acorns of the live oak and other white oaks whose acorns mature the year they are fertilized and are usually nondormant. If simply cached, the acorns would likely sprout before being recovered by the squirrels, so before storing them, they excise the seed embryo (Fox, 1982). Acorns of the red oak group, including laurel and water oaks, have delayed germination so may be safely stored over winter.

Gray squirrels are highly arboreal, spending much time in trees. However, when island animals are foraging on the ground, they exhibit odd behavior when danger is perceived. Rather than run up the nearest adequate tree, they may bypass many to get to a particular one, although the canopy appears fairly tight. This habit may have developed from a lack of cruising predators on the island and may change depending on the duration of the introduced bobcat population and now coyotes.

Gray squirrels can swim, but most observations of that activity have been when the animals were under duress of emigration. It is unlikely they deliberately enter a body of water at other times, which reduces their chances of colonizing a barrier island. I once watched one jump to a dead branch that broke from its weight, and the animal fell into a small tidal creek. It bobbed to the surface and immediately began dog-paddling to shore with the front third of its body well out of water. Once on land it remained motionless for several minutes, apparently recovering from the exertion.

Island populations of gray squirrels definitely fluctuate but studies have not been done to reveal the magnitude or cause. Squirrels were reported as "plentiful" on the island by Isaac F. Arnow in the 1920s (Harper, 1927) but were apparently "scarce" in 1947 when the Carnegie caretaker stated that they did not want any shooting of them south of Plum Orchard. Nor are data collected opportunistically adequate to show patterns or trends due to the dynamic human factor on the island. The number of animals found dead on the road might be used to judge a change in population numbers with over three decades of data, but the number of people and vehicles has not remained constant for that period. Hunting pressure has also changed as has the island fire regime, all of which combined introduce too many variables for speculation on past population numbers.

On Cumberland Island, the only month specimens revealed no reproductive activity was June. Embryos were collected in July and October, and lactating females or nursing young appeared in September to April, but the sample size was relatively small. Collecting methods also could bias the results. Most specimens were provided by domestic cats.

Squirrels have many predators but predation is considered of minor importance in overall population dynamics. Island fatalities recorded as a result of domestic cats, vehicles, and people (hunting or nuisance removal) are about equally represented numerically and seasonally. Snake predation no doubt increases in the autumn when diamondback rattlesnakes are attracted to areas with ripening nuts and much squirrel activity. Several pecan trees and a large hickory grow in the area near my house, and rattlesnake sightings can almost be guaranteed in the autumn. At other seasons, snake predation may be generally more happenstance, although rat snakes may search out nest cavities in trees. An island camper witnessed a large yellow rat snake wrapped tightly around a gray squirrel fall to the ground beneath a live oak. Ultimately the snake ate the squirrel. Besides mortality from the few domestic cats, island squirrels have had to adjust their behavior to introduced bobcats. Squirrels rank third in the diet of bobcats on the island, based on feces.

Most literature accounts do not attribute much impact to squirrel populations from sport hunting, however, spatial restrictions of an island may influence that impact. Early hunting pressure on Cumberland Island is unknown, but between 1885 and 1911, a twenty-six-year period, fewer than seventy were reportedly killed for sport, mostly on the south end. W. W. Brown, a collector of scientific specimens for O. Bangs (1898), secured eighteen squirrels on Cumberland Island in 1897. Between 1974 and 1980, a six-year period, a dozen were reported killed. The National Park Service has never had an open season for squirrels, so hunting pressure on the island over the last century has been minimal.

Depending upon the vegetation type and time since the last burn, fire may move swiftly through an area and catch squirrels with no available refuge. Mortality was documented in the 1981 island fire.

Discussion. Why gray squirrels were not on some of the older, Pleistocene core, barrier islands, such as Ossabaw and Sapelo, in historic times is unclear. The most important factor for their survivorship is food availability. Gray squirrel distribution in the US mirrors that of deciduous forests, and plant species variety within contributes to stability of the food resources. Cumberland Island, being the largest barrier island, has a wide variety of species that may compensate for oscillations in mast production. The juvenile survival rate plummets with a mast failure, and successive years of drought, which are not uncommon on the barrier islands, may cause longer shortages of mast than on the adjacent mainland. Mainland areas would also have a better likelihood of being recolonized after a severe depletion of animals.

One young gray squirrel from Jekyll Island, Georgia, was brought to Cumberland Island as a pet and ultimately released at Stafford. Its fate is unknown.

_____. Family Sciuridae. **Eastern Fox Squirrel**. *Sciurus niger* Linnaeus, 1758. Larger and heavier than a gray squirrel, this is the largest tree squirrel in the US. Dentition is I 1/1, C 0/0, PM 1/1, and M 3/3 for a total of 20 teeth, which is a way to separate skulls of gray and fox squirrels. Gray squirrels have an extra small premolar in the upper tooth row, which results in a total of 22 teeth.

Fox squirrels are found statewide in Georgia but are not common in the mountains or upper piedmont and are not naturally occurring on the barrier islands at this time, although they are reportedly good swimmers. Fire is compatible as it opens the understory and thins the oaks.

Hillestad et al. (1975) listed the fox squirrel as a member of the island fauna based on a specimen collected by K. Doutt in 1957, which is in the Carnegie Museum. The authors speculated that this species was introduced between 1927 and 1957. An attempt by curator S. McLaren (pers. comm.) to verify the identification revealed that the specimen had been incorrectly identified and was, in fact, a young eastern gray squirrel.

J. B. Peeples, long-time property manager for L. R. Ferguson, said he never saw a fox squirrel on Cumberland Island and that they introduced none. Dr. Coleman Johnston, a Carnegie descendant, knew of no releases.

_____. Family Geomyidae. **Southeastern Pocket Gopher**. *Geomys pinetis* Rafinesque, 1817. Taxonomy. Rafinesque (1817) published a description of what had been called the Georgia hamster in Screven County and placed this new species, *pinetis*, in his newly established genus, *Geomys*. From a collection made at "Stafford Place" on Cumberland Island in 1896, O. Bangs (1898) designated the pocket gophers on Cumberland a distinct species, *Geomys cumberlandius* (Fig. 32). He also identified a colony of another species of pocket gopher, *G. colonus*, about four miles west of St. Marys. With a much larger sample size, Williams and Genoways (1980) examined specimens of all three nominal species for morphological variation and concluded that all should be lumped under *G. pinetis* and were not distinct even at the subspecific level. Although Cumberland Island individuals averaged the largest, it is not unusual for small mammals on restricted islands to become larger than their mainland counterparts.

These rodents are specialized to live in underground tunnels. Their front feet have stout claws for digging and their large shoulders and arms support that activity. Their hair is short and originally described as bright cinnamon to russet, darkening along the middle of the back into a well-defined darker dorsal stripe. Hair on the under parts is plumbeous at base and cinnamon at the tips, and there are irregular white markings under the chin and about wrists. The hairs on the feet are grayish white (Bangs, 1898). The ears and eyes are tiny. Dentition is I 0/0, C 1/1, PM 1/1, M 3/3 for a total of 20 teeth and the incisors, which may be used for digging, grow throughout life. A biting louse is known from the Cumberland Island specimens. See Appendix VI C.

Charles Lyell (1845) reported an animal from Screven County, "which they call a salamander, because, I believe, it is often seen to appear when the woods are burnt." In the region of the Okefenokee Swamp, Francis Harper (1927) commented that the animal was known by the local inhabitants as "salamander" because, he speculated, in its subterranean retreats it was not harmed by fire, as the fabled salamander. George Merrow (1916–996), born on Cumberland Island, also referred to pocket gophers as salamanders, as did Lucy R. Ferguson (1899–1989).

Northernmost records in Georgia are just south of the fall line. In 1897, a collector for Bangs reported that he hunted for pocket gophers on Amelia Island but did not find any. He added that they were said to be there. Bangs (1898) collected along the Georgia coast and commented that Cumberland was the only one of the Sea Islands on which a pocket gopher occurred. On Cumberland Island, he found a colony "centered in some old fields on the Stafford Place" and said that their hills (mounds) straggled off through the pine woods for miles. His collections were made at Stafford Place, while his paid collector trapped on the north end with success. In the 1930s, several colonies were reported on Cumberland Island, and in 1959, K. Doutt, from the Carnegie Museum, collected some in the vicinity of Stafford. By 1970, sign of gopher activity was found in only one old field near Stafford. A month later, the field was plowed for agriculture (Johnson et al., 1974). Island resident George Merrow in 1974 recalled his youth, when he worked as a caddie for the Carnegies on the golf course at Stafford and said that he "killed a many" there. He used to trap them and said they were all over the island. Long-time employee of Lucy R. Ferguson, J. B. Peeples said in 1985 that he remembered mounds only at the Stafford airstrip and golf course. Tunneling with resulting mound-building in the gopher's last stand habitats in the late 1960s and early 1970s was, unfortunately, in conflict with human endeavors, and the last few known on Cumberland Island were deliberately killed. Lucy R. Ferguson recalled (1978, pers. comm.) that she and her foreman killed all they could to relieve danger on the airstrip and even tried running a hose from the exhaust of a vehicle down the tunnels. No animals or sign have been seen on Cumberland Island since that time and the species is presumed extirpated on the island.

All *Geomys* species are characterized as fiercely aggressive and will predictably try to bite any threatening object. When individuals are put together, unfamiliar gophers will fight violently. Lowery (1974) reported much intolerance existed between immatures and adults and between the young themselves and suggested that may be responsible for early dispersal of the young.

Discussion. After learning of all the attention biologists were focusing on the island pocket gophers, Lucy R. Ferguson suggested (January 1978, pers. comm.) that the rodents were not unique as biologists thought. She said there were none on Cumberland Island until the caddies at the golf course brought them over from the mainland to watch them fight. So the story goes, the caddies would put them in buckets and the animals would fight until death. I was able to find no reference to gambling or fighting pocket gophers, although due to their pugnacious nature, it seemed plausible. However, they are found in the island archaeological record. The steamroller to create the golf course at Stafford was purchased in 1901 (Bullard, 2003), and the animals were "all over the island" in 1898, so the story seems unlikely. A clear test would have been to examine burrows for arthropods, which live in close association (commensal). At least fourteen commensals with an obligate relationship have been identified from burrows on the mainland.

_____. Family Castoridae. **American Beaver**. *Castor canadensis* Kuhl, 1820. The American beaver is one of the largest rodents. Their size is maximum in northern latitudes and decreases to the south, and their weight is said to range between 11 kilograms (24 pounds) to 26 kilograms (57 pounds).

The color may vary between shades of brown and also between populations, each hair being uniformly colored. There is no seasonal color change, and under parts, throat, and cheeks is usually lighter than the back. The pelt is lush with dense, short, fine underfur overlain with coarse, long guard hairs. The nose, feet, and tail are black. The unusual tail of the beaver eliminates any mistaking the identity of the animal. Digits two and three on the hind feet have long, broad, very strong nails, and the nail of the fourth digit is specialized for grooming. The eyes and ears are small and positioned high on the head, allowing maximum sensory input while swimming with minimal exposure to the animal.

The skeleton is robust, sturdy, and strongly built. The skull is noticeably heavy, and dentition is I 1/1, C 0/0, PM 1/1, M 3/3 for a total of 20 teeth. The incisors are large and the exposed outer surface is bright orange enamel. The upper incisors act as levers while the lowers do the actual gnawing. Both grow continuously. The cheek teeth are flat with folds of enamel.

The present distribution of the American beaver in the Eastern US is from Labrador south to northern Florida. They occur throughout Georgia and continue to increase in numbers through introductions and protection and along the coast by continued reduction of large alligators. In the 1950s, a restocking program was carried out in Georgia because of greatly reduced numbers.

On Cumberland in January 1976, there was an active beaver dam and pond on a small, intermittent stream in a forested wetland with an understory of fetterbush. It remained active through February of 1977; subsequently the beaver disappeared. Beaver sign was reported in the vicinity of Duckhouse in the spring of 1987, and a beaver skeleton was found on Duckhouse Road in the spring of 1992. Beaver have been active up Coastal Plain rivers for some time, and one was found dead on the Cumberland Island beach in December 1997. Another was reported dead on the beach in January of 1998, and a live one was seen on the beach in February of 1998. They are common on the adjacent mainland at this time.

Few references ever mention the alligator as a beaver predator because most accounts address the beaver in northern latitudes. By the early 1940s, beavers were nearly gone from Georgia and the South. Restocking programs, managed hunting seasons, and decline in demand for pelts allowed reestablishment and perhaps range extensions.

Discussion. Beaver distribution poses some interesting questions. The beaver is awkward on land but is adapted to and requires an aquatic environment for long-term survival. Prior to European influence, every aquatic system in the Georgia Lower Coastal Plain was populated with alligators, many very large and all premier predators of mammals. How would beavers and alligators coexist, or could they? Large alligators eat primarily mammals, and moderate-sized mammalian species that share aquatic habitat with alligators on the island change their behavior based on alligator activity during the warmer months. Beavers are not seasonally flexible, nor can they for extended periods, forsake water deep enough in which to submerge and forage. One study in Mississippi found that alligators would reduce beaver populations but that alligators moved out of shallow impoundments during hot weather.

One of the earliest accounts describing natural history of the Southeast was by Mark Catesby from 1731 to 1743. Catesby said that beavers inhabited all of North America between latitudes 30 and 60. The 30-degree latitude stretches across Georgia just south of the fall line from Muscogee County in the west to Bulloch and Effingham counties in the east. At that time, the alligator ranged north to the fall line in Georgia but was never considered abundant along the northern fringe. In other words, the ranges of the two species did not overlap. Francis Moore (1983 [1744]) made a voyage to coastal Georgia in 1735 and, among other things, described the "beasts" he saw. He made no mention of beavers. William Bartram (Harper, 1958), who spent much time along the Georgia coast in the 1770s, said there were a few beavers in east Florida and Georgia but that they were more common in north Georgia and west Florida "near the mountains." He added that muskrats were never seen within 100 miles of the sea coast. George White (1849) compiled "Statistics of the State of Georgia," in which he reported that beavers were between Milledgeville and Macon (near the fall line) but rare. Charles Cory (1970 [1896]), who detailed hunting and fishing in Florida in 1894, said the beaver had not been taken in that state. In 1936, when alligator populations were presumably still quite low, H. B. Sherman acknowledged that an attempt had been made to introduce beavers (and muskrats) to Florida, but success was problematical, so he did not list the beaver as a recent mammal of Florida.

Beaver lower incisors are sharp and durable, and were used by early Americans as chisels. Were they traded as valuable tools and carried from place to place? Beaver remains have been found in the archaeological record of Florida; one jaw here, three there, and seven jaws minus incisors elsewhere. No other anatomical parts have been represented. Absence of the species from Florida archaeological sites is more the rule (Neill et al., 1956).

Williams and Jones (2006) suggested a possible commensal relationship between the native inhabitants of the Oconee River Valley in north central Georgia and beavers beginning around AD 1350. Beaver dams slow water in a stream and trap sediment, which over time accumulates and finally makes the site untenable for the beaver. When they move on to another location, the flat rich ground is more easily and productively farmed than the adjacent hillsides. If the natives protected the beavers in that situation, a symbiotic relationship, conceivably the practice could have been followed in other suitable areas. Is it possible that such a relationship modified the natural distribution of the beaver before historic documentation? Francis Harper (1927) suggested that the southern range of the beaver may be limited by the presence of the alligator, and if that was a primary obstacle to range extension, it could have been removed in specific areas. Precise pre-European natural range delineations in the Southeast may not be possible at this late date, considering that both the alligator and the beaver have been subject to great human manipulation and extensive mortality. Even today large alligators are not tolerated, except in protected areas, so natural populations of both species are highly modified.

_____. Family Cricetidae. **Marsh Oryzomys**. *Oryzomys palustris* (Harlan, 1837). The marsh oryzomys or rice rat is smaller than the hispid cotton rat and has silky, rather short (57 millimeters middorsal) water-repellent hair which lacks the amount of grizzling seen in cotton rats. Cumberland Island specimens range from a dorsal coloration of dark brown to reddish, rusty brown with tan hairs interspersed in both color phases. The base of all body hair is dark gray to black, which gives the belly a dirty white appearance. The hair on the ankles and feet is all white. The toes are noticeably long and the ones on the hind feet are partially webbed to facilitate its semiaquatic habits. The ears are relatively small and haired to match the dorsum. The moderately long tail is uniformly sparsely haired and lighter colored below than above. Dentition is I 1/1, C 0/0, PM 0/0, M 3/3 which totals 16 teeth. The molars have opposite cusps in two longitudinal rows. Measurements of twenty-nine adult island animals averaged: total length 234.1 millimeters, tail 112, hind foot 27.8, and ear 15.2. Males averaged slightly larger than females in total length and tail length, but there was no more than a millimeter of difference in hind foot or ear length. Skull measurements of the sexes were similar.

The marsh oryzomys is found throughout Georgia and is on most of the Holocene as well as the older Georgia barrier islands. Bottomland forests or mixed-forest types with open, grassy areas, especially along streams, as well as grassy marshes are preferred habitat. Along the coast, salt marshes provide ideal habitat.

Rice rats are referred to as semiaquatic rodents because they readily take to water as a defense, swim well on the surface or under water, and spend much of their time in aquatic situations. They are capable colonizers of brackish water areas and periodically stumble onto colonial nesting shore-birds, which choose unstable, washover areas for nesting to help avoid pre-dation. Nesting birds are probably an important but sporadic part of the rat's diet along the Georgia coast.

There are only two months in which no individuals at all were record-ed on the island, July and August. Reproductive activity, either embryos, placental scars, juveniles, or descended testes, was recorded in January, Feb-ruary, and March, May and June, and September, October, and November. From the combined Cumberland Island data, it appears breeding occurs throughout the year in this area. Out of nine heavy island females, four had six embryos, while one each had two, three, four, five, or seven embryos.

One flea, one sucking louse, five mites, four chiggers, and two species of ticks have been found on island marsh oryzomys. See Appendix VI. C.

Out of twenty-eight alligator fecal samples collected on Cumberland Island, one contained hair of a rice rat (Shoop and Ruckdeschel, 1990). There is always the possibility that the rat had been eaten by another preda-tor, which was then consumed by the alligator, however, it is likely that small alligators would be attracted to rice rats.

_____. Family Muridae. **Cotton Deermouse.** *Peromyscus gossypinus* (LeConte, 1853). Taxonomic status. From twenty-eight specimens collected on the north end of Cumberland Island in 1897, O. Bangs (1898) described a new species of cotton deermouse based on size and color, *Peromyscus in-sulanus.* He described the adult color as a "dull yellowish drab," which was slightly darker along the middle of the back but with no marked dorsal stripe. Even the young were of a different color, he reported, than the typical *P. gossypinus* young, having more "drabby" coloring and no darker dorsal stripe. Its size was small for the species, its tail short, and its hind feet pro-portionally large.

In 1909, the Cumberland Island mouse was recognized as being the same as the cotton mouse found on Anastasia Island, Florida (Osgood, 1909), which had also been described by Bangs in 1898. Osgood lumped the two and reduced them to subspecific status, *Peromyscus gossypinus anastasae.* In 1993, based on morphometric and electrophoretic analyses, Boone et al. decided that even subspecific designation was not appropriate and returned the name to that of the local subspecies on the mainland, *Peromyscus gossypi-*

nus gossypinus. They found no significant differences between the island population and that of the adjacent mainland, St. Marys, and interestingly, no reduction in genetic variability on the island.

Adult deermice are tawny, a light yellow-brown, on the sides with a much less noticeable darker brown middorsal stripe than animals on the adjacent mainland and inland. The line between the brown of the back and the white of the belly is clearly defined and runs from the upper lip, across the top of the front limb, midway along the sides, and midway the length of the hind leg. The white hair on the belly has a dark base that gives it an overall gray cast. The short hair on the tail is distinctly bicolored, light brown on the top and white underneath. The feet are white and the hair covers the nails. The exophalmic eyes are black, the ears large, sparsely haired, rounded, and held erect. Young animals are gray with a lighter belly than back.

There is no sexual dimorphism in this species except for genitalia, so adult body measurements are usually lumped. Combined average measurements for island animals were: weight 29.9 grams, TL 161.0 millimeters, T 61.8, HF 21.5, E 17.0. Dentition is I 1/1, C 0/0, PM 0/0, M 3/3 for a total of 16 teeth.

This mouse occurs on all the older Georgia barrier islands and several Holocene inlands and is common on Cumberland. In 1971, it was the most common mammal trapped on Amelia Island, Florida (Layne, 1971). LeConte (1853), in his original description of the animal, commented that around 1800, it "was scarcely known to the inhabitants of the southern parts of Georgia."

Almost every habitat, other than open fields, may be occupied by this mouse. Bottomland hardwood forests, scrub with dense palmetto, and edges of salt marsh habitat are all acceptable to this adaptable species, as well as buildings, both abandoned and occupied. Although its specific name links it to cotton, the only association LeConte described was in material used for nest construction. He commented that they frequently used more than a pound of cotton per nest. Nests have been found four feet up under the bark of pine snags. Belowground nests have the advantage of moderating temperatures and offering some protection from wildfires, depending upon the depth of the hole.

Cotton deermice are good swimmers. Under duress, they may swim for an hour with occasional resting by floating with only the tip of their nose above water.

On Cumberland Island, embryos have been recorded in every month but July through September, with only two in April through June. The average litter was 3.9, with the extremes two and six.

Hot, dry summers and food availability are thought to limit reproduction.

External arthropod parasites on Cumberland Island deermice include, fleas, ticks, mites, and dipteran larvae. Botfly larvae have been recorded in June and January. See Appendix VI C.

Cotton deermice play an important role in the spread of Lyme disease. They act as reservoir hosts for the infectious spirochete, which is transmitted via a tick. Other species of small mammals, such as the short-tailed shrew, may be competent reservoir hosts for the spirochete but do not regularly host as great a number of ticks as cotton deermice. Spirochetes have been found in ticks on birds, such as the Carolina wren and common yellowthroat, but gray catbirds and deer appear to be unsuitable reservoir hosts for the bacterium. The significance of the bacterium to the cotton deermouse and other small mammal hosts is unknown.

Pentastomids, or parasitic tongue worms, hatch in the gut of a small mammal, a cotton deermouse, and the larvae migrate through the gut to the body cavity and viscera. Of ninety-six island deermice checked over a continuous 25-month period, 12.5% were infected with pentastome larvae. Infections have not been obvious in juveniles. Limited experiments with Cumberland Island mice showed above average interest in snake feces. Under what circumstances pentastome eggs are ingested by mice is still unknown, as is any handicap conferred by the parasite. One Cumberland Island mouse, which had recently given birth to four young, hosted forty-seven pentastome larvae and appeared to be in good condition.

Another parasitic infection of Cumberland Island deermice appears to be *Besnoitia* sp. (E. Greiner, pers. comm.), a toxoplasma-like protozoan parasite. It was not found in a sample of forty-two juvenile cotton mice, but 41% of adults were infected in 2003/2004. Cumberland Island mice have not been closely examined for internal parasites, but tapeworms have also been noted.

A corn snake has been recorded eating a cotton deermouse on Cumberland Island, and the fact that pentastomes are found with such frequency in adult mice suggests that crotaline snakes eat many. During the late 1980s, following the release of many bobcats on the island by the NPS, and through the 1990s, cotton deermice were not a significant part of the bobcat diet based on fecal analysis. They have become more important since 2000, vying in popularity with squirrels and rice rats.

Discussion. Because deermouse longevity is short and there is a rapid turnover in the population, if factors influencing breeding success vary, there will be population fluctuations; these have been documented. Environmental factors include hot, dry periods, which are more exaggerated on the barrier islands than the mainland and have been shown to affect mast production. Food resources affect cotton deermouse reproduction, and on Cumberland Island and some of the other barrier islands, food resources are under intense competition from feral animals. A full understanding of the natural ecology of the cotton deermouse on Cumberland Island will have to await the return of unmanipulated ecological conditions, which would require elimination of feral animals and return to a natural wildfire regime.

_____. Family Muridae. **Oldfield Deermouse.** *Peromyscus polionotus* (Wagner, 1843). The oldfield deermouse is a small, light-colored brown mouse, the shade of which may vary with habitat. Dentition is I 1/1, C 0/0, PM 0/0, M 3/3 for a total of 16 teeth.

This deermouse is truly an animal of the Southeast but does not occur on any of the Georgia barrier islands or on Amelia Island, Florida. Howell (1920) discussed subspecies of *Peromyscus polionotus* and stated that *P. p. phasma* was confined to Anastasia Island, Florida. In 1926, A. H. Wright published an article on vertebrate life in the Okefenokee Swamp, and in an attempt to place his findings in a larger context, listed *P. phasma* as being on Cumberland Island, which is the basis for it being listed as a species once found on the island. D. Wilson, Department of Vertebrate Zoology at the United States National Museum, Smithsonian Institution, said he found no indication in the literature of any *P. polionotus* on Cumberland Island and speculated that "it must have been a lapsus on the part of Wright" (email 8 June 2010).

_____. Family Cricetidae. **Eastern Harvest Mouse.** *Reithrodontomys humulis* (Audubon and Bachman, 1841). The eastern harvest mouse is a small mouse with a long tail and conspicuous ears. The dorsal pelage color is rich brown and sometimes gray, frequently with a darker middorsal stripe. The sides are light brown or gray with a lateral line often separating the light belly coloring. The tail is bicolored, the ears dusky, the feet grayish-white. Dentition is I 1/1, C 0/0, PM 0/0, M 3/3 for a total of 16 teeth. Grooved incisors are a clear characteristic for the species; an obvious groove runs longitudinally down the center of each upper incisor.

One specimen was collected from an owl pellet on Cumberland Island, but the species has not been reported from any of the other barrier islands despite much trapping. No specimens have been trapped on Cumberland Island, yet the species is common on the adjacent mainland. By nesting on or in proximity to the ground rather than in a burrow, the long-time presence of feral swine on Cumberland Island could certainly have had an impact. Another influence may be the restrictions on wildfire imposed by the National Park Service on the island. A study done at Tall Timbers in Florida found that the harvest mouse was abundant in a study plot until fire was excluded for several years. The species then disappeared.

_____. Family Cricetidae. **Hispid Cotton Rat.** *Sigmodon hispidus* Say and Ord, 1825. The hispid cotton rat is the largest native rat on Cumberland Island. It is generally brown with light golden, straw-colored streaks and has a thinly haired, noticeably annulated tail that is shorter than the head and body. O. Bangs (1898) commented on the range of color variation of this species, saying that the ones from Cumberland Island had "very dark colored underparts." The molars quickly differentiate this island rodent from all others, they are more or less flat crowned from a lateral perspective, with an "S" shaped pattern on the crown, which the generic name describes, and with no raised cusps. The molars, unlike those of the marsh oryzomys, vary little in size, with the first being only slightly larger than the third. Dentition is: I 1/1, C 0/0, PM 0/0, M 3/3 for a total of 16 teeth. Measurements of males and females on Cumberland Island varied little, but the sample was small. The average total length for males and for females was 251 millimeters.

The species is found statewide in Georgia, and there are specimens or literature references from nearly all the Georgia barrier islands. It also occurs on Amelia Island, Florida. The cotton rat is more common on high ground than in swampy and marshy areas and prefers open grass areas with thickets and good cover from aerial predators. On Cumberland Island, it is common in the scrub habitats, especially when water levels are low and the temporary ponds are filled with grass, on the high ground along the edge of the marsh, and in the interdune area when grass seed ripens. Under cover of darkness, the cotton rat will venture onto the primary dunes to feed. These rats roam all open spaces of Cumberland Island but perhaps primarily when populations are high and food is limited. Hispid cotton rats are one of the most abundant mammals in Georgia and also on Cumberland Island. Population numbers fluctuate in response to habitat changes. The large, dynamic area of scrub-flatwoods on the north end has thick vegetation to their liking, but when it burns, as it frequently does, the instant habitat change no doubt affects local cotton rat populations, as may direct mortality from the fire. When cattle roamed Cumberland Island, fewer habitats were likely acceptable to cotton rats. The interdune area, for example, offered no cover so was probably utilized much less. Grazing by horses at the edge of the high salt marsh may also affect rat populations in that area by opening it up and thus making it less desirable.

While grasses and sedges are their primary food, cotton rats are considered omnivorous, perhaps seasonally. On Cumberland Island they have been observed in bushes to reach ripe blackberries and suspected of eating the fruit off the hard seed of the saw palmetto when it is abundant.

Cotton rats are poor swimmers (Esher et al., 1978). Their coat quickly becomes wet upon entering the water and they begin sinking from the rear while continuously kicking to keep their head above water. There is rapid turnover in cotton rat populations with very few animals living over six months. Embryos have been reported on Cumberland Island in June and December. Maturity is reached in forty to sixty days. Several external parasites have been identified on cotton rats on Cumberland Island. See Appendix VI C.

On Cumberland Island, owl pellets containing cotton rat remains have been found, and a merlin was observed dropping an adult cotton rat as it took off. Introduced bobcats and domestic animals, both dogs and cats, are known to have killed these rats on the island. One rat was found dead in conjunction with the big 1981 fire, and it is likely many more died as a result of it.

Discussion. The cotton rat's habitat choice of dry, grassy uplands, and their inability to swim well beg the question of how they established populations on some of the Holocene barrier islands. Rafting is always a possibility, but with time, the physical connection of the Holocene deposits to the larger, older islands has also become more substantial and thus more easily traversed. Only one animal has been found dead on the beach, but details are lacking.

_____. Family Muridae. **Roof Rat**. *Rattus rattus* (Linnaeus, 1758). The roof rat is a medium-sized rat with variable color but is infrequently dark black; more often it is grayish brown above with a light gray to white belly. Cumberland Island animals are brown above and have light gray to warm tan bellies. The pelage is soft and glossy. The underfur is gray and the bases of the long, dark-tipped guard hairs are clear or light. On Amelia Island, Florida, their bellies are white. The ears and long tail are nearly free of hair, and the annulations on the tail earned this species the name "file-tailed rat" in the Okefenokee Swamp (Harper, 1927). The tail is usually longer than the head and body combined. The average measurements of ten Cumberland Island rats (two male, eight female) were: total length 330 millimeters, tail 191, hind foot 34, ear 21. Dentition is I 1/1, C 0/0, PM 0/0, M 3/3 for a total of 16 teeth. The three longitudinal rows of tubercles on the molars are characteristic of the genus and the entire family.

The other member of this genus potentially occurring on Cumberland Island, the Norway rat, *Rattus norvegicus*, has coarse pelage, and the naked tail is less than the length of the head and body combined.

This species was the first Old World rat to arrive via English colonists in the early 1600s. It was originally from Asia. In 1898, Bangs described the roof rat as the common rat of Georgia and Florida and said it occurred on all of the barrier islands. There are museum specimens from both Pleistocene and Holocene Georgia barrier islands and from Cumberland Island in the 1970s. Its documented occurrence on Cumberland Island has been irruptive.

Most species of *Rattus*, and there are many, live in forests away from humans, but the two species that made it to this continent are considered commensal with humans. They swim and dive well. Barns, especially with stored grain, and buildings are preferred to natural environments, and they frequently reside between walls of buildings. I found a rat refuse "midden" containing bones and crab shells between the ceiling of the living room and the floor of the attic in my island home when it was being renovated. The material was situated precisely where it would have received most warmth from the fireplace. No rat colonies have been found away from human development on Cumberland Island.

The sticktight flea has been reported on island roof rats.

Discussion. The rat's close association with humans, its restricted home range under normal conditions, and its short life expectancy all support the likelihood of fluctuating or even periodic roof rat populations on Cumberland Island. As the island human population has greatly fluctuated, so perhaps has that of the roof rat. During the mid-1970s, a nursery/production operation for quail and exotic birds was undertaken by L. R. Ferguson at Stafford. The barn housed birds, feed (grain), and incubators, along with many years' accumulation of junk, as barns are wont to do. It was a perfect situation for a colony of roof rats to become established and proliferate.

Interestingly, the rats made it to the north end of Cumberland Island at the same time, some nine miles away, and there the population also flourished. Effort was made to eliminate the species from both localities at that time and no other colonies on the island have been identified to date, 2015.

A bald eagle had been active on the south end of Cumberland Island in February of 2007, and a large regurgitated pellet was found in proximity to a scavenged bird carcass at South Point. The pellet contained remains of a roof rat. Queries were made on the island as to the presence of rats around developed areas, especially Dungeness, but all responses were negative. Unless an unidentified population exists on the island, away from development, it is likely the rat was caught on nearby Amelia Island, Florida, where roof rats are common. Arguing against isolated Cumberland Island populations of the roof rat is the fact that none have been identified in island bobcat scat.

ORDER LAGOMORPHA. Family Leporidae. **Marsh Rabbit.** *Sylvilagus palustris* (Bachman, 1837). The marsh rabbit is a medium-sized rabbit, smaller than its close relative the swamp rabbit and larger than a cottontail. It is darker brown than most rabbit species and has long toenails on both front and hind feet. The underside of the tail is usually tan or brown, not white. Dentition is I 2/1, C 0/0, PM 3/2, M 3/3 for a total of 28.

The marsh rabbit occurs in Georgia south of the fall line in the Coastal Plain. Marsh rabbits prefer dense vegetation near water, while cottontails remain on upland areas, both wooded and open. Layne (1971) found marsh rabbits on Amelia Island, Florida, to be common also in habitats that usually are occupied by cottontails and suggested that the paucity of cottontails allowed the marsh rabbits to exploit a wider range of habitats. The same may be true on Cumberland Island. Temporary ponds and sloughs are rarely brimming full of water, and they support a lush growth of grasses at their periphery. When dry, they are grasslands and excellent marsh rabbit habitat. Burrows in this low-relief habitat would periodically be inundated, which would restrict cottontails to much higher ground.

This rabbit is one of the few vertebrate species that occurs on all the Georgia barrier islands and is the only species of rabbit on Cumberland Island. One mite and four species of ticks have been identified on marsh rabbits on Cumberland Island. See Appendix VI C.

Availability of water is a specific habitat requirement for the marsh rabbit, and its affinity for water likely enabled it to colonize the Holocene islands and remain on the Pleistocene barrier islands. While they apparently have no specific physical adaptations to an aquatic life, they quickly take refuge in water and swim well. Their nests are frequently surrounded by water and on Cumberland Island have been found in proximity to alligator holes. In South Carolina, marsh rabbits reportedly prefer freshwater marshes, but in Georgia they are also numerous in brackish marshes with adjacent high ground on which to retreat during spring tides. On Cumberland Island, before the NPS introduction of bobcats, marsh rabbits occupied all densely vegetated inland areas, as well as brackish marshes. A particularly favorite island habitat, when the species was abundant, was the then savanna-like area on the north end known as Cedar Dock. Temporary wetlands on Cumberland Island are numerous and provide lush herbaceous cover when they are not full of water.

On Cumberland Island, rabbits have been recorded feeding on rushes and sedges, saw palmetto, dogfennel, seaoats, and gallberry. Dates of island gallberry fruit availability, as suggested by occurrence of fruit in raccoon feces and general observations, are from October through March. Island rabbits have been recorded cutting or stripping gallberry stems in December and January.

They spend daylight hours on what is termed a "form," which is a well-used platform that they may construct themselves in a protected place. Fire ants were documented on Cumberland Island in the 1980s and have since preempted the use of most large basal clumps of grass as forms by vertebrates during times of high water.

Marsh rabbits may breed throughout the year, but on Cumberland Island there is a noticeable lack of records of young animals in the autumn and early winter, September through December.

Nests have been found in May. One was near human habitation but in a well-concealed spot. The other was at the edge of an alligator hole in a temporary pond, which was fairly dry at the time. There was water in the alligator hole and it was occupied by an adult American alligator.

The NPS introduction of thirty-two bobcats on the island acutely changed rabbit habits and demographics. Rabbit droppings and cuttings were obvious and abundant on the island up to 1986, after which mortality was recorded, and little (1991 to 1992) to no sign (1993 to 1997) was observed. After 2000, sign was scarce but frequent enough to suggest that the rabbits were low in numbers but not extirpated.

Hunting has always been popular on the barrier islands and rabbits have been taken, as well as larger game. The Carnegies took rabbits "often," and on the north end there were infrequent rabbit hunts without dogs. The amount of hunting pressure exerted by hotel guests at the turn of the twentieth century and the hunt club that followed is unknown.

Discussion. At low tide there are frequently freshwater seeps along the edge of Cumberland Island salt marsh that would provide a source of freshwater even in times of drought, if you did not mind getting your feet wet. Drought might be devastating to cottontails. And with drought comes fire to further reduce habitat and force exposure, if only temporarily.

Whatever the habitat partitioning characteristics between the marsh rabbit and the eastern cottontail, they are manifest on the barrier islands. Cottontails are common on the adjacent mainland but absent on all the Georgia barrier islands (without bridges), and there is no reason to believe they were not here when sea level rose, isolating the islands. In that case, as with so many other species, colonization was not the issue, it was survival under changing environmental conditions. A small population of cottontails occurs on Amelia Island, Florida (Layne, 1971), which has a bridge to the mainland. Perhaps some interspecific competition coupled with habitat limitations restricted cottontails to the mainland along the Georgia coast.

FERAL LIVESTOCK

Horses, cattle, and swine arrived in the Southeast US with early explorers during the mid1500s. None are native to this continent at this time. By 1597, the native chief on Cumberland Island, don Juan, had been given a personal horse, and at a time when horses were a luxury for most Spanish in Florida (Lanning, 1935; Hann, 1996). Horses were used for transportation and work, especially in conjunction with military efforts, but even by 1743, William Stephens, secretary of the Colony of Georgia, commented that horses "able and sufficient for cattle hunting" were not yet to be had in Georgia (Coulter, 1958). By the 1780s, horses had been stocked on Cumberland Island by early owners and the population was estimated at 200 to 300 (Torres, 1977).

Cuban cattle were apparently imported by Spanish governors in St. Augustine in 1574 and were to be kept on "near-by coastal islands" (Bushnell, 1978). By the early 1700s, the Spanish had developed a substantial cattle industry and bred various stocks to find a type adapted to the rigors of the Florida environment. Whether deliberately released or escaped, feral cattle roamed the countryside along the St. Marys and Satilla rivers, as noted by Jonathan Bryan in 1753 (Wood and Bullard, 1996), and possibly on Cumberland Island as well. Owners of cattle on the Sea Islands were ordered to remove all animals to the mainland during the Revolution in 1776 so they would not be available for the enemy (Bullard, 2003), but the roundups were incomplete.

Hogs are more difficult to control than horses or cattle (Fig. 33), and those that escaped in the early 1500s proliferated and quickly spread across the Southeast, despite one complaint that they were difficult to raise because of all the alligators in the swamps (Grant, 1980). In 1560, natives supplied pork to the French (Hanson and Karstad, 1959), and around St. Augustine feral hogs were "common" in 1604 (Bushnell, 1994). Owners of Cumberland Island commented on the profit to be made from the number of hogs on the island in 1785 and referred to the abundance of acorns, suggesting in 1788 that even more animals could be supported (Torres, 1977).

The tenure of feral livestock populations in the Southeast has been locally erratic. Pressure on the animals increased periodically, especially during military episodes when animals were killed either for food or to inconvenience the enemy. Protecting agricultural crops from feral animals was always a concern, even as early as the 1600s, when friars and soldiers expressed concerns about introducing cattle for fear they would plunder the native's corn fields (Lanning, 1935). Shortly after 1695, there were complaints that a wandering herd of horses on Amelia Island destroyed four fields of beans and one of maize (Bushnell, 1994), and around 1700, a report of damage done by horses came from St. Catherines Island (Ross Papers). As agriculture increased during the Plantation era, tolerance for feral livestock decreased. Fences were required to protect fields from feral horses and cattle, but there was no protection from marauding feral swine or native animals other than killing them, as described at a plantation on St. Simons Island in

1857, where a large hog escaped from its pen and had to be shot to protect the cornfield (Pavich-Lindsay, 2002). Feral populations were likely greatly reduced or eliminated in some areas during this period.

Circumstances changed with the Civil War, when the Plantation era came to an end. A newspaper account in 1876 described Cumberland Island as having not one acre in cultivation (Torres, 1977). The intense pressure on remaining feral animals was, at least temporarily, relieved. Thomas Carnegie and family arrived on Cumberland Island in the 1880s. Island life necessitates self-sufficiency, and the island families established herds of cattle, riding horses, and brought in blooded stock they thought would improve the quality of the rangy feral hogs. Because hogs prospered on the island, most were released to fend for themselves but bore the mark of their owner so they could be reclaimed at a later date. Boars were castrated before release. Earmarks, a combination of holes and/or "lops" (slices), were recorded in the Camden County Courthouse until open range was no longer legal. Carnegies sold feral animals for profit from at least 1926 through the 1950s. In the late 1940s, the Carnegie caretaker reported that the prediction for the acorn crop was poor and hog prices were high, so they would "thin the hogs down," selling the young boars and gilts and keeping small pigs and sows. They also tried to catch all the "old sand hill, long nose, piney woods boars which would destroy any young boars of good blood turned loose to improve the stock" (GDAH). In 1954, in a contract between the estate of Lucy C. Carnegie and J. B. Peeples to catch and market island hogs, it was stipulated that only the boars and unproductive sows be taken to market and that productive sows be released (GDAH). So not only was the pressure to reduce or eliminate feral hogs relieved, their proliferation on the island was encouraged.

The same was true for feral horses, if any survived the Plantation era. James Silva (1976) remembered "wild ponies" that subsisted on the salt marsh on Robert Stafford's land, which were occasionally sold. Of course, Stafford had many slaves, and as Thomas (1923) recalled, slaves had horses and cows that they pastured in the salt marsh, so the animals referred to at Stafford's were not necessarily completely unattended. Having a fondness for horses, in 1921, the Carnegies brought a Seaboard Airline Railway Company carload of mustangs from Globe, Arizona, to Fernandina, Florida, and barged them across to the island for release. They were feral animals and formed the foundation of the present island herd.

The few remaining island cattle were rounded up and removed in 1987. Prior to that, Lucy Ferguson, who brought some Herefords over during World War II (J. Graves, pers. comm.), had a roundup in 1976 that removed most of the animals on the north end of the island. It was a brutal affair and captured the one remaining horned animal. Early on, the Carnegies maintained a herd of dairy cattle in Beach Field at Dungeness. Nancy C. Rockefeller (1993) recalled that their herd of 200 animals was reduced or eliminated in 1918 due to her father's asthma.

In their native land, Western Europe and Central Asia, horses, cattle, and swine all evolved along with their habitats, which means that the resources the animals depended on had adapted to accommodate the various pressures they imposed. A herd of cattle or horses might graze while wandering over a grassland, but they had ample room to continue on to other pastures to allow regrowth and recovery. They were adapted to the quality of the food available and received adequate nutrition without damaging the resource. The same was true for omnivorous swine. Through time, species success is marked by adaptations that permit sustainability. When animals are introduced to habitats foreign to them, ones in which they did not evolve nor for which they have any special adaptations, they simply do the best they can. Some, such as cattle, horses, and swine, can eke out a living even in such alien terrain as Cumberland Island, but at a cost to them and the environment.

Visitors to Cumberland Island who are not closely acquainted with horses are fascinated by them and empathize with their freedom. What they don't see are the thousands of ticks on every animal, the throats swollen shut from snake bites, the founder from improper habitat and nutrition, snapped leg bones, and the ranks of parasites in their guts. Two species of ticks have been identified on island feral horses. Worn teeth which cannot properly prepare the poor quality fodder for digestion and the blankets of deadly encephalitis-bearing mosquitoes are also usually out of sight, as is the agony of watching an animal bogged down in the low salt marsh hopelessly struggling to free itself as the tide rises and finally drowns it. Horses are not woodland or salt-marsh animals, so are unfamiliar with the hazards the local environment presents. Once entangled in vines, healthy big stallions may die for lack of food and water, and they have even died on the island wedged between two closely spaced trees, something not found in grassland habitat.

Swine, being smaller and more adaptable than horses, fare somewhat better on Cumberland Island. They are subject to disease and parasites, which sometimes are debilitating, especially when the hog population is high. Four species of ticks have been identified on island feral hogs. Swine brucellosis and pseudorabies are swine diseases but have not been reported from the island. Pseudorabies, a viral infection, has been found on Ossabaw Island. Nine species of internal parasites have been recorded from Cumberland Island swine, all nematodes, but there was no evidence that they caused mortality (Pence et al., 1988). Most adults suffer tooth problems, getting coarse vegetation packed down between the molars, which finally causes infection and ultimately tooth loss. Island food resources are likely not the same as in their native habitat. Snake bites are not uncommon.

Cattle are subject to numerous parasites and diseases, and attempts were made to protect the island herds. Dipping vats were constructed and all cattle, regardless of ownership, were dipped to eradicate Texas cattle fever, as the disease was called. It spread over the Southeast by 1890 and was a serious problem in Camden County and on Cumberland Island. The cause of the disease, transmitted by a single-host native tick species (*Boophilus annulatus*), was a protozoan parasite (*Babesia bigemina*), which entered and destroyed red blood cells, quickly developing enormous populations that could cause death to the host in four to eight days. In 1914, the first cattle-dipping vat was constructed in Camden County, and soon they were constructed on Cumberland Island. The idea was to swim the cattle through a pesticide bath to kill the ticks. The recipe for the potent bath water used on the island was: 8# white arsenic, 24# Sal Soda, one gallon of pine tar. Dissolve arsenic and soda in boiling water. Drip in pine tar when half cool. Add 500 gallons of water. The vats were cement troughs with sides that sloped outward making a broad "V." There is a trough located on the west side of the island between Brickhill Bluff and Hawkins Creek that was used for the animals on the north end. The vat/bath technique proved successful and the disease and the native tick were eliminated from the Southeast US in 1954.

Another problem Cumberland Island cattle and deer faced was screwworm. Larvae of a species of fly in the blowfly family feed in open wounds, enlarging them and destroying tissue. Screwworm flies were eliminated from the Southeast near the end of 1961. In 1954, the Carnegie caretaker commented that the cattle were fat and remarkably free of screwworm.

Bang's disease or brucellosis is yet another problem that introduced island cattle encountered. It is a bacterial infection transmitted by the close association of animals and a contaminated environment.

Impact

Cattle accept a wider range of vegetation types as forage than do horses and more frequently browse. They maintain larger groups, which may contribute to their more noticeable impact. During the time of free-ranging cattle, the understory on Cumberland Island was greatly reduced and presented a park-like appearance. The cattle spent much time on the beach to escape biting insects (Fig. 34) and there eliminated the typical interdune wax myrtle habitat by keeping the myrtle bushes browsed 30 to 45 centimeters (1 to 1.5 feet) in height. They also consumed other dune-stabilizing vegetation, which frustrated normal dune dynamics. Blowing sand was stopped by the inland tree line, but there was nothing to stop it between there and the ocean, so the community was greatly compromised. On the south end of the island where accretion was predominant due to the effect of the jetty, primary dunes were lacking and unable to become established because of the lack of vegetation. This precluded use of that area by sea turtles, and it was not until several years after the cattle were removed that the beach on the south end was suitable for sea turtle nesting. With a fifteen to twenty-five year maturity period, and young returning to their natal beach to nest, only recently has the island sea turtle nesting distribution begun to equilibrate between the north and south ends. In the 1970s there was rarely a turtle nest from Willow Pond Road south.

Loss of the dune and interdune habitat no doubt affected many species, but it is only the more obvious ones of which we are aware. Some migrating birds rely on wax myrtle for food and shelter, and resident species that are more or less restricted to that habitat, such as the amber snail and the island glass lizard, were probably reduced in number. Horses also graze the dune vegetation, reducing its effectiveness in stabilizing the dunes. They prefer grasses to shrubs, so the myrtle and other pioneering species in the dunes, such as cabbage palm and live oak, have a chance to become established. Inland, horses consume much Spanish moss, both fallen and still on the trees. This changes the appearance of the forest and eliminates certain habitats. Ground-nesting birds are affected by all feral animals.

The salt marsh suffers enormous damage from feral livestock. Heavy animals, such as horses, churn and chop the stabilizing marsh cordgrass, turning the area into a quagmire. Horses trample and smash the delicate ribbed mussels, which usually crowd the edge of the high marsh and filter the water for their livelihood. Mussels have been mostly eliminated from areas horses frequent. Hogs swim the small tidal creeks at high tide to forage in areas for mussels and crabs. Feces from feral animals are caught in the numerous depressions left by their feet, and there it stews in the low water and sun, producing toxic bacteria and creating an unhealthy situation for all and compromising water quality. Island shellfish areas have had to be closed to harvest because of feral livestock.

Freshwater areas, too, feel the effects of feral animals. Horses regularly frequent the temporary ponds and sloughs of the island to graze. They follow each other in single file on narrow trails to their preferred feeding sites. In so doing, many times they create a connection between small bodies of water that otherwise would have remained distinct. The connection allows fish access to some areas that would have been fish-free, decreasing amphibian breeding success. During times of drought, hogs completely uproot vegetation in temporary ponds, capturing the hapless amphibians and reptiles that took refuge there and altering the vegetation pattern of the wetlands.

In summary, the list of effects from feral animals is great and includes compacting soil, erosion, nutrient cycling, water pollution and regime changes that affect amphibian reproduction, altering the quality and quantity of vegetation, which then affects fire characteristics, impacting dune stability and fauna and flora of the high marsh, ground-nesting birds, and interspecies competition. There is much competition between hogs, horses, deer, and native species that share their dietary preferences or habitats, such as turkeys, squirrels, mice, and raccoons. Acorns, for example, are eaten by all the above-mentioned animals. Annual acorn production varies, but in years of low production the competition from hogs and horses is certainly felt by native species. In season, hogs fill their stomachs daily with several pounds of acorns, which adds up to tons of mast unavailable for native species or for oak reproduction. Less-preferred plants must then be eaten by native wildlife deprived of nutritious acorns, so the effects of feral animals ripple through the entire ecosystem and result in atypical functioning and stressed communities.

National Park Service policies require control or eradication if an exotic species damages the natural ecosystem or competes with native species. Georgia law waffles on feral hogs because they are a popular "sport" animal, and the state does not address feral horses. The Wilderness Act requires that the managing agency, the National Park Service, maintain wilderness character to promote a naturally functioning ecosystem.

Figure 24
Alligator.
(S. Willie)

Figure 25
Tracks beneath nest tree.

Figure 26
Sweetwater heronry, 1997.

Figure 27
Supper.

Figure 28
Eastern mole burrow on ocean beach.

Figure 29
Fumigating Carriage House, Dungeness.
(National Park Service)

Figure 30
White deer at Dungeness.
(National Park Service)

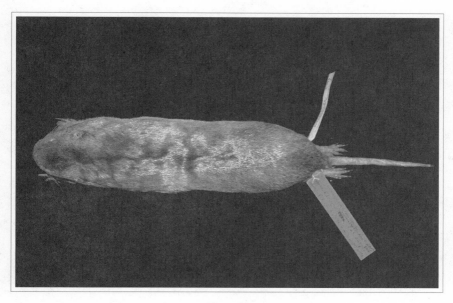

Figure 31
Cumberland Island Pocket Gopher.
(MCZ)

Figure 32
Feral hog.

Figure 33
Cattle were numerous in 1974.

Personal Correspondence References

Arnow, I. F. (1870–1957) Naturalist, ornithologist in Camden County, Georgia.

Bailey, Jesse (1918–1982) Island caretaker for Candler property.

Bell, R. Long-time resident of Little Cumberland Island.

Bursey, C. Professor of biology, Pennsylvania State University.

Candler, S. O. Island landowner.

Clapp, R. Smithsonian Institution, Ornithology Department.

CIM. Cumberland Island Museum, established in 1985. See www.cimuseum.org.

Ferguson, Lucy R. (1899–1989) A granddaughter of Lucy and Thomas Carnegie.

Foster, Lucy S. (1928–2008) A great-granddaughter of Lucy and Thomas Carnegie.

Fries, C. Employed by the National Park Service on Cumberland Island from 1987 through 1998. Resident of north Florida.

Gerwin, J. Curator of Ornithology, North Carolina Museum of Natural Sciences.

Graves, J. A great-grandson of Lucy and Thomas Carnegie.

Greenway, J. C., Jr. (1903–1989) Ornithologist, naturalist, author of *Extinct and Vanishing Birds of the World*. New York: American Committee for International Wild Life Protection, Special Publication (13), 1958.

Greiner, E. Department of Pathology, College of Veterinary Medicine, University of Florida, Gainesville.

Hall, C. Biology Department, Berry College, Georgia.

Helme, Arthur. (1860–1947) Professional ornithologist.

Hendricks, S. Naturalist employed at Greyfield Inn for several years.

Henry, Vernon J., Jr. (1931–2010) Oceanographer, Marine Institute, Sapelo Island, National Science Foundation, Applied Coastal Research Lab, Skidaway Island.

Hodges, M. Conservation biologist with the Nature Conservancy.

Hopkins, M. N. (1926–2007) Ornithologist, naturalist, farmer in south Georgia.

Johnston, D. W., PhD (1926–2015) University of California, Berkeley. Ornithologist. Professor, Mercer University, Wake Forest, University of Florida, George Mason University. Published many scientific papers, five books, and edited several books.

Jordan, Helen B., PhD (1907–1993) Protozoology, University of California, Berkeley. Professor Georgia State University 1954–1974. Studied lizard malaria.

Kingsley, M. Landowner on Little Cumberland Island.

Leary, Pat. Ornithologist, naturalist, artist.

Mahoney, A. Athens, Georgia. Bird watcher.

Makemson, D. Owned property on Little Cumberland Island.

McCollough, L. Logged on Cumberland Island in the 1940s. Residence in Kingsland, Georgia.

McLaren, Suzanne. Collections Manager, Mammals, Carnegie Museum of Natural History, Pittsburgh, Pennsylvania.

Merrow, George. (1916–1996) Born on Cumberland Island. Worked for Carnegies and Candlers.

Merrow, Josie. Born on Cumberland Island. Older brother of George Merrow.

Miller, Mary. (1903–1999) Landowner on Cumberland Island. Related to Bunkleys.

Olsen, O. H., Jr. Cumberland Island landowner. His father worked for the Candler family.

Peeples, J. B. (1911–1987) Worked on Cumberland Island for L. R. Ferguson

Quitmyer, I. R. Collections manager for Environmental Archaeology, Florida Museum of Natural History, Gainesville.

Rockefeller, N. C. (1900–1994) A granddaughter of Lucy and Thomas Carnegie.

Sanders, Jennie Whitby. Interview 1979, Fernandina, Florida. Came to island as a teacher.

Sciple, G. (1921–2013) Avocation ornithology. Brunswick and Little Cumberland Island, GA.

Thrift, Mark. Farmer, naturalist, Charlton County, Georgia.

West, Sandy. Heir to Ossabaw Island. Sold to state of Georgia.

Whitehead, F. Photographer and tour guide employed by Greyfield Inn for many years.

Willis, Sheila. Naturalist, ornithologist based in Waycross, Georgia.

References

Allen, G. M. 1916. "Whalebone Whales of New England." *Memoirs of the Boston Society of Natural History* 8 (2): 107–322.

Allen, G. W. 1948. "The Management of Georgia Deer." *Journal of Wildlife Management* 12 (4): 428–32.

Allen, J. A. 1878. "The West Indian Seal." *Bulletin of the American Museum of Natural History* 2 (1): 1–34.

Anderson, S. 1972. "Report on St. Catherines Island Mammals." Unpublished report to landowner. Cumberland Island Museum.

Andrews, E. W., and C. M. Andrews, eds. 1985. *Jonathan Dickinson's Journal.* Port Salerno: Florida Classics Library. Originally published in Philadelphia, 1699.

Arnow, I. F. 1950–1953. "History of St. Marys, Georgia and Vicinity." Unpublished manuscript. Microfilm. Georgia Department Archives and History.

Art, H. W., F. H. Bormann, and G. M. Woodwell. 1974. "Barrier Island Forest Ecosystem: Role of Meteorological Nutrient Inputs." *Science* 184 (4132): 60–62.

Audubon, J. J., and J. Bachman. 1845–1854. *The Viviparous Quadrupeds of North America.* New York: privately published by J. J. Audubon. Vol. 1:1–389 (1846); Vol. 2:1–334 (1851); Vol. 3:1–348 (1854).

Baker, L. A., R. J. Warren, D. R. Diefenbach, and W. E. James. 2001. "Prey Selection by Reintroduced Bobcats (*Lynx rufus*) on Cumberland Island, Georgia." *American Midland Naturalist* 145: 80–93.

Bangs, O. 1898. "The Land Mammals of Peninsular Florida and the Coast Region of Georgia." *Proceedings of the Boston Society of Natural History* 28 (7): 157–235.

Barnabe, C., R. Yaeger, O. Pung, and M. Tibayrenc. 2001. "*Trypanosoma cruzi*: A Considerable Phylogenetic Divergence Indicates That the Agent of Chagas Disease Is Indigenous to the Natural Fauna of the United States." *Experimental Parasitology* 99: 73–79.

Baughman, J. L. 1946. "Some Early Notices on American Manatees and the Method of Their Capture." *Journal of Mammalogy* 27 (3): 234–39.

Beaton, G., P. W. Sykes, and J. W. Parrish. 2003. "Annotated Checklist of Georgia Birds." *Georgia Ornithological Society, Occasional Publication* 14.

Bellis, V. J. 1995. "Ecology of Maritime Forests of the Southern Atlantic Coast: A Community Profile." *National Biological Service*, Report 30.

Belt, Thomas. 1985. *The Naturalist in Nicaragua.* Chicago: University of Chicago Press. Originally published in London: J. Murray, 1874.

Bent, A. C. 1940. "Life Histories of North American Cuckoos, Goatsuckers, Hummingbirds, and Their Allies." U.S. National Museum Bulletin 176.

Berry, W. 1916. "The Fossil Plants from Vero, Florida." Florida Geological Survey. *Additional Studies in the Pleistocene at Vero*: 19–33.

Blount, R. 1993. Spirits of Turpentine, A History of Florida Naval Stores, 1528–1950. Tallahassee: Florida Agricultural Museum.

Bond, S. C., Jr. 1987. "The Development of the Naval Stores Industry in St. Johns County, Florida." *Florida Anthropologist* 40 (3): 187–202.

Boone, J. L., J. Laerm, and M. Smith. 1993. "Taxonomic Status of *Peromyscus gossypinus anastasae* (Anastasia Island Cotton Mouse)." *Journal of Mammalogy* 74 (2): 363–75.

Bourdeau, P., and H. J. Oosting. 1959. "The Maritime Live Oak Forest in North Carolina." *Ecology* 40 (1): 148–52.

Bozeman, J. R. 1975. "Vegetation." In H. O. Hillestad, J. R. Bozeman, A. S. Johnson, C. W. Biersford, and J. I. Richardson, *The Ecology of Cumberland Island National Seashore, Camden County, Georgia.* University of Georgia Technical Report Series: 63–115.

Brill, W. J. 1979. "Nitrogen Fixation: Basic to Applied." *American Scientist* 67 (4): 458–66.

Brisse, P. 1986. "From the Field." *Oriole* 51 (2–3): 50.

Brown, C. A. 1945. "Louisiana Trees and Shrubs." Louisiana Forestry Commission Bulletin 1.

Bruce, J. G., D. L. Stoneburner, J. I. Richardson, and J. Worthington. 1979. "*Vittaria lineata* Rediscovered in Georgia." *American Fern Journal* 69 (1): 29.

Bullard, M. R. 1982. An Abandoned Black Settlement on Cumberland Island, Georgia. DeLeon Springs, FL: E. O. Painter.

———. 1986. Robert Stafford of Cumberland Island: Growth of a Planter. DeLeon Springs, FL: E. O. Painter.

———. 2003. *Cumberland Island, A History.* Athens: University of Georgia Press.

Burleigh, T. D. 1958. *Georgia Birds.* Norman: University of Oklahoma Press.

Bushnell, A. T. 1978. "The Menendez Marquez Cattle Barony at la Chua and the Determinants of Economic Expansion in Seventeenth-Century Florida." *Florida Historical Quarterly* 56 (4): 407–31.

———. 1994. "Situado and Sabana: Spain's Support System for the Presidio and Mission Provinces of Florida." *American Museum of Natural History, Anthropological Paper* 74.

Cadle, F. W. 1991. *Georgia Land Surveying, History and Law.* Athens and London: University of Georgia Press.

Caldwell, D. K., and M. C. Caldwell. 1969. "The Harbor Seal, *Phoca vitulina concolor*, in Florida." *Journal of Mammalogy* 50 (2): 379–80.

Carr, A. F. 1994. *A Naturalist in Florida.* New Haven, CT, and London: Yale University Press.

Carr, A., and C. J. Goin. 1959. *Guide to the Reptiles, Amphibians and Fresh-water Fishes of Florida.* Gainesville: University of Florida Press.

Catesby, M. 1731–1743. *The Natural History of Carolina, Florida, and the Bahama Islands.* London.

Chabreck, R. H. 1968. "The American Alligator—Past, Present and Future." Proceedings of the 21st Annual Conference of the Southeastern Association of Game and Fish Commissions: 554–58.

Clewel, A. F. 1985. *Guide to the Vascular Plants of the Florida Panhandle.* Tallahassee: University Presses of Florida, Florida State University Press.

REFERENCES

Cofer-Shabica, S. 1993. "Ocean Shoreline Changes." *Georgia Geological Society Guidebook* 13 (1): 12–15.

Coker, W. C., and H. R. Totten. 1934. *Trees of the Southeastern States*. Chapel Hill: University of North Carolina Press.

Coleman, K. 1985. *The Colonial Records of the State of Georgia. Trustee's Letter Book*. Vols. 30 (1738–1745) and 31 (1745–1752). Athens: University of Georgia Press.

Conant, R. 1975. A Field Guide to Reptiles and Amphibians of Eastern and Central North America. Boston: Houghton Mifflin.

Cooke, C. W. 1939. "Scenery of Florida Interpreted by a Geologist." Florida Geological Bulletin 17.

Cory, C. B. 1970. *Hunting and Fishing in Florida*. New York: Arno Press. Reprint. Originally published in Boston: The Barta Press, 1896.

Coulter, E. M. 1958. *The Journal of William Stephens: 1741–1743*. 2 vols. Athens: University of Georgia Press.

Crane, V. W. 1928. *The Southern Frontier*. Ann Arbor: University of Michigan Press.

Crites, J. L. 1964. "A Millipede, *Narceus americanus*, as a Natural Intermediate Host of an Acanthocephalan. J." *Parasitology* 50 (2): 293.

Cumbaa, S. L. 1980. "Aboriginal Use of Marine Mammals in the Southeastern United States." Southeast Archaeological Conference Bulletin 17: 6–10.

Dahlberg, M. D., and D. C. Scott. 1971. "The Freshwater Fishes of Georgia." Bulletin of the Georgia Academy of Science 29: 1–64.

Darlington, W., complier. 1969. *Reliquiae Baldwinianae*. New York and London: Hafner Publishing. Reprint. Originally published in Philadelphia in 1843 by Kimberly and Sharpless.

Davidson, W. R., V. F. Nettles, C. E. Couvillion, and H. W. Yoder Jr. 1982. "Infectious Sinusitis in Wild Turkeys." *Avian Diseases* 26 (2): 402–405.

Davis, J. H., Jr. 1943. "The Natural Features of Southern Florida." Florida Geological Survey Bulletin 25.

Deagan, K. 1978. "Cultures in Transition: Fusion and Assimilation among the Eastern Timucua." In *Tacachale: Essays of the Indians of Florida and Southeast Georgia during the Historic Period*. Edited by J. Milanich and S. Proctor. Gainesville: University Press of Florida: 89–119.

DePratter, C. B., and J. D. Howard. 1977. "History of Shoreline Changes Determined by Archeological Dating: Georgia Coast, U.S.A." *Transactions of the Gulf Coast Association Geological Society* XXVII: 252–58.

———. 1980. "Indian Occupation and Geologic History of the Georgia Coast: A 5,000 Year Summary." In *Excursions in Southeastern Geology, The Archaeology-Geology of the Georgia Coast*. Edited by J. D. Howard, C. B. DePratter, and R. W. Frey. *Geological Society of America, Guidebook* 20: 1–65.

DeVorsey, L., Jr., ed. 1971. *DeBrahm's Report of the General Survey in the Southern District of North America*. Tricentennial Edition No. 3. Columbia: University of South Carolina Press.

Doutt, J. K. 1954. "The Swimming of the Opossum." *Journal of Mammalogy* 35 (4): 581–83.

Duncan, W. H. 1982. "The Vascular Vegetation of Sapelo Island, Georgia." Botany Department. Athens: University of Georgia. Atlanta: Georgia Department of Natural Resources.

Duncan, W. H., and M. B. Duncan. 1987. *Seaside Plants of the Gulf and Atlantic Coasts*. Washington, DC, and London: Smithsonian Institution Press.

Dyer, C. D. 1963. "History of the Gum Naval Stores Industry." *American Turpentine Farmers Association Journal* 25 (January 1963): 1–6.

Elliott, C. 1943. *Fading Trails*. Boston: Macmillan.

Elliot, W. 1828. "On the Cultivation and High Prices of Sea-Island Cotton." *Southern Agriculturist* 1 (April): 151–63.

———. 1994. *Carolina Sports by Land and Water*. Columbia: University of South Carolina Press. Originally published in 1846.

Engles, W. L. 1933. "Notes on the Mammals of St. Joseph County, Indiana." *American Midland Naturalist* 14 (1): 1–16.

Esher, R. D., J. L. Wolfe, and J. N. Layne. 1978. "Swimming Behavior of Rice Rats (*Oryzomys palustris*) and Cotton Rats (*Sigmodon hispidis*)." *Journal of Mammalogy* 59 (3): 551–58.

Feldhamer, G. A., B. G. Thompson, and J. C. Chapman. 2003. *Wild Mammals of North America*. Baltimore and London: Johns Hopkins University Press.

Fernald, M. L., and A. C. Kinsey. 1943. *Edible Wild Plants of Eastern North America*. New York: Idlewild Press.

Fitch, H. S., Jr. 1963. "Natural History of the Racer *Coluber constrictor*." *University of Kansas Museum of Natural History* 15 (8): 351–468.

Floyd, C. R. 1835. "Marmaduke Hamilton and Dolores Boisfeullet Papers." Savannah: Georgia Historical Society, Box 21.

Fogarty, M. J., and H. Campbell. 1978. "American Alligator." In *Rare and Endangered biota of Florida*. Volume 3. Edited by P. C. H. Pritchard and R. W. McDiarmid. Gainesville: University Presses of Florida. 65–67.

Foshee, A. G. 1988. "Vegetable Hair: The Spanish Moss Industry in Florida." *Florida Historical Quarterly* LXVI (3): 265–79.

Fowells, H. A. 1965. *Silvics of Forest Trees of the United States*. United States Department of Agriculture, Forest Service. Agriculture Handbook 271.

Fox, J. F. 1982. "Adaptation of Gray Squirrel Behavior to Autumn Germination by White Oak Acorns." *Evolution* 36: 800–809.

Frey, R. W., and M. R. Voorhies. 1975. "Fossil and Recent Skeletal Remains in Georgia Estuaries." *In Estuaries of the Georgia Coast, U.S.A.* 7: 257–95.

Gallay, A. 1989. *The Formation of a Planter Elite*. Athens: University of Georgia Press.

Garth, R. E. 1964. "The Ecology of Spanish Moss (*Tillandsia usneoides*): Its growth and Distribution." *Ecology* 45 (3): 470–81.

Georgia Division of Archives and History (GDAH). Carnegie estate records of Cumberland Island, 1798–1969.

Gibbons, E. 1962. *Stalking the Wild Asparagus*. New York: Van Rees Press.

Gibson, C. D. 1948. *Sea Islands of Georgia, Their Geologic History*. Athens: University of Georgia Press.

Ginn, E. H. 1987. *Recollections of Glynn*. Brunswick, GA: The Glover Printing Co.

REFERENCES

Godfrey, R. K., and J. W. Wooten. 1979. *Aquatic and Wetland Plants of Southeastern United States.* Athens: University of Georgia Press.

Golley, F. B. 1962. *Mammals of Georgia.* Athens: University of Georgia Press.

Granberry, J. 1993. *A Grammar and Dictionary of the Timucua Language.* Tuscaloosa: University of Alabama Press.

Grant, C. L., ed. 1980. Letters, Journals, and Writings of Benjamin Hawkins, 1796–1801. Vol. 1. Savannah, GA: Beehive Press.

Griffin, M. M., and V. J. Henry. 1984. "Historical Changes in the Mean High Water Shoreline of Georgia, 1857–1982." Georgia Department of Natural Resources, Georgia Geological Survey Bulletin 98.

Gubbins, C. 2002. "Use of Home Ranges by Resident Bottlenose Dolphins (*Tursiops truncatus*) in a South Carolina Estuary." *Journal of Mammalogy* 83 (1): 178–87.

Hallock, C., ed. 1876. Camp Life in Florida: A Handbook for Sportsman and Settlers. New York: Forest and Stream.

Handley, C. O., Jr. 1966. "A synopsis of the Genus *Kogia* (Pygmy Sperm Whales)." In *Whales, Dolphins and Porpoises.* Edited by K. S. Norris. University of California Press: 62–69.

Haney, J. C., P. Brisse, D. R. Jacobson, M. Oberle, and J. M. Paget. 1986. "Annotated Checklist of Georgia Birds." *Georgia Ornithological Society, Occasional Publication* 10.

Hann, J. H. 1996. *A History of the Timucua Indians and Missions.* University Press of Florida, R. P. Bullen Series, Florida Museum of Natural History.

Hanson, R. P., and L. Karstad. 1959. "Feral Swine in the Southeastern United States." *Journal of Wildlife Management* 23 (1): 64–74.

Harden, J. M. B. 1845. "Observations on the Soil, Climate, and Diseases of Liberty County, Georgia." *Southern Medical and Surgical Journal* 1 (10): 545–69.

Harper, F. 1927. "Mammals of the Okefenokee Swamp Region of Georgia." *Proceedings of the Boston Society of Natural History* 38 (March): 191–396.

———. 1958. *The Travels of William Bartram.* Naturalist's Edition. New Haven, CT: Yale University Press.

Harper, R. M. 1914. "Geography and Vegetation of Northern Florida." Florida Geological Survey, 6th Annual Report.

Harriot, T. 1972. *Brief and True Report of the New Found Land of Virginia.* New York: Dover. Originally printed by T. de Bry, Frankfurt a/M in 1590.

Hemmings, E. T., and K. A. Deagan. 1973. "Excavations on Amelia Island in Northeast Florida." Contribution of the Florida State Museum, Anthropology and History (18). Gainesville: University of Florida.

Herndon, M. 1968. "Naval Stores in Colonial Georgia." *Georgia Historical Quarterly* 52 (4): 426–33.

Hersh, S. L. 1987. "Characterization and Differentiation of Bottlenose Dolphin Populations (Genus *Tursiops*) in the Southeastern United States Based on Mortality Patterns and Morphometrics." PhD diss., University of Miami.

Heyward, F. 1939. "The Relation of Fire to Stand Composition of Longleaf Pine Forests." *Ecology* 20 (2): 287–304.

Hillestad, H. O., J. R. Bozeman, A. S. Johnson, C. W. Berisford, and J. I. Richardson. 1975. "The Ecology of the Cumberland Island National Seashore, Camden County, Georgia." *University of Georgia Technical Report Series*. Georgia Marine Science Center, Skidaway Island, Georgia.

Hilmon, J. B. 1968. "The Autecology of the Saw Palmetto." PhD diss., Duke University.

Hoelzel, A. R., C. W. Potter, and P. B. Best. 1998. "Genetic Differentiation between Parapatric Nearshore and Offshore Populations of the Bottlenose Dolphin." *Proceedings of the Royal Society of London* 265 (1402): 1177–83.

Holbrook, J. E. 1976. *North American Herpetology*. Society for the Study of Amphibians and Reptiles (SSAR). Reprint. Originally published in Philadelphia by J. Dobson in 1842.

Howell, A. H. 1920. "Description of a New Species of Beach Mouse from Florida." *Journal of Mammalogy* 1 (5): 237–40.

Huddlestun, P. F. 1988. "A Revision of the Lithostratigraphic Units of the Coastal Plain of Georgia, the Miocene through Holocene." Georgia Geological Survey Bulletin 104.

Hudson, C. 1976. *The Southeastern Indians*. Knoxville: University of Tennessee Press.

Humphries, R. L., ed. 1991. *The Journal of Archibald C. McKinley*. Athens: University of Georgia Press.

Humphry, S. R. 1974. "Zoogeography of the Nine-banded Armadillo (*Dasypus novemcinctus*) in the U.S." *Bioscience* 24 (8): 457–62.

"Hunter Tract Prospectus, 1894." Georgia Division of Archives and History, Rare Book Collection: Morrow, Georgia.

Imhof, T. A. 1976. *Alabama Birds*. Tuscaloosa: University of Alabama Press.

Ivers, L. E. 1974. British Drums on the Southern Frontier: The Military Colonization of Georgia. Chapel Hill: University of North Carolina Press.

Jackson, C. J. 2006. "Historical Back-barrier Shoreline Changes along Cumberland Island, Georgia, 1857–2002." Report for the National Park Service.

Jenkins, J. H. 1953. "The Game Resources of Georgia." Georgia Game and Fish Commission, Federal Aid Project, GA W-1-R.

Jensen, J. B., C. D. Camp, W. Gibbons, and M. J. Elliott, eds. 2008. *Amphibians and Reptiles of Georgia*. Athens: University of Georgia Press.

Johnson, A. S., H. O. Hillestad, S. F. Shanholtzer, and G. F. Shanholtzer. 1974. "An Ecological Survey of the Coastal Region of Georgia." *National Park Service Monograph Series* 3.

Johnson, G. G. 1930. *A Social History of the Sea Islands*. Chapel Hill: University of North Carolina Press.

Jordan, H. B., and M. B. Friend. 1971. "The Occurrence of *Shellackia* and *Plasmodium* in two Georgia Lizards." *Journal of Protozoology* 18 (3): 485–87.

Kilgo, J. C., and R. F. Labisky. 1995. "Nutritional Quality of Three Major Deer Forages in Pine Flatwoods of Northern Florida." *Florida Scientist* 58 (4): 327–34.

Koprowski, J. L. 1994. "*Sciurus carolinensis*." *Mammalian Species* 480: 1–9.

Kozel, T. R. 1991. "Surface Water Quality in Three Interdunal Ponds, South End Ponds Ecosystem, Cumberland Island, Georgia." Proceedings of the 1991 Georgia Water Resources Conference, University of Georgia.

REFERENCES

Kushlan, J. A. 1972. "An Ecological Study of an Alligator Pond in the Big Cypress Swamp of Southern Florida." Master's thesis, University of Miami.

Laerm, J., T. C. Carter, M. A. Menzel, T. S. McCay, J. L. Boone, W. M. Ford, L. T. Lepardo, D. M. Krishon, G. Balkcom, N. L. Van Der Maath, and M. J. Harris. 1999. "Amphibians, Reptiles, and Mammals of Sapelo Island, Georgia." *Journal of the Elisha Mitchell Scientific Society* 115 (2): 104–26.

Laessle, A. M. 1942. "The Plant Communities of the Welaka Area." *University of Florida Publications, Biological Science Series* IV (1).

Laessle, A. M., and C. D. Monk. 1961. "Some Live Oak Forests of Northeastern Florida." *Quarterly Journal of the Florida Academy of Science* 24 (1): 39–55.

LaGory, K. E., C. Bagshaw, and I. L. Brisbin. 1991. "Niche Differences between Male and Female White-tailed Deer on Ossabaw Island, Georgia." *Applied Animal Behavior Science* 29: 205–14.

Lanning, J. T. 1935. *The Spanish Missions of Georgia.* Chapel Hill: University of North Carolina Press.

Larsen, C. S. 1980. "Human Skeletal and Dental Health Changes on the Prehistoric Georgia Coast." In *Excursions in Southeastern Geology, The Archaeology-Geology of the Georgia Coast.* Edited by J. D. Howard, C. B. DePratter, and R. W. Frey. *Geological Society of America Guidebook* 20: 192–201. Georgia Department of Natural Resources.

———. 1982. "Prehistoric Human Biological Adaptation." The Anthropology of St. Catherines Island. *Anthropological Papers of the American Museum of Natural History* 57 (3).

Larson, L. H. 1980. Aboriginal Subsistence Technology on the Southeastern Coastal Plain During the Late Prehistoric Period. Gainesville: University Presses of Florida.

Layne, J. N. 1971. "Mammals of Amelia Island." In *Amelia Island, Nassau County, Florida: A Preliminary Ecological Inventory.* Report to Amelia Island Company, Fernandina Beach, FL, by Jack McCormick and Associates: 237–359.

———. 2003. "Armadillo, *Dasypus novemcinctus.*" In *Wild Mammals of North America.* Edited by G. A. Feldhamer, B. C. Thompson, and J. A. Chapman. Baltimore and London: Johns Hopkins University Press.

Leary, P. 2009. "Arctic Tern." *Oriole* 74 (1–4): 60.

LeConte, J. L. 1853. "Description of Three New Species of American Arvicolae, with Remarks Upon Some Other American Rodents." *Proceedings of the Academy of Natural Sciences* 6: 404–15.

Little, E. A., and J. C. Andrews. 1982. "Drift Whales at Nantucket: The Kindness of Moshup." *Man in the Northeast* 23 (Spring): 17–38.

Lockey, J., J. W. Byrne, and J. W. Caughey, eds. 1949. *East Florida, 1783–1785.* University of California Press.

Lotze, J. 1979. "The Raccoon (*Procyon lotor*) on St. Catherines Island, Georgia. Comparisons of Home Ranges Determined by Livetrapping and Radiotracking." *American Museum Novitates* 2664: 1–25.

Lovell, C. C. 1933. *The Golden Isles of Georgia.* Boston: Little and Brown.

Lowery, G. H. 1974. *The Mammals of Louisiana and Its Adjacent Waters*. Kingsport, TN: Louisiana State University Press.

Lowery, W. 1911. The Spanish Settlements within the Present Limits of the U.S., Florida 1562–1574. New York and London: G. B. Putnam's Sons.

Lyell, Charles. 1845. *Travels in North America*. London: John Murray.

———. 1849. A Second Visit to the United States of North America. 2 vols. New York: Harper Bros.

Mackaness, F. P. 1942. "Bryophytes of the Live Oak Forest." *Louisiana Academy of Science* 6: 48–49.

Mager, K. J., and T. A. Nelson. 2001. "Roost-site Selection by Eastern Red Bats (*Lasiurus borealis*)." *American Midland Naturalist* 145 (1): 120–26.

McCallie, S. W. 1898. "A Preliminary Report on the Artesian-Well System in Georgia." Georgia Geological Survey Bulletin 7.

McLemore, W. H., C. T. Swann, P. B. Wigley, M. C. Turlington, V. J. Henry, G. J. Nash, J. Martinez, R. E. Carver, and J. T. Thurmond. 1981. "Geology as Applied to Land-use Management on Cumberland Island, Georgia." Georgia Department of Natural Resources, Georgia Geological Survey.

McManus, J. J. 1974. "*Didelphis virginana*." *Mammalian Species* 40: 1–6.

McMichael, A. E. 1977. "A Model for Barrier Island Settlement Pattern." *Florida Anthropologist* 30 (4): 179–95.

McNab, B. K. 1980. "Energetics and the Limits to a Temperate Distribution in Armadillos." *Journal of Mammalogy* 61 (4): 606–27.

McPherson, R., ed. 1962. *The Journal of the Earl of Egmont*. Athens: University of Georgia Press.

Mead, J. G., and C. W. Potter. 1995. "Recognizing Two Populations of the Bottlenose Dolphin (*Tursipos truncatus*) off the Atlantic Coast of North America." International Marine Biology Research Institute: IBI Reports 5:31–44.

Meader, E. A., and W. E. Page. 1898–1905. Map: Dungeness and Stafford Place. Property of Lucy C. Carnegie. Georgia Department of Archives and History: Morrow, GA.

Milanich, J. T. 1972. "Tacatacuru and the San Pedro De Mocamo Mission." *Florida Historical Quarterly* L (3): 283–91.

———. 1973. "The Southeastern Deptford Culture: A Preliminary Definition." Florida Bureau of Historic Sites and Properties Bulletin 3: 51–63.

Milanich, J. T., and W. C. Sturtevant. 1972. "Francisco Pareja's 1613 Confessionario, a Documentary Source for Timucuan Ethnography." Tallahassee: Division of Archives, History and Records Management, Florida Department of State.

Miller, M. 1990. "Cumberland Island, The Unsung Northend." *Darien* (GA) *News*.

Miller, S. K. 1988. "Reproductive Biology of White-tailed Deer on Cumberland Island, Georgia." Master's thesis, University of Georgia.

Mitchell, J. C. 1994. *The Reptiles of Virginia*. Washington and London: Smithsonian Institution Press.

Mitchell, J. C., and C. Ruckdeschel. 2008. "*Crotalus adamanteus*." *Herpetological Review* 39 (4): 467–68.

REFERENCES

Monk, C. B. 1966. "An Ecological Significance of Evergreeness." *Ecology* 47 (3): 504–505.

Moore, F. 1983. *A Voyage to Georgia, Begun in the Year 1735.* Brunswick, GA: Glover Printing Company. Georgia Historical Society Reprint. Originally printed in London for Jacob Robinson in 1744.

Moore, T. 1986. "King Eider at Cumberland Island National Seashore." *Oriole* 51 (4): 69–70.

Murphy, R. C. 1936. *Oceanic Birds of South America.* 2 vols. MacMillan.

Neill, W. T. 1952. "The Spread of the Armadillo in Florida." *Ecology* 33 (2): 282–84.

———. 1958. "The Occurrence of Amphibians and Reptiles in Saltwater Areas and Bibliography." Bulletin of Marine Science, Gulf and Caribbean 8: 1–97.

Neill, W. T., H. J. Gut, and P. Brodkorb. 1956. "Animal Remains from Four Preceramic Sites in Florida." *American Antiquity* 21 (4): 383–95.

Neuhauser, H. N., and W. W. Baker. 1974. "Annotated List of Mammals of the Coastal Islands of Georgia." In *An Ecological Survey of the Coastal Region of Georgia,* A. S. Johnson, H. O. Hillestad, S. F. Shanholzer, and G. F. Shanholzer. *National Park Service Monograph Series* 3.

Neuhauser, H. N., and C. Ruckdeschel. 1978. "Whales (Cetacea) of Georgia." Proceedings of the Rare & Endangered Wildlife Symposium, Georgia Department of Natural Resources Technical Bulletin WL4: 38–53.

Ober, F. A. 1880. "Dungeness. General Greene's Sea Island Plantation." *Lippincott's Magazine,* (26 August): 241–49.

Odum, W. E., and J. W. Harvey. 1988. "Barrier Island Interdunal Freshwater Wetlands." Association of Southern Biologists Bulletin 35 (4): 149–55.

Olson, D. F., Jr., and S. G. Boyce. 1971. "Factors Affecting Acorn Production and Germination and Early Growth of Seedlings and Seedling Sprouts." Oak Symposium, Proceedings 44–48, USDA, Northeast Forest Experiment Station.

Oritz, R. M., and G. A. W. Worthy. 2006. "Body Composition and Water Turnover Rates of Bottlefed West Indian Manatee Calves." *Aquatic Mammals* 32 (1): 41–45.

Osborne, J. S., A. S. Johnson, P. E. Hale, R. L. Marchinton, C. V. Vansant, and J. M. Wentworth. 1992. "Population Ecology of the Blackbeard Island White-tailed Deer." Tall Timbers Research Inc. Bulletin 26.

Osgood, W. H. 1909. "Revision of the Mice of the American Genus *Peromyscus.*" *North American Fauna* 28: 1–285.

Osowski, S. L. 1992. "The Role of Environmental Contaminants in the Decline of Mink (*Mustela vison*) in the Coastal Plain of Georgia, North Carolina, and South Carolina." Final Report to South Carolina Wildlife and Marine Resources Department, North Carolina Wildlife Resources Commission, and Georgia Department of Natural Resources.

Pavich-Lindsay, M., ed. 2002. Anna, the Letters of a St. Simons Island Plantation Mistress, Anna Matilda Page King. Athens: University of Georgia Press.

Pearson, T. G. 1922. "Notes on the Birds of Cumberland Island, Georgia." Wilson Bulletin 34: 84–90.

Pence, D. B., R. J. Warren, and G. R. Ford. 1988. "Visceral Helminth Communities of an Insular Population of Feral Swine." *Journal of Wildlife Diseases* 24 (1): 105–12.

Peter Kalm's Travels in North America. New York: Dover Publications, 1966. Edited by A. B. Benson. Originally published in Toronto, Canada: General Publishing Company, 1937.

Petrides, G. A. 1949. "Sex and Age Determination in the Opossum." *Journal of Mammalogy* 30 (4): 364–78.

Pirkle, F. L., E. C. Pirkle, and J. G. Reynolds. 1993. "Yulee Heavy-mineral Deposits." In *Geomorphology and Facies Relationships of Quaternary Barrier Island Complexes Near St. Marys, Georgia.* Edited by K. M. Farrell, C. W. Hoffman, and V. J. Henry Jr., *Georgia Geological Society Guidebook* 13 (1): 68–73.

Plummer, G., and J. C. Purvis. 1991. "Tornadoes in Georgia, 1950–1989." Southeast Regional Climate Center, South Carolina Water Resources Commission, Technical Paper 110191.

Porcher, F. P. 1970. *Resources of the Southern Fields and Forests.* New York: Arno. *The New York Times*, Reprint. Originally printed in Charleston, SC, by Walker, Evans, and Cogswell, 1869.

Porcher, R. D. 1995. *Wildflowers of the Carolina Lowcountry and Lower Pee Dee.* Columbia: University of South Carolina Press.

Ray, C. E. 1961. "The Monk Seal in Florida." *Journal of Mammalogy* 42 (1): 113.

Reitz, E. J. 1991. "Evidence for Animal Use at the Missions of Spanish Florida." *Florida Anthropologist* 44 (2–4): 295–306.

Rhea, M. W. 1986. "Comparison of Quaternary Shoreline Systems in Georgia: Morphology, Drainage, and Inferred Processes of Formation." Master's thesis, University of Georgia.

Rice, D. W. 1998. *Marine Mammals of the World.* Society for Marine Mammalogy, Special Publication 4.

Richardson, J. I. 1973. "A Confirmed Occurrence of the Rough-toothed Dolphin (*Steno bredanensis*) on the Atlantic Coast of the United States." *Journal of Mammalogy* 54 (1): 275.

Rigdon, T. A., and A. J. Green. 1980. Soil Survey of Camden and Glynn Counties, Georgia. USDA, Soil Conservation Service in Cooperation with University of Georgia Agricultural Experiment Station.

Robertson, W. B., and G. E. Woolfenden. 1992. *Florida Bird Species: An Annotated List.* Gainesville: Florida Ornithological Society.

Romans, B. 1961. *A Concise Natural History of East and West Florida.* New Orleans, LA: Pelican Publishing. Reprint. Originally printed in New York for Romans, 1775.

Ross, M. 1926. "The Restoration of the Spanish Missions in Georgia, 1598–1606." *Georgia Historical Quarterly* 10 (3): 171–99.

Ross Papers. Georgia Division of Archives and History. Folder 103 (1): Morrow, GA.

Ruckdeschel, C. 1996. "First Specimen of a White-tailed Tropicbird from Georgia." *Oriole* 60 (2–3): 39–41.

———. 2003. "Chuck-will's-widow: Fatal Forage." *Oriole* 68 (1–2): 13–14.

———. 2005. "First Georgia Specimen of the Brown Booby." *Florida Field Naturalist* 33 (2): 50.

REFERENCES

———. 2008. "New Georgia Specimens." *Oriole* 73 (1–4): 30.

———. 2012. "*Rhadinea flavilata*, Geographic Distribution." *Herpetological Review* 43 (1): 107.

Ruckdeschel, C., L. Ellis, and C. R. Shoop. 1982. "*Dermochelys coriacea*, Nesting." *Herpetological Review* 13 (4): 126.

Ruckdeschel, C., and H. B. Jordan. 1982. "Observations on the Cumberland Island Fire of 16 July–24 August, 1981, and Subsequent Recovery." Final Report, National Park Service Contract PX 5630-1-531.

Ruckdeschel, C., and C. R. Shoop. 1986. "The Fauna of Cumberland Island, I: On the Occurrence of the Opossum and Gray Fox." *Georgia Journal of Science* 44: 90–95.

———. 1987. "Aspects of Wood Stork Nesting Ecology on Cumberland Island, Georgia." *Oriole* 52 (2–3): 21–27.

———. 1998a. "*Eretmochelys imbricata*, Geographic Distribution." *Herpetological Review* 29 (4): 247.

———. 1998b. "Georgia Specimens of the Sooty Shearwater." *Oriole* 61 (2–3): 42–43.

———. 2006. Sea Turtles of the Atlantic and Gulf Coasts of the United States. Athens and London: University of Georgia Press.

Ruckdeschel, C., C. R. Shoop, and G. W. Sciple. 1994. "A Mass Stranding of Leach's Storm-petrel in Georgia and Florida." *Florida Scientist* 57 (1–2): 48–49.

Ruckdeschel, C., C. R. Shoop, and D. Sibley. 1996. "First Sighting of the Shiny Cowbird in Georgia." *Oriole* 61 (2–3): 29–30.

Ruckdeschel, C., C. R. Shoop, and B. Winn. 1990. "Brown Pelican Nesting in Georgia." *Oriole* 55 (4): 65–69.

Ruckdeschel, C., C. R. Shoop, and G. R. Zug. 2000. Sea turtles of the Georgia Coast. Occasional Publications of the Cumberland Island Museum.

Ruckdeschel, C. and J. O. Whitaker Jr. 2007. "The American Kestrel on Cumberland Island, Georgia." *Oriole* 72 (1–4): 8–11.

Sabine, J. B., S. H. Schwitzer, and M. T. Meyers. 2006. "Nest Fate and Productivity of American Oystercatchers, Cumberland Island National Seashore, Georgia." *Waterbirds* 29 (3): 308–14.

Say, Thomas. 1818. "Account of Two New Genera and Several New Species of Freshwater and Land Shells." *Journal of the Academy of Natural Sciences of Philadelphia.* 1 (2): 276–84.

Schemmel, B. 1975. "Golden Sand, Golden Sunsets, Cumberland Island, Georgia." *Travel* September: 40–45.

Schmalzer, P. A., and C. R. Hinkle. 1992. "Species Composition and Structure of Oak-Saw Palmetto Scrub Vegetation." *Castanea* 57 (4): 220–51.

Seibert, N. D. 1966. "History of the Downes Family." Unpublished manuscript. Cumberland Island Museum.

Sharpe, J. 1977. "Plant Checklist, Georgia Coastal Islands." Manuscript. Athens: University of Georgia Herbarium.

Shelley, R. M., and W. D. Sissom. 1995. "Distributions of the Scorpions *Centruroides vittatus* (Say) and *Centruroides hentzi* (Banks) in the United States and Mexico (Scorpiones, Buthidae)." *Journal of Arachnology* 23: 100–10.

Sherman, H. B. 1969. Georgia Division of Archives and History, Morrow, GA. Manuscripts (Carnegie Estate): AC 1969. 501 M.

Shoop. C. R., and C. Ruckdeschel. 1986. "New Herpetological Records for Cumberland Island, Georgia." *Herpetological Review* 17 (2): 51.

———. 1990. "Alligators as Predators on Terrestrial Mammals." *American Midland Naturalist* 124: 407–12.

———. 1997. "Geographic Distribution: *Ophisaurus compressus.*" *Herpetological Review* 28 (3):157.

———. 2003. "Herpetological Biogeography of the Georgia Barrier Islands: An Alternative Interpretation." *Florida Scientist* 66 (1): 43–51.

Silva, J. S. 1976. Early Reminiscence of Camden County, Georgia, by an Old St. Marys Boy in his 82nd Year. Kingsland, GA: Southeast Georgian.

Simberloff, D., and J. Cox. 1987. "Consequences and Costs of Conservation Corridors." *Conservation Biology* 1 (1): 63–71.

Slonaker, J. R. 1920. "Some Morphological Changes for Adaptation in the Mole." *Journal of Morphology* 34 (2): 335–73.

Smith, J. F. 1985. *Slavery and Rice Culture in Low Country Georgia, 1750–1860.* Knoxville: University of Tennessee Press.

Smith, M. H., J. B. Gentry, and J. Pinder. 1974. "Annual Fluctuations in Small Mammal Populations in an Eastern Hardwood Forest." *Journal of Mammalogy* 55 (1): 231–34.

Sprunt, A., Jr. 1933. "The Glossy Ibis in Georgia." *Auk* 50 (3): 352.

———. 1936. "Some Observations on the Bird Life of Cumberland Island, Georgia." *Oriole* 1 (1): 1–6.

———. 1954. *Florida Bird Life.* New York: Coward-McCann.

Sprunt, A., Jr., and E. B. Chamberlain. 1949. *South Carolina Bird Life.* Columbia: University of South Carolina Press.

Stoddard, H. L. 1947. "Examination of Cumberland Island." Memorandum. Tallahassee, FL: Archives of Tall Timbers Research Station.

Stoneburner, D. L., and L. A. Smock. 1979. "The Physical and Chemical Limnology of an Insular, Brown-water Lake in Coastal Georgia." *Archiv fur Hydrobiologie* 87: 364–78.

Sullivan, B. 1990. *Early Days on the Georgia Tidewater, The Story of McIntosh County and Sapelo, Georgia.* Darien, GA: The Darien News.

Swanson, V. E., and J. G. Palacas. 1965. "Humate in Coastal Sands of Northwest Florida." Contributions to Geochemistry, Geologic Survey Bulletin 1214-B.

Swanton, J. R. 1922. "Early History of the Creek Indians and Their Neighbors." Smithsonian Institution, Bureau of American Ethnology Bulletin 73.

———. 1946. "The Indians of the Southeastern United States." Washington, DC: Bureau of American Ethnology Bulletin 137.

Tanner, W. F. 1992. "3000 Years of Sea Level Change." Bulletin of the American Meteorological Society 73 (3): 297–303.

Teal, M., and J. Teal. 1964. *Portrait of an Island.* New York: Atheneum.

Thom, B. G. 1967. "Humate and Coastal Geomorphology." Louisiana State University, Coastal Studies Series Bulletin 1.

REFERENCES

Thomas, E. J. 1923. *Memoirs of a Southerner.* Savannah: Privately Printed.

Timm, R. M., R. M. Salazar, and A. T. Peterson. 1997. "Historical Distribution of the Extinct Tropical Seal, *Monachus tropicalis* (Carnivora: Phocidae)." *Conservation Biology* 11 (2): 549–51.

Tomkins, I. R. 1965. "Absence of the Blue Jay on Some of Georgia's Coastal Islands." *Oriole* 30 (2): 77–79.

Torres, L. 1977. "Historic Resource Study, Cumberland Island National Seashore, Georgia." Historic Preservation Division, USDI, National Park Service, Denver.

Turner, S. No date (~1984). "The Fire History of Cumberland Island National Seashore, 1900–1983." National Park Service Cooperative Unit and Institute of Ecology, University of Georgia, Technical Report 7.

Vignoles, C. 1979. *Observations on the Floridas.* Facsimile Edition, University Presses of Florida. Originally published in New York by E. Bliss and E. White, 1823.

Wagner, R. H. 1964. "Ecology of *Uniola paniculata* L. in the Dune-Strand Habitat of North Carolina." *Ecological Monographs* 34 (1): 79–96.

Walker, K. J. 1985. "The Protohistoric and Historic Indian Occupation at King's Bay: An Overview." In *Aboriginal Subsistence and Settlement Archaeology of the King's Bay and Devil's Walking Stick Sites.* Edited by W. H. Adams. University of Florida, Department of Anthropology, Report of Investigations, 1: 55–71.

Warren, M. A. 1944. "Artesian Water in Southeastern Georgia." Georgia Geological Survey Bulletin 49.

Wassmer, D. A, D. D. Guenther, and J. N. Layne. 1988. "Ecology of the Bobcat in South-Central Florida." Bulletin of the Florida State Museum 33 (4): 159–228.

Watkins, L. C. 1972. "*Nycticeius humeralis.*" *Mammalian Species* 23: 1–4.

Watts, W. A. 1971. "Postglacial and Interglacial Vegetation History of Southern Georgia and Central Florida." *Ecology* 52 (4): 676–90.

Webb, S. D. 1974. *Pleistocene Mammals of Florida.* Gainesville: University Presses of Florida.

Webster's New World Dictionary, 2nd edition. 1970. Edited by David B. Guralnik. New York and Cleveland, OH: World Publishing.

Wharton, C. H. 1960. "Birth and Behavior of a Brood of Cottonmouths, *Agkistrodon piscivorus,* with Notes on Tail-luring." *Herpetologica* 16 (2): 125–29.

Whitaker, J. O., Jr., and C. Ruckdeschel. 2006. "Food of the Southern Short-tailed Shrew on Cumberland Island, Georgia." *Southeastern Naturalist* 5 (2): 361–66.

———. 2009. "Diet of *Amphiuma means* from Cumberland Island, Georgia, U.S.A." *Herpetological Review* 40 (2): 154–56.

———. 2010. "Spanish Moss, the Unfinished Chigger Story." *Southeast Naturalist* 9 (1): 85–94.

———. 2013. "Food of Eastern Moles, *Scalopus aquaticus,* on Cumberland Island, Georgia." *Georgia Journal of Science* 71 (3): 167–72.

Whitaker, J. O., Jr., C. Ruckdeschel, and L. Bakken. 2012a. "Food of the Armadillo, *Dasypus novemcinctus,* from Cumberland Island, Georgia." *Southeastern Naturalist* 11 (3): 487–506.

———. 2012b. "Food of Some Lizards from Cumberland Island, Georgia." *Herpetological Review* 43 (4): 569–571.

White, G. 1849. *Statistics of the State of Georgia*. Savannah, GA: W. T. Williams.

Williams, S. L., and H. H. Genoways. 1980. "Morphological Variation in the Southeastern Pocket Gopher, *Geomys pinetis*, (Mammalia: Rodentia)." *Annals of the Carnegie Museum* 49 (23): 405–53.

Williams, M., and S. Jones. 2006. "Lithics, Shellfish, and Beavers." In *Light on the Path: The Anthropology and History of the Southeastern Indians*. Edited by T. J. Pluckhann. Tuscaloosa: University of Alabama Press.

Williston, H. L., and F. W. Shropshire. 1980. "Cypress Management: A Forgotten Opportunity." USDA, Forest Service, Forestry Report SA-FR8.

Wing, E. S., and I. R. Quitmyer. 1985. "Screen Size for optimal Data Recovery: a Case Study." In *Aboriginal Subsistnce and Settlement Archaeology of the Kings Bay Locality, Volume 2, Zooarchaeology*. Edited by W. H. Adams. Gainesville: University of Florida, Department of Anthropology, Reports of Investigations 2: 49–58.

Wood, G. W., and D. N. Roark. 1980. "Food Habits of Feral Hogs in Coastal South Carolina." *Journal of Wildlife Management* 44 (2): 506–11.

Wood, V. S. 1981. *Live Oaking*. Boston: Northeastern University Press.

Wood, V. S., and M. R. Bullard, eds. 1996. Journal of a Visit to the Georgia Islands of St. Catherines, Green, Ossabaw, Sapelo, St. Simons, Jekyll, and Cumberland. Macon, GA: Mercer University Press.

Worth, J. E. 1995. "The Struggle for the Georgia Coast: An 18th Century Spanish Retrospective on Guale and Mocama." Anthropological Papers of the American Museum of Natural History, No. 75.

Wright, A. H. 1926. "The Vertebrate Life of the Okefenokee Swamp in Relation to the Atlantic Coastal Plain." *Ecology* 7: 72–95.

Wunderlin, R. F., and B. F. Hansen. 2011. *Guide to the Vascular Plants of Florida*. 3rd Edition. University Press of Florida.

Yabsley, M. J., A. E. Ellis, C. A. Cleveland, and C. Ruckdeschel. 2015. "High Prevalence of *Porocephalus crotali* Infection on a Barrier Island (Cumberland Island) Off the Coast of Georgia, with Identification of Novel Intermediate Hosts." *J. Parasitology* 101 (5): 603–607.

Yabsley, M. J., G. P. Noblet, and O. J. Pung. 2001. "Use of the Indirect Immunofluorescent Antibody Test (IFAT) and Blood Culture to Detect *Trypanosoma cruzi* Infections in Raccoons from Georgia." *Journal of Parasitology* 87 (5): 1155–59.

Yesner, D. R. 1980. "Maritime Hunter-Gathers: Ecology and Prehistory." *Current Anthropology* 21 (6): 727–50.

Youngken, H. W. 1948. *Textbook of Pharmacognosy*. Philadelphia and Toronto: Blakiston.

Zeigler, J. M. 1973. "Origin of the Sea Islands of the Southeastern U.S." In *Barrier Islands*. Edited by M. L. Schwartz. Stroudsberg, PA: Dowden, Hutchinson, and Ross.

Zoodsma, B. J. 1991. "Distribution and Behavioral Ecology of Manatees in Southeastern Georgia." Kings Bay Environmental Monitoring Program. National Park Service Report to the Southeast Region: 91.

APPENDIX I. PLANT LIST FOR CUMBERLAND ISLAND, GEORGIA

*= exotic

Scientific name	Family	Common name
Acacia farnesiana	Fabaceae	Sweet Acacia
Acalypha gracilens	Euphorbiaceae	Threeseeded Mercury
Acalypha ostryifolia	Euphorbiaceae	Pineland Threeseed Mercury
Acer rubrum	Aceraceae	Red Maple
Aeschynomene viscidula	Fabaceae	Sticky Jointvetch
Aesculus pavia	Sapindaceae	Red Buckeye
Agalinis fasciculata	Orobanchaceae	Beach False Foxglove
Agalinis maritima	Orobanchaceae	Saltmarsh False Foxglove
Agalinis obtusifolia	Orobanchaceae	Tenlobe False Foxglove
Agalinis purpurea	Orobanchaceae	Purple False Foxglove
Ageratina altissima	Asteraceae	White Snakeroot
Ageratina jucunda	Asteraceae	Hammock Snakeroot
* *Albizia julibrissin*	Fabaceae	Silktree; Mimosa
* *Aleurites fordii*	Euphorbiaceae	Tungoil Tree
* *Ailanthus altissima*	Simaroubaceae	Tree-of-Heaven
* *Alpinia zerumbet*	Zingiberaceae	Shellflower
* *Alternanthera philoxeroides*	Amaranthaceae	Alligatorweed
* *Amaranthus viridis*	Amaranthaceae	Slender Amaranth
Ambrosia artemisiifolia	Asteraceae	Common Ragweed
Ammannia latifolia	Lythraceae	Pink Redstem
Amoglossum ovatum	Asteraceae	Ovateleaf Indian Plantain
Amorpha fruticosa	Fabaceae	Bastard False Indigo
Ampelopsis arborea	Vitaceae	Peppervine
Anagallis minima	Primulaceae	Chaffweed
Andropogon glomeratus	Poaceae	Bushy Bluestem
Andropogon gyrans	Poaceae	Elliott's Bluestem
Andropogon ternarius	Poaceae	Splitbeard Bluestem
Andropogon virginicus	Poaceae	Broomsedge Bluestem
* *Antigonon leptopus*	Polygonaceae	Coral Vine
Aralia spinosa	Araliaceae	Devil's Walkingstick
Arenaria serpyllifolia	Caryophyllaceae	Thymeleaf Sandwort
Argemone albiflora	Papaveraceae	Bluestem Pricklypoppy
Argemone mexicana	Papaveraceae	Mexican Pricklypoppy
Arisaema triphyllum	Araceae	Jack- in-the-Pulpit
Aristida lanosa	Poaceae	Woolysheath Threeawn
Aristida longespica	Poaceae	Slimspike Threeawn

Aristida purpurascens	Poaceae	Arrowfeather Threeawn
Aristida spiciformis	Poaceae	Bottlebrush Threeawn
Aristolochia serpentaria	Aristolochiaceae	Virginia Snakeroot
Arundinaria gigantea	Poaceae	Switchcane
* *Arundo donax*	Poaceae	Giant Reed
Asclepias amplexicaulis	Apocynaceae	Clasping Milkweed
Asclepias humistrata	Apocynaceae	Pinewoods Milkweed
Asclepias longifolia	Apocynaceae	Longleaf Milkweed
Asclepias pedicellata	Apocynaceae	Savannah Milkweed
Asclepias verticillata	Apocynaceae	Whorled Milkweed
Asimina angustifolia	Annonaceae	Slimleaf Pawpaw
Asimina incana	Annonaceae	Wooly Pawpaw
Asimina parviflora	Annonaceae	Smallflower Pawpaw
Asimina pygmea	Annonaceae	Dwarf Pawpaw
* *Asparagus setaceus*	Asparagaceae	Common Asapragus-fern
Asplenium platyneuron	Aspleniaceae	Ebony Spleenwort
Astragalus villosus	Fabaceae	Bearded Milk-vetch
Atriplex pentandra	Amaranthaceae	Seabeach Orach
Axonopus compressus	Poaceae	Tropical Carpetgrass
Axonopus fissifolius	Poaceae	Common Carpetgrass
Axonopus furcatus	Poaceae	Big Carpetgrass
Azolla filiculoides	Azollaceae	American Waterfern
Baccharis angustifolia	Asteraceae	Falsewillow
Baccharis halimifolia	Asteraceae	Groundsel Tree
Bacopa caroliniana	Plantaginaceae	Blue Waterhyssop
Bacopa monnieri	Plantaginaceae	Herb-of-Grace
* *Bambusa multiplex*	Poaceae	Hedge Bamboo
Bartonia verna	Gentianaceae	White Screwstem
Batis maritima	Bataceae	Saltwort
Bejaria racemosa	Ericaceae	Tarflower
Berchemia scandens	Rhamnaceae	Rattan Vine
Bidens alba	Asteraceae	Beggarticks
Bidens bipinnata	Asteraceae	Spanish Needles
Bidens laevis	Asteraceae	Smooth Beggarticks
Bignonia capreolata	Bignoniaceae	Crossvine
Boehmeria cylindrica	Urticaceae	False Nettle
Boerhavia diffusa	Nyctaginaceae	Red Spiderling
Borrichia frutescens	Asteraceae	Bushy Seaside Oxeye
Brasenia schreberi	Cabombaceae	Watershield
* *Briza minor*	Poaceae	Little Quakinggrass
* *Bromus catharticus*	Poaceae	Rescuegrass
Buchnera americana	Orobanchaceae	American Bluehearts

*	*Bulbostylis barbata*	Cyperaceae	Watergrass
	Bulbostylis ciliatifolia	Cyperaceae	Capillary Hairsedge
	Bulbostylis stenophylla	Cyperaceae	Sandy Field Hairsedge
	Burmannia biflora	Burmanniaceae	Bluethread
*	*Butia capitata*	Arecaceae	Pindo Palm
	Cabomba caroliniana	Cabombaceae	Carolina Fanwort
	Cakile edentula	Brassicaceae	American Searocket
	Callicarpa americana	Laminaceae	American Beautyberry
	Calystegia sepium	Convolvulaceae	Hedge False Bindweed
*	*Camellia japonica*	Theaceae	Camellia
	Campsis radicans	Bignoniaceae	Trumpet Creeper
	Cardamine pensylvanica	Brassicaceae	Pennsylvania Bittercress
	Carex atlantica	Cyperaceae	Atlantic Sedge
	Carex bromoides	Cyperaceae	Bromelike Sedge
	Carex comosa	Cyperaceae	Longhair Sedge
	Carex dasycarpa	Cyperaceae	Sandywoods Sedge
	Carex festucacea	Cyperaceae	Fescue Sedge
	Carex fissa var. *aristata*	Cyperaceae	Hammock Sedge
	Carex joorii	Cyperaceae	Cypress Swamp Sedge
	Carex longii	Cyperaceae	Long's Sedge
	Carex lupulina	Cyperaceae	Hop Sedge
	Carex lurida	Cyperaceae	Shallow Sedge
	Carex muhlenbergii	Cyperaceae	Muhlenberg's Sedge
	Carex nigromarginata	Cyperaceae	Blackedge Sedge
	Carex normalis	Cyperaceae	Greater Straw Sedge
	Carex stipata	Cyperaceae	Awlfruit Sedge
	Carex verrucosa	Cyperaceae	Warty Sedge
	Carphephorus odoratissimus	Asteraceae	Vanillaleaf; Deer's Tongue
	Carya glabra	Juglandaceae	Pignut Hickory
*	*Carya illinoinensis*	Juglandaceae	Pecan
	Castanea pumila	Fagaceae	Chinquapin
*	*Cedrus deodara*	Pinaceae	Deodar Cedar
	Celtis laevigata	Celtidaceae	Hackberry
	Cenchrus echinatus	Poaceae	Southern Sandspur
	Cenchrus spinifex	Poaceae	Coastal Sandbur
	Cenchrus tribuloides	Poaceae	Sanddune Sandbur
	Centella asiatica	Araliaceae	Spadeleaf
	Centrosema virginianum	Fabaceae	Spurred Butterfly Pea
	Cephalanthus occidentalis	Rubiaceae	Common Buttonbush
*	*Cerastium glomeratum*	Caryophyllaceae	Mouse-ear Chickweed
	Ceratophyllum demersum	Ceratophyllaceae	Coontail
	Ceratophyllum echinatum	Ceratophyllaceae	Spiny Hornwort

	Cercis canadensis	Fabaceae	Redbud
	Chamaecrista fasciculata	Fabaceae	Partridge Pea
	Chamaecrista nictitans	Fabaceae	Sensitive Pea
*	*Chamaerops humilis*	Arecaceae	Dwarf Fan Plam
	Chamaesyce bombensis	Euphorbiaceae	Dixie Sandmat
	Chamaesyce hirta	Euphorbiaceae	Pillpod Sandmat
	Chamaesyce hypericifolia	Euphorbiaceae	Graceful Sandmat
	Chamaesyce hyssopifolia	Euphorbiaceae	Hyssopleaf Sandmat
	Chamaesyce maculata	Euphorbiaceae	Spotted Sandmat
	Chamaesyce polygonifolia	Euphorbiaceae	Seaside Sandmat
	Chamaesyce prostrata	Euphorbiaceae	Prostrate Sandmat
	Chasmanthium laxum	Poaceae	Slender Woodoats
*	*Chenopodium album*	Amaranthaceae	Lamb's-quarters
*	*Chenopodium ambrosioides*	Amaranthaceae	Mexican Tea
	Chionanthus virginicus	Oleaceae	White Fringetree
	Chrysopsis mariana	Asteraceae	Maryland Goldenaster
*	*Cinnamomum camphora*	Lauraceae	Camphortree
	Cirsium horridulum	Asteraceae	Purple Thistle
	Cirsium nuttallii	Asteraceae	Nuttall's Thistle
	Cirsium repandus	Asteraceae	Sandhill Thistle
	Cirsium virginianum	Asteraceae	Virginia Thistle
*	*Citrus Xaurantium*	Rutaceae	Sour Orange
*	*Citrus Xparadisi*	Rutaceae	Grapefruit
	Cladium jamaicense	Cyperaceae	Jamaica Swamp Sawgrass
	Clematis reticulata	Ranunculaceae	Netleaf Leatherflower
	Clitoria mariana	Fabaceae	Atlantic Pigeonwings
	Cnidoscolus stimulosus	Euphorbiaceae	Tread-softly
*	*Colocasia esculenta*	Araceae	Wild Taro
	Commelina erecta	Commelinaceae	Whitemouth Dayflower
	Commelina virginica	Commelinaceae	Virginia Dayflower
	Conyza canadensis	Asteraceae	Canadian Horseweed
	Corallohriza wisteriana	Orchidaceae	Spring Coralroot
	Cornus florida	Cornaceae	Flowering Dogwood
	Cornus foemina	Cornaceae	Swamp Dogwood
	Corydalis micrantha	Paapaveraceae	Smallflower Fumewort
*	*Crinum asiaticum*	Amaryllidaceae	Poisonbulb
*	*Crotalaria pallida*	Fabaceae	Smooth Rattlebox
	Crotalaria purshii	Fabaceae	Pursh's Rattlebox
	Crotalaria rotundifolia	Fabaceae	Rabbitbells
	Crotalaria sagittalis	Fabaceae	Arrowhead Rattlebox
*	*Crotalaria spectabilis*	Fabaceae	Showy Rattlebox
	Croton glandulosus	Euphorbiaceae	Vente Conmigo

302

Croton punctatus	Euphorbiaceae	Gulf Croton
Croton sp.	Euphorbiaceae	Rushfoil
* *Cuphea carthagenensis*	Lythraceae	Columbian Waxweed
* *Cupressus sempervirens*	Cupressaceae	Italian Cypress
Cuscuta pentagona	Convolvulaceae	Fiveangled Dodder
* *Cycas revoluta*	Cycadaceae	Sago Palm
* *Cyclospermum leptophyllum*	Apiaceae	Marsh Parsley
* *Cymbopogon citratus*	Poaceae	Lemon Grass
Cynanchum angustifolium	Apocynaceae	Gulf Coast Swallowwort
Cynanchum scoparium	Apocynaceae	Leafless Swallowwort
* *Cynodon dactylon*	Poaceae	Bermuda Grass
Cyperus croceus	Cyperaceae	Baldwin's Flatsedge
Cyperus distinctus	Cyperaceae	Swamp Flatsedge
Cyperus erythrorhizos	Cyperaceae	Redroot Flatsedge
* *Cyperus esculentus*	Cyperaceae	Nutgrass; Chufa Flatsedge
Cyperus filiculmis	Cyperaceae	Wiry Flatsedge
Cyperus haspan	Cyperaceae	Haspan Flatsedge
Cyperus odoratus	Cyperaceae	Fragrant Flatsedge
Cyperus ovatus	Cyperaceae	Pinebarren Flatsedge
Cyperus plukenetii	Cyperaceae	Plukenet's Flatsedge
Cyperus polystachyos	Cyperaceae	Manyspike Flatsedge
Cyperus pseudovegetus	Cyperaceae	Marsh Flatsedge
* *Cyperus rotundus*	Cyperaceae	Nutgrass
Cyperus surinamensis	Cyperaceae	Tropical Flatsedge
Cyperus tetragonus	Cyperaceae	Fourangle Flatsedge
Cyperus virens	Cyperaceae	Green Flatsedge
* *Dactyloctenium aegyptium*	Poaceae	Durban Crowfootgrass
Datura stramonium	Solanaceae	Jimsonweed
Decodon verticillatus	Lythraceae	Swamp Loosestrife
Descurainia pinnata	Brassicaceae	Western Tansymustard
* *Desmodium incanum*	Fabaceae	Zarzabacoa Comun
Desmodium lineatum	Fabaceae	Sand Ticktrefoil
Desmodium paniculatum	Fabaceae	Panicled Ticktrefoil
Dicerandra linearifolia	Lamiaceae	Coastalplain Balm
Dichanthelium aciculare	Poaceae	Needleleaf Witchgrass
Dichanthelium acuminatum	Poaceae	Tapered Witchgrass
Dichanthelium commutatum	Poaceae	Variable Witchgrass
Dichanthelium dichotomum	Poaceae	Cypress Witchgrass
Dichanthelium ensifolium	Poaceae	Dwarf Cypress Witchgrass
Dichanthelium laxiflorum	Poaceae	Openflower Witchgrass
Dichanthelium leucothrix	Poaceae	Rough Witchgrass
Dichanthelium oligosanthes	Poaceae	Heller's Witchgrass

Dichanthelium portoricense	Poaceae	Hemlock Witchgrass
Dichanthelium strigosum	Poaceae	Roughhair Witchgrass
Dichondra caroliniensis	Convolvulaceae	Carolina Ponysfoot
Digitaria ciliaris	Poaceae	Southern Crabgrass
Digitaria serotina	Poaceae	Blanket Crabgrass
Diodia teres	Rubiaceae	Rough Buttonweed
Diodia virginiana	Rubiaceae	Virginia Buttonweed
* *Dioscorea bulbifera*	Dioscoreaceae	Air-Potato
Diospyros virginiana	Ebenaceae	Persimmon
Distichlis spicata	Poaceae	Saltgrass
Drosera brevifolia	Droseraceae	Dwarf Sundew
Drosera intermedia	Droseraceae	Water Sundew
Dryopteris ludoviciana	Dryopteridaceae	Southern Wood Fern
Dulichium arundinaceum	Cyperaceae	Threeway Sedge
Dyschoriste oblongifolia	Acanthaceae	Oblongleaf Twinflower
* *Echinochloa crus-galli*	Poaceae	Barnyardgrass
Echinochloa muricata	Poaceae	Rough Barnyardgrass
Echinochloa walteri	Poaceae	Coast Cockspur
Eclipta prostrata	Asteraceae	False Daisy
* *Elaeagnus pungens*	Elaeagnaceae	Silverthorn
* *Elaeagnus umbellata*	Elaeagnaceae	Silverberry
Eleocharis albida	Cyperaceae	White Spikerush
Eleocharis equisetoides	Cyperaceae	Jointed Spikerush
Eleocharis fallax	Cyperaceae	Creeping Spikerush
Eleocharis flavescens	Cyperaceae	Yellow Spikerush
Eleocharis montevidensis	Cyperaceae	Sand Spikerush
Eleocharis obtusa	Cyperaceae	Blunt Spikerush
Eleocharis robbinsii	Cyperaceae	Robbins' Spikerush
Eleocharis vivipara	Cyperaceae	Viviparous Spikerush
Elephantopus nudatus	Asteraceae	Smooth Elephantsfoot
Elephantopus tomentosus	Asteraceae	Devil's Grandmother
* *Eleusine indica*	Poaceae	Goosegrass
Epidendrum conopseum	Orchidaceae	Green-fly Orchid
Equisetum sp.	Equisetaceae	Horsetail
* *Eragrostis amabilis*	Poaceae	Feather Lovegrass
Eragrostis elliottii	Poaceae	Elliott's Lovegrass
Eragrostis pectinacea	Poaceae	Tufted Lovegrass
* *Eragrostis pilosa*	Poaceae	Indian Lovegrass
Eragrostis secundiflora	Poaceae	Red Lovegrass
Eragrostis spectabilis	Poaceae	Purple Lovegrass
Eragrostis virginica	Poaceae	Coastal Lovegrass
Erechtites hieraciifolius	Asteraceae	American Burnweed

*	*Eremochloa ophiuroides*	Poaceae	Centipedegrass
	Erigeron quercifolius	Asteraceae	Oakleaf Fleabane
	Erigeron vernus	Asteraceae	Early Whitetop Fleabane
	Eriocaulon sp.	Eriocaulaceae	Pipewort
	Erythrina herbacea	Fabaceae	Coralbean
	Eubotrys racemosa	Ericaceae	Swamp Doghobble
	Eupatorium album	Asteraceae	White Thoroughwort
	Eupatorium capillifolium	Asteraceae	Dogfennel
	Eupatorium compositifolium	Asteraceae	Yankeeweed
	Eupatorium leptophyllum	Asteraceae	Falsefennel
	Eupatorium mohrii	Asteraceae	Mohr'sThoroughwort
	Eupatorium serotinum	Asteraceae	Lateflowering Thoroughwort
	Eustachys glauca	Poaceae	Saltmarsh Fingergrass
	Eustachys petraea	Poaceae	Pinewoods Fingergrass
	Euthamia caroliniana	Asteraceae	Slender Flattop Goldenrod
*	*Facelis retusa*	Asteraceae	Annual Trampweed
*	*Ficus carica*	Moraceae	Common Fig
*	*Ficus pumila*	Moraceae	Climbing Fig
	Fimbristylis autumnalis	Cyperaceae	Slender Fimbry
	Fimbristylis caroliniana	Cyperaceae	Carolina Fimbry
	Fimbristylis cymosa	Cyperaceae	Hurricanegrass
	Fimbristylis puberula	Cyperaceae	Hairy Fimbry
	Fimbristylis spadicea	Cyperaceae	Marsh Fimbry
	Forestiera segregata	Oleaceae	Florida Swampprivet
	Fraxinus caroliniana	Oleaceae	Carolina Ash
	Froelichia floridana	Amaranthaceae	Cottonweed
	Fuirena pumila	Cyperaceae	Dwarf Umbrellasedge
	Fuirena squarrosa	Cyperaceae	Hairy Umbrellasedge
	Gaillardia aestivalis	Asteraceae	Lanceleaf Blanketflower
	Gaillardia pulchella	Asteraceae	Firewheel
	Galactia elliottii	Fabaceae	Elliott's Milkpea
	Galactia regularis	Fabaceae	Downy Milkpea
	Galactia volubilis	Fabaceae	Eastern Milkpea
*	*Galanthus nivalis*	Amaryllidaceae	Snowdrop
	Galium hispidulum	Rubiaceae	Coastal Bedstraw
	Galium obtusum	Rubiaceae	Bluntleaf Bedstraw
	Galium pilosum	Rubiaceae	Hairy Bedstraw
	Gamochaeta antillana	Asteraceae	Caribbean Purple Everlasting
	Gamochaeta pensylvanica	Asteraceae	Pennsylvania Everlasting
	Gamochaeta purpurea	Asteraceae	Spoonleaf Purple Everlasting
	Gaura angustifolia	Onagraceae	Southern Beeblossom
	Gaylussacia frondosa	Ericaceae	Blue Huckleberry

Gelsemium sempervirens	Gelsemiaceae	Jessamine
Geranium carolinianum	Geraniaceae	Carolina Cranesbill
* *Gladiolus* sp.	Iridaceae	Gladiolus
* *Glandularia pulchella*	Verbenaceae	Moss Verbena
* *Gloriosa superba*	Colchicaceae	Flamelily
Gonolobus suberosus	Apocynaceae	Angle Pod
Gordonia lasianthus	Theaceae	Loblolly Bay
Gratiola ramosa	Plantaginaceae	Branched Hedgehyssop
Habenaria repens	Orchidaceae	Waterspider False Reinorchid
Hamamelis virginiana	Hamamelidaceae	American Witchhazel
* *Hedera helix*	Araliaceae	English Ivy
Helenium amarum	Asteraceae	Bitterweed
Helianthemum carolinianum	Cistaceae	Carolina Frostweed
Helianthemum corymbosum	Cistaceae	Pinebarren Frostweed
Helianthemum georgianum	Cistaceae	Georgia Frostweed
* *Helianthus argophyllus*	Asteraceae	Silverleaf Sunflower
Heliotropium curassavicum	Boraginaceae	Seaside Heliotrope
Heterotheca subaxillaris	Asteraceae	Camphorweed
Hibiscus grandiflorus	Malvaceae	Swamp Rosemallow
Hibiscus moscheutos	Malvaceae	Crimsoneyed Rosemallow
Hieracium gronovii	Asteraceae	Queen-devil
Hippeastrum X*hybridum*	Liliaceae	Hippeastrum
Houstonia procumbens	Rubiaceae	Innocence
Hydrocotyle bonariensis	Araliaceae	Largeleaf Marshpennywort
Hydrocotyle rununculoides	Araliaceae	Floating Marshpennywort
Hydrocotyle unbellata	Araliaceae	Manyflower Marshpennywort
Hydrocotyle verticillata	Araliaceae	Whorled Marshpennywort
Hypericum cistifolium	Clusiaceae	Roundpod St. John'swort
Hypericum crux-andraea	Clusiaceae	St. Peter'swort
Hypericum fasciculatum	Clusiaceae	Sandweed
Hypericum gentianoides	Clusiaceae	Pineweed
Hypericum hypericoides	Clusiaceae	St. Andrew's-Cross
Hypericum mutilum	Clusiaceae	Dwarf St. John'swort
Hypericum tetrapetalum	Clusiaceae	Fourpetal St. John'swort
Hypoxis curtissii	Hypoxidaceae	Common Yellow Stargrass
Hypoxis juncea	Hypoxidaceae	Fringed Yellow Stargrass
Ilex ambigua	Aquifoliaceae	Carolina Holly
Ilex cassine	Aquifoliaceae	Dahoon
Ilex glabra	Aquifoliaceae	Gallberry; Inkberry
Ilex opaca	Aquifoliaceae	American Holly
Ilex vomitoria	Aquifoliaceae	Yaupon
* *Illicium parviflorum*	Illiciaceae	Star Anise

Indigofera caroliniana	Fabaceae	Carolina Indigo
Ipomoea hederifolia	Convolvulaceae	Ivyleaf Morning-glory
Ipomoea pandurata	Convolvulaceae	Man-of-the-earth
Ipomoea pes-caprae	Convolvulaceae	Railroad Vine
* *Ipomoea quamoclit*	Convolvulaceae	Cypressvine
Ipomoea sagittata	Convolvulaceae	Saltmarsh Morning-glory
Ipomoea cordatotriloba	Convolvulaceae	Tievine
Ipomoea imperati	Convolvulaceae	Beach Moring-glory
Iva frutescens	Asteraceae	Marsh Elder
Iva imbricata	Asteraceae	Beach Elder
Jacquemontia tamnifolia	Convolvulaceae	Hairy Clustervine
Juncus acuminatus	Juncaceae	Tapertip Rush
Juncus bufonius	Juncaceae	Toad rush
Juncus coriaceus	Juncaceae	Leathery Rush
Juncus dichotomus	Juncaceae	Forked Rush
Juncus effusus	Juncaceae	Common or Soft Rush
Juncus marginatus	Juncaceae	Shore Rush
Juncus megacephalus	Juncaceae	Bighead Rush
Juncus repens	Juncaceae	Lesser Creeping Rush
Juncus roemerianus	Juncaceae	Needle Rush
Juncus scirpoides	Juncaceae	Needlepod Rush
Juncus tenuis	Juncaceae	Path Rush
Juniperus virginiana	Cupressaceae	Red Cedar
Kalmia hirsuta	Ericaceae	Wicky Hairy Laurel
Kosteletzkya pentacarpos	Malvaceae	Virginia Saltmarsh Mallow
Krigia virginica	Asteraceae	False Dandelion
* *Kyllinga brevifolia*	Cyperaceae	Shortleaf Spikesedge
Kyllinga pumila	Cyperaceae	Low Spikesedge
Lactuca graminifolia	Asteraceae	Grassleaf Lettuce
Lagerstroemia indica	Lythraceae	Crapemyrtle
* *Lamium amplexicaule*	Lamiaceae	Henbit Deadnettle
* *Landoltia punctata*	Araceae	Dotted Duckweed
* *Lantana camara*	Verbenaceae	Lantana
* *Lantana depressa*	Verbenaceae	Pineland Lantana
Lechea mucronata	Cistaceae	Hairy Pinweed
Lechea pulchella	Cistaceae	Leggett's Pinweed
Lechea torreyi	Cistaceae	Piedmont Pinweed
* *Lecojum vernum*	Amaryllidaceae	Spring Snowflake
Lemna aequinoctialis	Araceae	Lesser Duckweed
Lemna valdiviana	Araceae	Valdivia Duckweed
* *Leonotis nepetifolia*	Lamiaceae	Lion's-ear
Lepidium virginicum	Brassicaceae	Virginia Pepperweed

	Lespedeza hirta	Fabaceae	Hairy Lespedeza
	Eubotrys racemosa	Ericaceae	Swamp Doghobble
	Liatris gracilis	Asteraceae	Slender Gayfeather
	Liatris tenuifolia	Asteraceae	Shortleaf Gayfeather
*	*Ligustrum sinense*	Oleaceae	Chinese Privet
*	*Ligustrum japonicum*	Oleaceae	Japanese Privet
*	*Ligustrum lucidum*	Oleaceae	Glossy Privet
	Lilaeopsis chinensis	Apiaceae	Eastern Grasswort
	Limnobium spongia	Hydrocharitaceae	Frog's-bit
	Limonium carolinianum	Plumbaginaceae	Carolina Sealavender
	Linaria canadensis	Plantaginaceae	Canadian Toadflax
	Linum floridanum	Linaceae	Florida Yellow Flax
	Lipocarpha micrantha	Cyperaceae	Smallflower Halfchaf Sedge
	Liquidambar styraciflua	Altingiaceae	Sweetgum
*	*Livistona chinensis*	Arecaceae	Chinese Fan Palm
*	*Lolium perenne*	Poaceae	Italian Rye Grass
*	*Lonicera japonica*	Caprifoliaceae	Japanese Honeysuckle
	Lonicera sempervirens	Caprifoliaceae	Coral Honeysuckle
	Ludwigia alata	Onagraceae	Winged Primrosewillowox
	Ludwigia alternifolia	Onagraceae	Seedbox
	Ludwigia arcuata	Onagraceae	Piedmont Primrosewillow
	Ludwigia brevipes	Onagraceae	Long Beach Primrosewillow
	Ludwigia lanceolata	Onagraceae	Lanceleaf Primrosewillow
	Ludwigia leptocarpa	Onagraceae	Anglestem Primrosewillow
	Ludwigia linearis	Onagraceae	Narrowleaf Primrosewillow
	Ludwigia maritima	Onagraceae	Seaside Primrosewillow
	Ludwigia palustris	Onagraceae	Marsh Seedbox
	Ludwigia suffruticosa	Onagraceae	Shrubby Primrosewillow
	Lupinus villosus	Fabaceae	Lady Lupine
	Lycium carolinianum	Solanaceae	Christmasberry
*	*Lygodium japonica*	Schizacaceae	Japanese Climbing Fern
	Lyonia ferruginea	Ericaceae	Rusty Staggerbush
	Lyonia fruticosa	Ericaceae	Coastalplain Staggerbush
	Lyonia lucida	Ericaceae	Fetterbush
	Lyonia mariana	Ericaceae	Piedmont Staggerbush
	Lysimachia sp.	Primulaceae	Loosestrife
	Magnolia figo	Magnoliaceae	Bananashrub
	Magnolia grandifolia	Magnoliaceae	Southern Magnolia
	Magnolia virginiana	Magnoliaceae	Sweetbay
*	*Manihot grahamii*	Euphorbiaceae	Graham's Cassava
*	*Medicago minima*	Fabaceae	Burr Medick
	Melanthera nivea	Asteraceae	Snow Squarestem

*	*Melia azedarach*	Meliaceae	Chinaberrytree
	Melica mutica	Poaceae	Twoflower Melicgrass
	Melothria pendula	Cucurbitaceae	Creeping Cucumber
	Micranthemum umbrosum	Plantaginaceae	Shade Mudflower
	Mikania scandens	Asteraceae	Climbing Hempweed
	Mimosa quadrivalvis	Fabaceae	Sensitive Briar
	Mitchella repens	Rubiaceae	Partridge Berry
	Mitreola petiolata	Loganiaceae	Lax Hornpod
	Mitreola sessilifolia	Loganiaceae	Swamp Hornpod
*	*Mollugo verticillata*	Molluginaceae	Green Carpetweed
	Monotropa uniflora	Ericaceae	Indian Pipe
	Morus rubra	Moraceae	Red Mulberry
	Muhlenbergia capillaris	Poaceae	Hairawn Muhly
	Myrica cerifera	Myricaceae	Wax Myrtle
*	*Myriophyllum aquaticum*	Haloragaceae	Parrotfeather Water Milfoil
*	*Narcissus tazetta*	Amaryllidaceae	Cream Narcissus
	Nelumbo lutea	Nelumbonaceae	American Lotus
*	*Nerium oleander*	Apocynaceae	Common Oleander
	Nothoscordum bivalve	Alliaceae	False garlic
	Nuphar advena	Nymphaeaceae	Yellow Pondlily
	Nymphaea odorata	Nymphaeaceae	American White Waterlily
	Nymphoides aquatica	Menyanthaceae	Big Floatingheart
	Nyssa aquatica	Cornaceae	Water Tupelo
	Nyssa sylvatica var. *biflora*	Cornaceae	Swamp Tupelo
	Nyssa sylvatica var. *sylvatica*	Cornaceae	Blackgum
	Oclemena reticulata	Asteraceae	Pine Barren White Top
	Oenothera humifusa	Onagraceae	Seabeach Eveningprimrose
	Oenothera laciniata	Onagraceae	Cutleaf Eveningprimrose
*	*Oenothera speciosa*	Onagraceae	Pinkladies
*	*Oldenlandia corymbosa*	Rubiaceae	Flattop Mille Graines
	Oldenlandia uniflora	Rubiaceae	Clustered Mille Graines
*	*Olea europaea*	Oleaceae	Common Olive
	Ophioglossum nudicaule	Ophioglossaceae	Slender Adder's-tongue
	Ophioglossum pycnostichum	Ophioglossaceae	Stalked Adder's-tongue
	Ophioglossum vulgatum	Ophioglossaceae	Southern Adder's-tongue
	Oplismenus hirtellus	Poaceae	Woodgrass
	Opuntia humifusa	Cactaceae	Pricklypear
	Opuntia pusilla	Cactaceae	Cockspur Pricklypear
	Ornithogalum sp.	Liliaceae	Star of Bethlehem
	Osmanthus americanus	Oleaceae	Wild Olive
	Osmunda cinnamomea	Osmundaceae	Cinnamon Fern
	Osmunda regalis	Osmundaceae	Royal Fern

*	*Oxalis articulata*	Oxalidacaeae	Windowbox Woodsorrel
	Oxalis corniculata	Oxalidacaeae	Common Yellow Woodsorrel
	Oxalis macrantha	Oxalidacaeae	Tuffted Yellow Woodsorrel
*	*Oxalis violacea*	Oxalidacaeae	Violet Woodsorrel
	Panicum amarum	Poaceae	Bitter Panicgrass
	Panicum anceps	Poaceae	Beaked Panicum
	Panicum hemitomon	Poaceae	Maidencane
*	*Panicum repens*	Poaceae	Torpedograss
	Panicum rigidulum	Poaceae	Redtop Panicum
	Panicum verrucosum	Poaceae	Warty Panicgrass
	Panicum virgatum	Poaceae	Switchgrass
	Parietaria floridana	Urticaceae	Florida Pellitory
	Paronychia baldwinii	Caryophyllaceae	Baldwin's Nailwort
	Parthenocissus quinquefolia	Vitaceae	Virginia Creeper
*	*Paspalum notatum*	Poaceae	Bahia Grass
	Paspalum repens	Poaceae	Water Paspalum
	Paspalum setaceum	Poaceae	Thin Paspalum
*	*Paspalum urvillei*	Poaceae	Vaseygrass
	Paspalum vaginatum	Poaceae	Seashore Paspalum
	Passiflora incarnata	Passifloraceae	Purple Passionflower
	Passiflora lutea	Passifloraceae	Yellow Passionflower
	Pediomelum canescens	Fabaceae	Buckroot
	Peltandra sagittifolia	Araceae	Spoonflower
	Pentodon pentandrus	Rubiaceae	Hale's Pentodon
	Persea borbonia	Lauraceae	Red Bay
	Persea palustris	Lauraceae	Swamp Bay
	Phlebodium aureum	Polypodicaeae	Golden Polypody
*	*Phoenix canariensis*	Arecaceae	Canary Island Date Palm
	Phoradendron leucarpum	Viscaceae	Oak Mistletoe
	Photinia pyrifolia	Rosaceae	Red Chokeberry
	Phyla nodiflora	Verbenaceae	Capeweed
	Phyllanthus abnormis	Phyllanthaceae	Drummond's Leafflower
	Phyllanthus caroliniensis	Phyllanthaceae	Carolina Leafflower
*	*Phyllanthus tenellus*	Phyllanthaceae	Mascarene Island Leafflower
*	*Phyllanthus urinaria*	Phyllanthaceae	Chamber Bitter
*	*Phyllostachys aurea*	Poaceae	Golden Bamboo
	Physalis walteri	Solanaceae	Walter's Groundcherry
	Phytolacca americana	Phytolaccaceae	American Pokeweed
	Pilea microphylla	Urticaceae	Artillery Plant
	Pinguicula pumila	Lentibulariaceae	Small Butterwort
	Pinus echinata	Pinaceae	Shortleaf Pine
	Pinus elliottii	Pinaceae	Slash Pine

Pinus glabra	Pinaceae	Spruce Pine
Pinus palustris	Pinaceae	Longleaf Pine
Pinus serotina	Pinaceae	Pond Pine
Pinus taeda	Pinaceae	Loblolly Pine
Piptochaetium avenaceum	Poaceae	Blackseed Needlegrass
Pityopsis graminifolia	Asteraceae	Narrowleaf Silkgrass
Pityopsis pinifolia	Asteraceae	Silkgrass
Planera aquatica	Ulmaceae	Waterelm
* *Plantago lanceolata*	Plantaginaceae	English Plantain
Plantago virginica	Plantaginaceae	Southern Plantain
* *Platanus occidentalis*	Platanaceae	American Sycamore
* *Platycladus orientalis*	Cupressaceae	Oriental Arborvitae
Pleopeltis polypodioides	Polypodiaceae	Resurrection Fern
Pluchea foetida	Asteraceae	Stinking Camphorweed
Pluchea odorata	Asteraceae	Sweetscent
Pluchea baccharis	Asteraceae	Rosy Camphorweed
* *Poa annua*	Poaceae	Annual Bluegrass
Poinsettia cyathophora	Euphorbiaceae	Paintedleaf
Poinsettia heterophylla	Euphorbiaceae	Mexican Fireplant
* *Polycarpon tetraphyllum*	Caryophyllaceae	Fourleaf Manyseed
Polygala lutea	Polygalaceae	Orange Milkwort
Polygala nana	Polygalaceae	Candyroot
Polygala violacea	Polygalaceae	Showy Milkwort
Polygonella gracilis	Polygonaceae	Tall Jointweed
* *Polygonum cespitosum*	Polygonaceae	Oriental Lady's-thumb
Polygonum glabrum	Polygonaceae	Denseflower Knotweed
Polygonum glaucum	Polygonaceae	Glaucous Knotweed
Polygonum hirsutum	Polygonaceae	Hairy Smartweed
Polygonum hydropiperoides	Polygonaceae	Swamp Smartweed
Polygonum punctatum	Polygonaceae	Dotted Smartweed
Polygonum scandens	Polygonaceae	Climbing False Buckwheat
Polygonum setaceum	Polygonaceae	Bog Smartweed
Polypremum procumbens	Tetrachondraceae	Juniperleaf
Polystichum acrostichoides	Dryopteridaceae	Christmas fern
Pontederia cordata	Pontederiacaeae	Pickerelweed
Portulaca oleracea	Portulaceceae	Little Hogweed
Portulaca pilosa	Portulaceceae	Pink Purslane
Potamogeton sp.	Potamogetonaceae	Pondweed
Proserpinaca pectinata	Haloragaceae	Combleaf Mermaidweed
Prunus angustifolia	Rosaceae	Chickasaw Plum
Prunus caroliniana	Rosaceae	Carolina Laurelcherry
Prunus serotina	Rosaceae	Black Cherry

Prunus umbellata	Rosaceae	Hog Plum
Pseudognaphalium obtusifolium	Asteraceae	Rabbit Tobbaco
* *Pseudosasa japonica*	Poaceae	Arrow Bamboo
Pteridium aquilinum	Dennstaedtiaceae	Bracken Fern
Pterocaulon pycnostachyum	Asteraceae	Blackroot
Ptilimnium capillaceum	Apiaceae	Mock Bishopweed
* *Pyracantha koidzumii*	Rosaceae	Formosa Firethorn
Pyrrhopappus carolinianus	Asteraceae	False Dandelion
Quercus austrina	Fagaceae	Bastard White Oak; Bluff Oak
Quercus chapmanii	Fagaceae	Chapman's Oak
Quercus falcata	Fagaceae	Southern Red Oak
Quercus geminata	Fagaceae	Sand Live Oak
Quercus incana	Fagaceae	Blueblack Oak
Quercus laevis	Fagaceae	Turkey Oak
Quercus laurifolia	Fagaceae	Laurel Oak
Quercus margaretta	Fagaceae	Sand Post Oak
Quercus myrtifolia	Fagaceae	Myrtle Oak
Quercus nigra	Fagaceae	Water Oak
Quercus stellata	Fagaceae	Post Oak
Quercus virginiana	Fagaceae	Virginia Live Oak
Rhamnus caroliniana	Rhamnaceae	Carolina Buckthorn
Rhexia mariana	Melastomataceae	Pale Meadowbeauty
* *Rhododendron simsii*	Ericaceae	Indian Azalea
Rhus copallinum	Anacardiaceae	Winged Sumac
Rhynchosia difformis	Fabaceae	Doubleform Snoutbean
Rhynchospora colorata	Cyperaceae	Whitetop
Rhynchospora corniculata	Cyperaceae	Shortbristle Horned Beaksedge
Rhynchospora decurrens	Cyperaceae	Swampforest Beaksedge
Rhynchospora fascicularis	Cyperaceae	Fascicled Beaksedge
Rhynchospora inexpansa	Cyperaceae	Nodding Beaksedge
Rhynchospora leptocarpa	Cyperaceae	Brownish Beaksedge
Rhynchospora megalocarpa	Cyperaceae	Sandyfield Beaksedge
Rhynchospora microcephala	Cyperaceae	Southern Beaksedge
Rhynchospora miliacea	Cyperaceae	Millet Beaksedge
Rhynchospora mixta	Cyperaceae	Mingled Beaksedge
Rhynchospora scirpoides	Cyperaceae	Longbeak Beaksedge
Rhynchospora wrightiana	Cyperaceae	Wright's Beaksedge
* *Richardia brasiliensis*	Rubiaceae	Tropical Mexican Clover
* *Richardia scabra*	Rubiaceae	Rough Mexican Clover
* *Ricinus communis*	Euphorbiaceae	Castorbean
* *Rosa laevigata*	Rosaceae	Cherokee Rose

Rubus cuneifolius	Rosaceae	Sand Blackberry
Rubus pensilvanicus	Rosaceae	Sawtooth Blackberry
Rubus trivialis	Rosaceae	Southern Dewberry
Ruellia caroliniensis	Acanthaceae	Carolina Wild Petunia
Rumex hastatulus	Polygonaceae	Heartwing Dock
Ruppia maritima	Ruppiaceae	Widgeongrass
* *Ruscus aculeatus*	Ruscaceae	Butcher's Broom
Sabal palmetto	Arecaceae	Cabbage Palm
Sabatia stellaris	Gentianaceae	Rose-of-Plymouth
Saccharum giganteum	Poaceae	Sugarcane Plumegrass
Sacciolepis striata	Poaceae	American Cupscale
Sageretia minutiflora	Rhamnaceae	Smallflower Mock Buckthorn
Sagina decumbens	Caryophyllaceae	Trailing Pearlwort
Sagittaria filiformis	Alismataceae	Threadleaf Arrowhead
Sagittaria graminea	Alismataceae	Grassy Arrowhead
Sagittaria lancifolia	Alismataceae	Bulltongue Arrowhead
Sagittaria latifolia	Alismataceae	Duck Potato
Sagittaria subulata	Alismataceae	Awl-leaf Arrowhead
Salicornia bigelovii	Amaranthaceae	Annual Glasswort
Salicornia depressa	Amaranthaceae	Slender Glasswort
Salix caroliniana	Salicaceae	Carolina Willow
* *Salsola kali*	Amaranthaceae	Prickly Russian Thistle
Salvia coccinea	Lamiaceae	Blood Sage
Salvia lyrata	Lamiaceae	Lyreleaf Sage
Sambucus nigra	Adoxaceae	Elderberry
Samolus valerandi	Samolaceae	Pineland Pimpernel
Sanicula canadensis	Apiaceae	Canadian Blacksnakeroot
Sapindus saponaria	Sapindaceae	Soapberry
* *Sapium sebiferum*	Euphorbiaceae	Chinese Tallow Tree
Sarcocornia ambigua	Amaranthaceae	Perennial Glasswort
Sassafras albidum	Lauraceae	Sassafras
Saururus cernuus	Saururaceae	Lizard's Tail
Schoenoplectus pungens	Cyperaceae	Threesquare Bulrush
Schoenoplectus robustus	Cyperaceae	Saltmarsh Bulrush
Schoenoplectus tabernaemontanii	Cyperaceae	Softstem Bulrush
Scirpus cyperinus	Cyperaceae	Woolgrass
* *Scleranthus annuus*	Caryophyllaceae	Knawel Annual
Scleria oligantha	Cyperaceae	Littlehead Nutrush
Scleria reticularis	Cyperaceae	Netted Nutrush
Scleria triglomerata	Cyperaceae	Whip Nutrush
Scutellaria integrifolia	Lamiaceae	Helmet Skullcap

*	*Senecio vulgaris*	Asteraceae	Common Groundsel
*	*Senna obtusifolia*	Fabaceae	Sicklepod; Coffeeweed
*	*Senna occidentalis*	Fabaceae	Septicweed
	Serenoa repens	Arecaceae	Saw Palmetto
	Sesbania herbacea	Fabaceae	Danglepod
*	*Sesbania punicea*	Fabaceae	Rattlebox
	Sesuvium maritimum	Aizoaceae	Slender Seapurslane
	Sesuvium portulacastrum	Aizoaceae	Shoreline Seapurslane
	Setaria corrugata	Poaceae	Coastal Bristlegrass
*	*Setaria faberi*	Poaceae	Japanese Bristlegrass
	Setaria magna	Poaceae	Giant Bristlegrass
	Setaria parviflora	Poaceae	Yellow Bristlegrass
	Seymeria sp.	Orobanchaceae	Blacksenna
	Sida rhombifolia	Malvaceae	Indian Hemp
	Sida ulmifolia	Malvaceae	Common Wireweed
	Sideroxylon tenax	Sapotaceae	Tough Bully
	Silene antirrhina	Caryophyllaceae	Sleepy Catchfly
	Sisyrinchium albidum	Iridaceae	White Blue-eyed Grass
*	*Sisyrinchium rosulatum*	Iridaceae	Annual Blue-eyed Grass
	Smilax auriculata	Smilacaceae	Earleaf Greenbrier
	Smilax bona-nox	Smilacaceae	Saw Greenbrier
	Smilax glauca	Smilacaceae	Cat Greenbrier
	Smilax laurifolia	Smilacaceae	Laurel Greenbrier
	Smilax pumila	Smilacaceae	Sarsaparilla Vine
	Smilax tamnoides	Smilacaceae	Bristly Greenbriar
	Solanum americanum	Solanaceae	American Black Nightshade
	Solanum carolinense	Solanaceae	Carolina Horsenettle
	Solanum pseudogracile	Solanaceae	Glowing Nightshade
	Solidago odora	Asteraceae	Sweet Goldenrod
	Solidago sempervirens	Asteraceae	Seaside Goldenrod
	Solidago tortifolia	Asteraceae	Twistedleaf Goldenrod
*	*Sonchus asper*	Asteraceae	Spiny Sowthistle
*	*Sonchus oleraceus*	Asteraceae	Common Sowthistle
	Sorghastrum nutans	Poaceae	Yellow Indiangrass
	Sorghastrum secundum	Poaceae	Lopsided Indiangrass
	Spartina alterniflora	Poaceae	Smooth Cordgrass
	Spartina bakeri	Poaceae	Sand Cordgrass
	Spartina patens	Poaceae	Salt-meadow Cordgrass
*	*Spergularia marina*	Caryophyllaceae	Salt Sandspurrey
	Sphenopholis obtusata	Poaceae	Prairie Wedgescale
	Spiranthes praecox	Orchidaceae	Greenvein Ladiestresses
	Spiranthes tuberosa	Orchidaceae	Little Ladiestresses

Spiranthes vernalis	Orchidaceae	Spring Ladiestresses
Spirodela polyrhiza	Araceae	Common Duckweed
Spirodela sp.	Araceae	Big Duckweed
Sporobolus compositus	Poaceae	Hidden Dropseed
* *Sporobolus indicus*	Poaceae	Smutgrass
Sporobolus junceus	Poaceae	Pineywoods Dropseed
Sporobolus teretifolius	Poaceae	Wireleaf Dropseed
Sporobolus virginicus	Poaceae	Seashore Dropseed
Stachys floridana	Lamiaceae	Florida Hedgenettle
* *Stellaria media*	Caryophyllaceae	Common Chickweed
Stenotaphrum secundatum	Poaceae	St. Augustinegrass
Stillingia sylvatica	Euphorbiaceae	Queensdelight
Strophostyles helvola	Fabaceae	Trailing Fuzzybean
Strophostyles umbellata	Fabaceae	Pink Fuzzybean
Stylisma patens	Convolvulaceae	Coastalplain Dawnflower
Stylosanthes biflora	Fabaceae	Sidebeak Pencilflower
Suaeda linearis	Amaranthaceae	Sea Blite
Symphyotrichum dumosum	Asteraceae	Rice Button Aster
Symphyotrichum subulatum	Asteraceae	Annual Saltmarsh Aster
Symphyotrichum tenuifolium	Asteraceae	Perennial Saltmarsh Aster
Symplocos tinctoria	Symplocaceae	Horse Sugar
Tamarix canariensis	Tamaricaceae	Canary Island Tamarisk
Taxodium ascendens	Cupressaceae	Pond-Cypress
Taxodium distichum	Cupressaceae	Bald-Cypress
Tephrosia florida	Fabaceae	Florida Hoarypea
Ternstroemia gymnanthera	Pentaphlacaceae	Cleyera
Teucrium canadense	Lamiaceae	Wood Sage
Thalia dealbata	Marantaceae	Powdery Alligatorflag
Thalia geniculata	Marantaceae	Alligatorflag
Thelypteris kunthii	Thelypteridaceae	Widespread Maiden Fern
Thelypteris palustris	Thelypteridaceae	Marsh Fern
* *Thuja occidentalis*	Cupressaceae	Arbor Vitae
Tilia americana	Malvaceae	Southern Basswood
Tillandsia recurvata	Bromeliaceae	Ballmoss
Tillandsia setacea	Bromeliaceae	Southern Needleleaf
Tillandsia usneoides	Bromeliaceae	Spanish Moss
Tipularia discolor	Orchidaceae	Cranefly Orchid
Toxicodendron radicans	Anacardiaceae	Poison Ivy
* *Trachelospermum jasminoides*	Apocynaceae	Confederate Jasmine
Tradescantia ohiensis	Commelinaceae	Ohio Spiderwort
Tragia urens	Euphorbiaceae	Wavyleaf Noseburn
Trichostema dichotomum	Lamiaceae	Forked Bluecurls

	Trichostema setaceum	Lamiaceae	Narrowleaf Bluecurls
	Tridens flavus	Poaceae	Tall Redtop
*	*Trifolium dubium*	Fabaceae	Low Hop Clover
	Triglochin striata	Juncaginaceae	Arrowgrass
	Triodanis perfoliata	Campanulaceae	Clasping Venus' Looking-glass
	Triplasis americana	Poaceae	Perennial Sandgrass
	Triplasis purpurea	Poaceae	Purple Sandgrass
	Tripsacum dactyloides	Poaceae	Eastern Gammagrass
*	*Triumfetta pentandra*	Malvaceae	Fivestamen Burrbark
*	*Triumfetta semitriloba*	Malvaceae	Sacramento Burrbark
	Typha domingensis	Typhaceae	Southern Cattail
	Typha latifolia	Typhaceae	Broadleaf Cattail
	Ulmus americana	Ulmaceae	American Elm
	Uniola paniculata	Poaceae	Seaoats
	Urochloa platyphylla	Poaceae	Broadleaf Signalgrass
	Urtica chamaedryoides	Urticaceae	Heartleaf Nettle
	Utricularia cornuta	Lentibulariaceae	Horned Bladderwort
	Utricularia gibba	Lentibulariaceae	Humped Bladderwort
	Utricularia inflata	Lentibulariaceae	Floating Bladderwort
	Utricularia purpurea	Lentibulariaceae	Eastern Purple Bladderwort
	Utricularia subulata	Lentibulariaceae	Zig-zag Bladderwort
	Vaccinium arboreum	Ericaceae	Sparkleberry
	Vaccinium corymbosum	Ericaceae	Highbush Blueberry
	Vaccinium myrsinites	Ericaceae	Shiny Blueberry
	Vaccinium stamineum	Ericaceae	Deerberry
*	*Verbascum thapsus*	Scrophulariaceae	Common Mullein
	Verbena scabra	Verbenaceae	Harsh Vervain
*	*Veronica arvensis*	Plantaginaceae	Corn Speedwell
	Viburnum odoratissimum	Adoxaceae	Sweet Viburnum
	Vicia acutifolia	Fabaceae	Fourleaf Vetch
	Vicia caroliniana	Fabaceae	Carolina Vetch
	Vicia lathyroides	Fabaceae	Spring Vetch
	Vicia minutiflora	Fabaceae	Pigmyflower Vetch
*	*Vicia tetrasperma*	Fabaceae	Lentil Vetch
	Vigna luteola	Fabaceae	Hairypod Cowpea
	Viola lanceolata	Violaceae	Bog White Violet
	Viola palmata	Violaceae	Early Blue Violet
	Viola sororia	Violaceae	Common Blue Violet
	Vitis aestivalis	Vitaceae	Summer Grape
	Vitis cinerea	Vitaceae	Florida Grape
	Vitis palmata	Vitaceae	Catbird Grape
	Vitis rotundifolia	Vitaceae	Muscadine

Vitis vulpina	Vitaceae	Frost Grape
Vittaria lineata	Vittariaceae	Shoestring Fern
* *Vulpia myuros*	Poaceae	Rattail Fescue
Vulpia octoflora	Poaceae	Sixweeks Fescue
* *Wahlenbergia marginata*	Campanulaceae	Southern Rockbell
* *Washingtonia robusta*	Arecaceae	Washington Fan Palm
Websteria confervoides	Cyperaceae	Algal Bulrush
Wisteria frutescens	Fabaceae	American Wisteria
* *Wisteria sinensis*	Fabaceae	Chinese Wisteria
Wolffia columbiana	Araceae	Columbian Watermeal
Wolffiella gladiata	Araceae	Florida Mudmidget
Woodwardia areolata	Blechnaceae	Netted Chain Fern
Woodwardia virginica	Blechnaceae	Virginia Chain Fern
Xanthium strumarium	Asteraceae	Cockleburr
Xyris elliottii.	Xyridaceae	Elliott's Yelloweyed Grass
Xyris platylepis	Xyridaceae	Tall Yelloweyed Grass
Youngia japonica	Asteraceae	Oriental False Hawksbeard
Yucca aloifolia	Agavaceae	Spanish Bayonet
Yucca filamentosa	Agavaceae	Bear-grass; Adam's Needle
Yucca gloriosa	Agavaceae	Moundlily Yucca
Zamia pumila	Zamiaceae	Coontie
Zanthoxylum clava-herculis	Rutaceae	Hercules-club
* *Zeuxine strateumatica*	Orchidaceae	Lawn Orchid
Zornia bracteata	Fabaceae	Viperina

APPENDIX II. FISH OF CUMBERLAND ISLAND, GEORGIA

Order	Family	Common Name	Scientific Name
Siluriformes	Ictaluridae	Yellow Bullhead	Ictalurus natalis (LeSueur, 1819)
Anguilliformes	Anguillidae	Americal Eel	Anguilla rostrata (LeSueur, 1817)
Cyprinodontiformes	Cyprinodontidae	Sheephead Minnow	Cyprinodon variegatus (Lacépède, 1803)
		Marsh Killifish	Fundulus confluentus Goode and Bean, 1879
		Mummichog	Fundulus heteroclitus (Linnaeus, 1766)
	Poeciliidae	Mosquitofish	Gambusia affinis (Baird and Girard, 1853)
		Sailfin Molly	Poecilia latipinna LeSueur, 1821)
Perciformes	Centrarchidae	Warmouth	Lepomis gulosus (Cuvier, 1829)
		Bluegill	Lepomis macrochirus Rafinesque, 1819
		Black Crappie	Pomoxis nigromaculatus (LeSueur, 1829)
		Largemouth Bass	Micropterus salmoides (Lacépède, 1802)
	Gerridae	Mojareras	Eucinostomus sp.
	Eleotridae	Fat Sleeper	Dormitator maculate (Bloch, 1792)
	Mugillidae	Striped mullet	Striped mullet

APPENDIX III. AMPHIBIANS AND REPTILES OF CUMBERLAND ISLAND, GEORGIA.			
Order	**Family**	**Common Name**	**Scientific Name**
AMPHIBIANS			
Anura	Bufonidae	Southern Toad	*Anaxyrus terrestris* (Bonnaterre, 1789)
	Hylidae	Southern Cricket Frog	*Acris gryllus* (LeConte, 1825)
		Green Treefrog	*Hyla cinerea* (Schneider, 1799)
		Pine Woods Treefrog	*Hyla femoralis* Bosc, 1800
		Barking Treefrog	*Hyla gratiosa* LeConte, 1856
		Squirrel Treefrog	*Hyla squirella* Bosc, 1800
		Cope's Gray Treefrog	*Hyla chrysoscelis* Cope, 1880
		Spring Peeper	*Pseudacris crucifer* (Wied-Neuwied, 1838)
		Little Grass Frog	*Pseudacris ocularis* (Bosc and Daudin, 1801)
		Southern Chorus Frog	*Pseudacris nigrita* LeConte, 1825
	Microhylidae	Eastern Narrow-mouthed toad	*Gastrophryne carolinensis* (Holbrook, 1836)
	Pelobatidae	Eastern Spadefoot	*Scaphiopus holbrookii* (Harlan, 1835)
	Ranidae	Pig Frog	*Lithobates grylio* (Stejneger, 1901)
		Southern Leopard Frog	*Lithobates sphenocephalus* Cope, 1889
Caudata	Ambystomatidae	Mole Salamander	*Ambystoma talpoideum* (Holbrook, 1838)
	Amphiumidae	Two-toed Amphiuma	*Amphiuma means* Garden, 1821
	Plethodontidae	Southern Dusky Salamander	*Desmognathus auriculatus* (Holbrook, 1838)
		Dwarf Salamander	*Eurycea quadrigitata* (Holbrook, 1842)
	Salmandridae	Eastern Newt	*Notophthalmus viridescens* (Rafinesque, 1820)
REPTILES			
Crocodilia	Alligatoridae	American Alligator	*Alligator mississippiensis* Daudin, 1801
Squamates	Anguidae	Eastern Glass Lizard	*Ophisaurus ventralis* (Linnaeus, 1766)

		Island Glass Lizard	*Ophisaurus compressus* (Cope, 1900)
	Polychrotidae	Green Anole	*Anolis carolinensis* Voight, 1832
		Eastern Fence Lizard	*Sceloporus undulatus* (Latreille, 1801)
	Scincidae	Mole Skink	*Plestiodon egregius* (Baird, 1859)
		Southeastern Five-lined Skink	*Plestiodon inexpectatus* Taylor, 1932
		Broad-headed Skink	*Plestiodon laticeps* (Schneider, 1801)
		Ground Skink	*Scincella lateralis* (Say, 1823)
	Teidae	Six-lined Racerunner	*Aspidoscelis sexlineata* (Linnaeus, 1766)
Squamata	Colubridae	Scarlet Snake	*Cemophora coccinea* (Blumenbach, 1738)
		Black Racer	*Coluber constrictor* Linnaeus, 1758
		Southern Ring-necked Snake	*Diadophis punctatus* (Linnaeus, 1766)
		Red Cornsnake	*Pantherophis guttatus* (Linnaeus, 1766)
		Yellow Rat Snake	*Pantherophis obsoletus* (Say, 1823)
		Eastern Mud Snake	*Farancia abacura* (Holbrook, 1836)
		Common Kingsnake	*Lampropeltis getula* (Linnaeus, 1766)
		Scarlet Kingsnake	*Lampropeltis elapsoides* (Holbrook, 1838)
		Coachwhip	*Masticophis flagellum* (Shaw, 1802)
		Rough Green Snake	*Opheodrys aestivus* (Linnaeus, 1766)
		Pine Woods Littersnake	*Rhadinea flavilata* (Cope, 1871)
		Southern Banded Water Snake	*Nerodia fasciata* (Linnaeus, 1766)
		Florida Red-bellied Snake	*Storeria occipitomaculata* Trapido, 1944
		Eastern Ribbon Snake	Thamnophis sauritus (Linnaeus, 1766)
		Common Garter Snake	*Thamnophis sirtalis* (Linnaeus, 1758)
	Viperidae	Cottonmouth	Agkistrodon piscivorus (Lacépède, 1789)
		Eastern Diamondback Rattlesnake	*Crotalus adamanteus* Beauvois, 1799
		Canebrake Rattlesnake	*Crotalus horridus* (Linnaeus, 1758)

Testudines	Cheloniidae	Loggerhead Sea Turtle	*Caretta caretta* (Linnaeus, 1758)
		Green Sea Turtle	*Chelonia mydas* (Linnaeus, 1758)
		Hawksbill Sea Turtle	*Eretmochelys imbricata* Linnaeus, 1766)
		Kemp's Ridley Sea Turtle	*Lepidochelys kempii* (Garman, 1880)
	Dermochelidae	Leatherback Sea Turtle	*Dermochelys coriacea* (Linnaeus, 1766)
	Chelydridae	Snapping Turtle	*Chelydra serpentina* (Linnaeus, 1758)
	Emydidae	Chicken Turtle	*Deirochelys reticularia* (Latreille, 1801)
		Diamond-backed Terrapin	*Malaclemys terrapin* (Schoepff, 1793)
		Florida Red-bellied Cooter	*Pseudemys nelsoni* Carr, 1938
		Yellow-bellied Pond Slider	*Trachemys scripta* (Schoepff, 1792)
	Kinosternidae	Eastern Mud Turtle	*Kinosternon subrubrum* (Lacépède, 1788)
		Striped Mud Turtle	*Kinosternon baurii* (Garman, 1891)
	Testudinidae	Gopher Tortoise	*Gopherus polyphemus* (Daudin, 1802)
	Trionchidae	Florida Softshell	*Apalone ferox* (Schneider, 1783)

APPENDIX IVA. BIRDS OF CUMBERLAND ISLAND, GEORGIA.			
Order	Family	Common Name	Scientific Name
Anseriformes	Anatidae	Fulvous Whistling Duck	*Dendrocygna bicolor* (Vieillot, 1816)
		Snow Goose	*Chen caerulescens* (Linnaeus, 1758)
		Brant	*Branta bernicla* (Linnaeus, 1758)
		Canada Goose	*Branta canadensis* (Linnaeus, 1758)
		Tundra Swan	*Cygnus columbianus* (Ord, 1815)
		Wood Duck	*Aix sponsa* (Linnaeus, 1758)
		Gadwall	*Anas strepera* Linnaeus, 1758
		Eurasian Wigeon	*Anas penelope* Linnaeus, 1758
		American Wigeon	*Anas americana* Gmelin, 1789
		American Black Duck	*Anas rubripes* Brewster, 1902
		Mallard	*Anas platyrhynchos* Linnaeus, 1758
		Mottled Duck	*Anas fulvigula* Ridgway, 1874
		Blue-winged Teal	*Anas discors* Linnaeus,1766
		Northern Shoveler	*Anas clypeata* Linnaeus, 1758
		Northern Pintail	*Anas acuta* Linnaeus, 1758
		Green-winged Teal	*Anas crecca* Linnaeus, 1758
		Canvasback	*Aythya valisineria* (Wilson, 1814)
		Redhead	*Aythya americana* (Eyton, 1838)
		Ring-necked Duck	*Aythya collaris* (Donovan, 1809)
		Greater Scaup	*Aythya marila* (Linnaeus, 1761)
		Lesser Scaup	Aythya affinis (Eyton, 1838)
		King Eider	*Somateria spectabilis* (Linnaeus, 1758)
		Common Eider	*Somateria mollissima* (Linnaeus, 1758)
		Surf Scoter	*Melanitta perspicillata* (Linnaeus, 1758)
		White-winged Scoter	*Melanitta fusca* (Linnaeus, 1758)

		Black Scoter	*Melanitta nigra* (Linnaeus, 1758)
		Long-tailed Duck	*Clangula hyemalis* (Linnaeus, 1758)
		Bufflehead	*Bucephala albeola* (Linnaeus, 1758)
		Common Goldeneye	*Bucephala clangula* (Linnaeus, 1758)
		Hooded Merganser	*Lophodytes cucullatus* (Linnaeus, 1758)
		Common Merganser	*Mergus merganser* Linnaeus, 1758
		Red-breasted Merganser	*Mergus serrator* Linnaeus, 1758
		Ruddy Duck	*Oxyura jamaicensis* (Gmelin, 1782)
Galliformes	Odontophoridae	Northern Bobwhite	*Colinus virginoanus* (Linnaeus, 1758)
	Phasianidae	Wild Turkey	*Meleagris gallopavo* Linnaeus, 1758
Gaviiformes	Gaviidae	Red-throated Loon	*Gavia stellata* (Pontoppidan, 1763)
		Common Loon	*Gavia immer* (Brunnich, 1764)
		Pied-billed Grebe	*Podilymbus podiceps* (Linnaeus, 1758)
Podicipediformes	Podicipedidae	Horned Grebe	*Podiceps auaritus* (Linnaeus, 1758)
		Red-necked Grebe	*Podiceps grisegena* (Boddaert, 1783)
Procellariiformes	Procellariidae	Cory's Shearwater	*Calonectris diomedea* (Scopoli, 1769)
		Cape Verde Shearwater	*Calonectris edwardsii* (Oustalet, 1883)
		Great Shearwater	*Puffinus gravis* (O'Reilly, 1818)
		Sooty Shearwater	*Puffinus griseus* (Gmelin, 1789)
		Audubon's Shearwater	*Puffinus lherminieri* Lesson, 1839
	Hydrobatidae	Wilson's Storm Petrel	*Oceanites oceanicus* (Kuhl, 1820)
		Leach's Storm Petrel	*Oceanodroma leucorhoa* (Vieillot, 1818)
		Band-rumped Storm Petrel	*Oceanodroma castro* (Harcourt, 1851)
Phaethontiformes	Phaethontidae	White-tailed Tropicbird	*Phaethon lepturus* Daudin, 1802
Ciconiiformes	Ciconiidae	Wood Stork	*Mycteria americana* Linnaeus, 1758

Suliformes	Fregatidae	Magnificent Frigatebird	*Fregata magnificens* Mathews, 1914
	Sulidae	Masked Bobby	*Sula dactylatra* Lesson, 1831
		Brown Booby	*Sula leucogaster* (Boddaert, 1783)
		Northern Gannet	*Morus bassanus* (Linnaeus, 1758)
	Phalacrocoracidae	Double-crested Cormorant	*Phalacrocorax auritus* (Lesson, 1831)
	Anhingidae	Anhinga	*Anhinga anhinga* (Linnaeus, 1766)
Pelecaniformes	Pelecanidae	American White Pelican	*Pelecanus erythrorhynchos* Gmelin, 1789
		Brown Pelican	*Pelecanus occidentalis* Linnaeus, 1766
	Ardeidae	American Bittern	*Botaurus lentiginosus* (Rackett, 1813)
		Least Bittern	*Ixobrychus exilis* (Gmelin, 1789)
		Great Blue Heron	*Ardea herodias* Linnaeus, 1758
		Great Egret	*Ardea alba* (Linnaeus, 1758)
		Snowy Egret	*Egretta thula* (Molina, 1782)
		Little Blue Heron	*Egretta caerulea* (Linnaeus, 1758)
		Tricolored Heron	*Egretta tricolor* (Muller, 1776)
		Reddish Egret	*Egretta rufescens* (Gmelin, 1789)
		Cattle Egret	*Bubulcus ibis* (Linnaeus, 1758)
		Green Heron	*Butorides virescens* (Linnaeus, 1758)
		Black-crowned Night Heron	*Nycticorax nycticorax* (Linnaeus, 1758)
		Yellow-crowned Night Heron	*Nyctanassa violacea* (Linnaeus, 1758)
	Threskiornithidae	White Ibis	*Eudocimus albus* (Linnaeus, 1758)
		Glossy Ibis	*Plegadis falcinellus* (Linnaeus, 1766)
		Roseate Spoonbill	*Platalea ajaja* (Linnaeus, 1758)
Accipitriformes	Cathartidae	Black Vulture	*Coragyps atratus* (Bechstein, 1793)
		Turkey Vulture	*Cathartes aura* (Linnaeus, 1758)
	Pandionidae	Osprey	*Pandion haliaetus* (Linnaeus, 1758)

		Accipitridae	Swallow-tailed Kite	*Elanoides forficatus* (Linnaeus, 1758)
			Mississippi Kite	*Ictinia mississippiensis* (Wilson, 1811)
			Bald Eagle	*Haliaeetus leucocephalus* (Linnaeus, 1766)
			Northern Harrier	*Circus cyaneus* (Linnaeus, 1766)
			Sharp-shinned Hawk	*Accipiter striatus* (Vieillot, 1807
			Cooper's Hawk	*Accipiter cooperii* (Bonaparte, 1828)
			Northern Goshawk	*Accipiter gentiles* (Linnaeus, 1758)
			Red-shouldered Hawk	*Buteo lineatus* (Gmelin, 1788)
			Broad-winged Hawk	*Buteo platypterus* (Vieillot, 1823)
			Red-tailed Hawk	(Gmelin, 1788)
			Rough-legged Hawk	*Buteo lagopus* (Pontoppidan, 1763)
			Golden Eagle	*Aquila chrysaetos* (Linnaeus, 1758)
Falconiformes	Falconidae		American Kestrel	*Falco sparverius* Linnaeus, 1758
			Merlin	*Falco columbarius* Linnaeus, 1758
			Peregrine Falcon	*Falco peregrinus* Tunstall, 1771
Gruiformes	Rallidae		Yellow Rail	*Coturnicops noveboracensis* (Gmelin, 1789)
			Black Rail	*Laterallus jamaicensis* (Gmelin, 1789)
			Clapper Rail	*Rallus longirostris* Boddaert, 1783
			King Rail	*Rallus elegans* Audubon, 1834
			Virginia Rail	*Rallus limicola* Vieillot, 1819
			Sora	*Porzana carolina* (Linnaeus, 1758)
			Purple Gallinule	*Porphyrio martinica* (Linnaeus, 1766)
			Common Moorhen	*Gallinula chloropus* (Linnaeus, 1758)
			American Coot	*Fulica americana* (Gmelin, 1789)
		Gruidae	Sandhill Crane	*Grus canadensis* (Linnaeus, 1758)

Charadriiformes	Charadriidae	Black-bellied Plover	*Pluvialis squatarola* (linnaeus, 1758)
		American Golden-Plover	*Pluvialis dominica* (Muller, 1776)
		Snowy Plover	*Charadrius nivosus* (Casssin, 1858)
		Wilson's Plover	*Charadrius wilsonia* Ord, 1814
		Semipalmated Plover	*Charadrius semipalmatus* Bonaparte, 1825
		Piping Plover	*Charadrius melodus* Ord, 1824
		Killdeer	*Charadrius vociferus* Linnaeus, 1758
	Haematopodidae	American Oystercatcher	*Haematopus palliatus* Temminck, 1820
	Recurvirostridae	Black-necked Stilt	*Himantoppus mexicanus* (Muller, 1776)
		American Avocet	*Recurvirostra americana* Gmelin, 1789
	Scolopacidae	Spotted Sandpiper	*Actitis macularia* (Linnaeus, 1766)
		Solitary Sandpiper	*Tringa solitaria* Wilson, 1813
		Greater Yellowlegs	*Tringa melanoleuca* (Gmelin, 1789)
		Willet	*Tringa semipalmatus* (Gmelin, 1789)
		Lesser Yellowlegs	*Tringa flavipes* (Gmelin, 1789)
		Upland Sandpiper	*Bartramia longicauda* (Bechstein, 1812)
		Whimbrel	*Numenius phaeopus* Linnaeus, 1758
		Long-billed Curlew	*Numenius americanus* (Bechstein, 1812)
		Marbled Godwit	*Limosa fedoa* (Linnaeus, 1758)
		Ruddy Turnstone	*Arenaria interpres* (Linnaeus, 1758)
		Red Knot	*Calidris canutus* (Linnaeus, 1758)
		Sanderling	*Calidris alba* (Pallas, 1764)
		Semipalmated Sandpiper	*Calidris pusilla* (Linnaeus, 1766)
		Western Sandpiper	*Calidris mauri* (Cabanis, 1857)
		Least Sandpiper	*Calidris minutilla* (Vieillot, 1819)

	White-rumped Sandpiper	*Calidris fuscicollis* (Vieillot, 1819)
	Pectoral Sandpiper	Calidris melanotos (Vieillot, 1819)
	Purple Sandpiper	Calidris maritima (Brunnich, 1764)
	Dunlin	Calidris allpina (Linnaeus, 1758)
	Stilt Sandpiper	Calidris himantopus (Bonaparte, 1826)
	Buff-brested Sandpiper	Tryngites subruficollis (Vieillot, 1819)
	Short-billed Dowitcher	Limnodromus griseus (Gmelin, 1789)
	Long-billed Dowitcher	Limnodromus scolopaceus (Say, 1823)
	Common Snipe	Gallinago gallinago (Linnaeus, 1758)
	American Woodcock	Scolopax minor Gmelin, 1789
	Wilson's Phalarope	*Phalaropus tricolor* (Vieillot, 1819)
	Red-necked Phalarope	*Phalaropus lobat*us (Linnaeus, 1758)
	Red Phalarope	*Phalaropus fulicaria* (Linnaeus, 1758)
Laridae	Black-legged Kittywake	*Rissa tridactyla* (Linnaeus, 1758)
	Sabine's Gull	*Xema sabini* (Sabine, 1819)
	Bonaparte's Gull	*Chroicocephalus philadelphia* Ord, 1815
	Laughing Gull	*Leucophaeus atricilla* Linnaeus, 1758
	Franklin's Gull	*Leucophaeus pipixcan* (Wagler, 1831)
	Ring-billed Gull	*Larus delawarensis* Ord, 1815
	Herring Gull	*Larus argentatus* Pontoppidan, 1763
	Iceland Gull	*Larus glaucoides* Meyer, 1822
	Lesser Black-backed Gull	*Larus fuscus* Linnaeus, 1758
	Glaucous Gull	*Larus hyperboreus* Gunnerus, 1767
	Great Black-backed Gull	*Larus marinus* Linnaeus, 1758
	Brown Noddy	*Anous stolidus* (Linnaeus, 1758)

		Sooty Tern	*Onychoprion fuscata* Linnaeus, 1766
		Bridled Tern	*Onychoprion anaethetus* Scopoli, 1786
		Least Tern	*Sternula antillarum* (Lesson, 1847)
		Gull-billed Tern	*Gelochelidon nilotica* Gmelin, 1789
		Caspian Tern	*Hydroprogne caspia* Pallas, 1770
		Black Tern	*Childonias niger* (Linnaeus, 1758)
		Common Tern	*Sterna hirundo* Linnaeus, 1758
		Arctic Tern	*Sterna paradisaea* Pontoppidan, 1763
		Forster's Tern	*Sterna forsteri* Nuttall, 1834
		Royal Tern	*Thalasseus maximus* Boddaert, 1783
		Sandwich Tern	*Thalasseus sandvicensis* Latham, 1787
		Black Skimmer	*Rynchops niger* Linnaeus, 1758
	Stercorariidae	South Polar Skua	*Catharacta maccormicki* (Saunders, 1893)
		Pomarine Jaeger	*Stercorarius pomarinus* (Temminick, 1815)
		Parasitic Jaeger	*Stercorarius parasiticus* (Linnaeus, 1758)
		Long-tailed Jager	*Stercorarius longicaudus* Vieillot, 1819
	Alcidae	Dovekie	*Alle alle* (Linnaeus, 1758)
		Razorbill	*Alca torda* Linnaeus, 1758
Columbiformes	Columbidae	Rock Dove	*Columba liva* Gmelin, 1789
		Eurasian Collared-dove	*Streptopelia decaocto* (Frivaldszky, 1836)
		Mourning Dove	*Zenaida macroura* (Linnaeus, 1758)
		Ground Dove	*Columbina passerina* (Linnaeus, 1758)
Cuculiformes	Cuculidae	Yellow-billed Cuckoo	*Coccyzus americanus* (Linnaeus, 1758)
		Black-billed Cuckoo	*Coccyzus erythropthalmus* (Wilson, 1811)
Strigiformes	Tytonidae	Barn Owl	*Tyto alba* (Scopoli, 1769)
	Strigidae	Eastern Screech Owl	*Megascops asio* (Linnaeus, 1758)

		Great Horned Owl	*Bubo virginianus* (Gmelin, 1788)
		Barred Owl	*Strix varia* Barton, 1799
		Long-eared Owl	*Asio otus* (Linnaeus, 1758)
		Short-eared Owl	*Asio flammeus* (Pontoppidan, 1763)
Caprimulgiformes	Caprimulgidae	Common Nighthawk	*Chordeiles minor* (Forster, 1771)
		Chuck-will's-widow	*Caprimulgus carolinensis* Gmelin, 1789
		Whip-poor-will	*Caprimulgus vociferous* Wilson, 1812
Apodiformes	Apodidae	Chimney Swift	*Chaetura pelagica* (Linnaeus, 1758)
	Trochilidae	Ruby-throated Hummingbird	*Archilochus colubris* (Linnaeus, 1758)
		Rufous Hummingbird	*Selasphorus rufus* (Gmelin, 1788)
Coraciiformes	Alcedinidae	Belted Kingfisher	*Megaceryle alcyon* (Linnaeus, 1758)
Piciformes	Picidae	Red-headed Woodpecker	*Melanerpes erythrocephalus* (Linnaeus, 1758)
		Red-bellied Woodpecker	*Melanerpes carolinus* (Linnaeus, 1758)
		Yellow-bellied Sapsucker	*Sphyrapicus varius* (Linnaeus, 1766)
		Downy Woodpecker	*Picoides pubescens* (Linnaeus, 1766)
		Hairy Woodpecker	*Picoides villosus* (Linnaeus, 1766)
		Red-cockaded Woodpecker	*Picoides borealis* (Vieillot, 1808)
		Northern Flicker	*Colapes auratus* Linnaeus, 1758
		Pileated Woodpecker	*Dryocopus pileatus* (Linnaeus, 1758)
Passeriformes	Tyranidae	Eastern Wood Pewee	*Cantopus virens* (Linnaeus, 1766)
		Acadian Flycatcher	*Empidonax virescens* (Vieillot, 1818)
		Least Flycatcher	*Empidonax minimus* (Baird and Baird, 1843)
		Eastern Phoebe	*Sayornis phoebe* (Bonaparte, 1825)
		Vermillion Flycatcher	*Pyrocephalus rubinus* (Boddaert, 1783)
		Great Crested Flycatcher	*Miarchus crinitus* (Linnaeus, 1758)

	Western Kingbird	*Tyrannus verticalis* Say, 1823
	Eastern Kingbird	*Tyrannus tyrannus* (Linnaeus, 1758)
	Gray Kingbird	*Tyrannus dominicensis* (Gmelin, 1788)
	Scissor-tailed Flycatcher	*Tyrannus forficata* (Gmelin, 1789)
Laniidae	Loggerhead Shrike	*Lanius ludovicianus* Linnaeus, 1766
Vireonidae	White-eyed Vireo	*Vireo griseus* (Boddaert, 1783)
	Yellow-throated Vireo	*Vireo flavifrons* Vieillot, 1808
	Solitary Vireo	*Vireo solitarius* (Wilson, 1810)
	Red-eyed Vireo	*Vireo olivaceus* (Linnaeus, 1766)
Corvidae	Blue Jay	*Cyanocitta cristata* (Linnaeus, 1758)
	American Crow	*Corvus brachyrhynochos* Brehm, 1822
	Fish Crow	*Corvus ossifragus* Wilson, 1812
Alaudidae	Horned Lark	*Eremophila alpestris* (Linneaus, 1758)
Hirundinidae	Purple Martin	*Progne subis* (Linnaeus, 1758)
	Tree Swallow	*Tachycineta bicolor* (Vieillot, 1808)
	Northern Rough-winged Swallow	*Stelgidopteryx serripennis* (Audubon, 1838)
	Bank Swallow	*Riparia riparia* (Linnaeus, 1758)
	Cliff Swallow	*Pterochelidon pyrrhonota* Vieillot, 1817
	Barn Swallow	*Hirundo rustica* Linnaeus, 1758
Paridae	Carolina Chickadee	*Poecile carolinensis* Audubon, 1834
	Tufted Titmouse	*Baeolophus bicolor* Linnaeus, 1766
Sittidae	Red-brested Nuthatch	*Sitta canadensis* Linnaeus, 1758
	White-breasted Nuthatch	*Sitta carolinensis* Latham, 1790
	Brown-headed Nuthatch	*Sitta pusilla* Latham, 1790
Certhiidae	Brown Creeper	*Certhia americana* Bonaparte, 1838
Troglodytidae	Marsh Wren	*Cistothorus palustris* (Wilson, 1810)

	Sedge Wren	*Cistothorus platensis* (Latham, 1790)
	Bewick's Wren	*Thyromanes bewickii* (Audubon, 1827)
	Carolina Wren	*Thyrothorus ludovicianus* (Latham, 1790)
	House Wren	*Troglodytes aedon* Vieillot, 1808
	Winter Wren	*Troglodytes troglodytes* (Linnaeus, 1758)
Polioptilidae	Blue-gray Gnatcatcher	*Polioptila caerulea* (Linnaeus, 1766)
Regulidae	Golden-crowned Kinglet	*Regulus satrapa* Lichtenstein, 1823
	Ruby-crowned Kinglet	*Regulus calendula* (Linnaeus, 1766)
Turdidae	Eastern Bluebird	*Siala sialis* (Linnaeus, 1758)
	Bicknell's Thrush	*Catharus bicknelli* (Ridgeway, 1882)
	Veery	*Catharus fuscesens* (Stehphens, 1817)
	Gray-cheeked Thrush	*Catharus minimus* (Lafresnaye, 1848)
	Swainson's Thrush	*Catharus ustulatus* (Nutall, 1840)
	Hermit Thrush	*Catharus guttatus* (Pallas, 1811)
	Wood Thrush	*Hylocichla mustelina* (Gmelin, 1789)
	American Robin	Turdus migratorius Linnaeus, 1766
Mimidae	Gray Catbird	*Dumetella carolinensis* (Linnaeus, 1766)
	Northern Mockingbird	*Mimus polyglottos* (Linnaeus, 1758)
	Brown Thrasher	*Toxostoma rufum* (Linnaeus, 1758)
Sturnidae	European Starling	*Sturnus vulgaris* Linnaeus, 1758
Motacillidae	American Pipit	*Anthus spinoletta* (Linnaeus, 1758)
	Sprague's Pipit	*Anthus spragueii* (Audubon, 1844)
Bombycillidae	Cedar Waxwing	*Bombycilla cedrorum* Vieillot, 1808
Calcariidae	Snow Bunting	*Plectrophenax nivalis* Linnaeus, 1758
Parulidae	Ovenbird	*Seiurus aurocapillus* (Linnaeus, 1766)

Worm-eating Warbler	*Helmitheros vermivorus* (Gmelin, 1789)
Louisiana Waterthrush	*Parkesia motacilla* (Vieillot, 1809)
Northern Waterthrush	*Parkesia noveboracensis* (Gmelin, 1789)
Blue-winged Warbler	*Vermiovra cyanoptera* (Olson & Reveal, 2009)
Black & white Warbler	*Mniotilta varia* (Linnaeus, 1766)
Prothonotary Warbler	*Protonotaria citrea* (Boddawert, 1783)
Swainson's Warbler	*Limnothlypis swainsonii* (Audubon, 1834)
Tennessee Warbler	*Oreothlypis peregrina* (Wilson, 1811)
Orange-crowned Warbler	*Oreothlypis celata* (Say, 1823)
Nashville Warbler	*Preothlypis ruficapilla* (Wilson, 1811)
Connecticut Warbler	*Oporornis agilis* (Wilson, 1812)
Kentucky Warbler	*Oporornis formosus* (Wilson,1811)
Common Yellowthroat	*Geothlypis trichas* (Linnaeus, 1766)
Hooded Warbler	*Setophaga citrina* (Boddaert, 1783)
American Redstart	*Setophaga ruticilla* (Linnaeus, 1758)
Kirtland's Warbler	*Setophaga kirtlandii* (Baird, 1852)
Cape May Warbler	*Setophaga tigrina* (Gmelin, 1789)
Northern Parula	*Setophaga americana* (Linnaeus, 1758)
Magnolia Warbler	*Setophaga magnolia* (Wilson, 1811)
Bay-breasted Warbler	*Setophaga castanea* (Wilson, 1810)
Blackburnian Warbler	*Setophaga fusca* (Müller, 1776)
Yellow Warbler	*Setophaga petechia* (Linnaeus, 1766)
Chestnut-sided Warbler	*Setophaga pensylvanica* (Linnaeus, 1766)
Blackpoll Warbler	*Setophaga striata* (Forster, 1772)
Black-throated Blue Warbler	*Setophaga caerulescens* (Gmelin, 1789)

	Palm Warbler	*Setophaga palmarum* (Gmelin, 1789)
	Pine Warbler	*Setophaga pinus* (Wilson, 1811)
	Yellow-rumped Warbler	*Setophaga coronata* (Linnaeus, 1766
	Yellow-throated Warbler	*Setophaga dominica* (Linnaeus, 1766)
	Prairie Warbler	Setophaga discolor (Vieillot,1809)
	Black-throated Green Warbler	*Setophaga virens* (Gmelin, 1789)
	Wilson's Warbler	*Cardellina pusilla* Wilson, 1811
	Yellow-breasted Chat	*Icteria virens* (Linnaeus, 1758)
Emberizidae	Eastern Towhee	*Pipilo erythrophthalmus* (Linnaeus, 1758)
	Bachman's Sparrow	*Peucaea aestivalis* (Lichtenstein, 1823)
	Chipping Sparrow	*Spizella passerina* (Bechsteil, 1798)
	Clay-colored Sparrow	*Spizella pallida* (Swainson, 1832)
	Field Sparrow	*Spizella pusilla* (Wilson, 1810)
	Vesper Sparrow	*Pooecetes gramineus* (Gmelin, 1789)
	Lark Sparrow	*Chondestes grammacus* (Say, 1823)
	Savannah Sparrow	*Passerculus sandwichensis* (Gmelin, 1789)
	Grasshopper Sparrow	*Ammodramus savannarum* (Gmelin, 1798)
	Nelson's Sparrow	*Ammodramus nelsoni* Allen, 1875
	Saltmarsh Sparrow	*Amodramus caudacutus* (Gmelin, 1788)
	Seaside Sparrow	*Ammodramus martimus* (Wilson, 1811)
	Fox Sparrow	*Passerella iliaca* (Merrem, 1786)
	Song Sparrow	*Melospiza melodia* (Wilson, 1810)
	Swamp Sparrow	*Melospiza georgiana* (Latham, 1790)
	White-throated Sparrow	*Zonotrichia albicollis* (Gmelin, 1789)
	Dark-eyed Junco	*Junco hyemalis* (Linnaeus, 1758)

Cardinalidae	Summer Tanager	*Piranga rubra* (Linnaeus, 1758)
	Scarlet Tanager	*Piranga olivacea* (Gmelin, 1789)
	Northern Cardinal	*Cardinalis cardinalis* (Linnaeus, 1758)
	Rose-breasted Grosbeak	*Pheucticus ludovicianus* (Linnaeus, 1766)
	Blue Grosbeak	*Passerina caerulea* (Linnaeus, 1758)
	Indigo Bunting	*Passerina cyanea* (Linnaeus, 1766)
	Painted Bunting	*Passerina ciris* (Linnaeus, 1758)
Icteridae	Bobolink	*Dolichonyx oryzivorus* (Linnaeus, 1758)
	Red-winged Blackbird	*Agelaius phoeniceus* (Linnaeus, 1766)
	Eastern Meadowlark	*Sturnella magna* (Linnaeus, 1758)
	Yellow-headed Blackbird	*Xanthocephalus xanthocephalus* (Bonaparte, 1826)
	Rusty Blackbird	*Euphagus carolinus* (Müller, 1776)
	Common Grackle	*Quiscalus quiscula* (Linnaeus, 1758)
	Boat-tailed Grackle	*Quiscalus major* Vieillot, 1819
	Shiny Cowbird	*Molothrus bonariensis* (Gmelin, 1789)
	Brown-headed Cowbird	*Molothus ater* (Boddaert, 1783)
	Orchard Oriole	*Icterus spurius* (Linnaeus, 1766)
	Baltimore Oriole	*Icterus galbula* (Linnaeus, 1758)
Fringillidae	Purple Finch	*Carpodacus purpureus* (Gmelin, 1789)
	House Finch	*Carpodacus mexicanus* (Müller, 1776)
	Pine Siskin	*Spinus pinus* (Wilson, 1810)
	American Goldfinch	*Spinus tristis* (Linnaeus, 1758)
	Evening Grosbeak	*Coccothraustes vespertinus* (Cooper, 1825)

APPENDIX IV B. BIRD MUSEUM SPECIMENS FROM
CUMBERLAND ISLAND, GEORGIA.

List compiled by D.W. Johnston. DMNH = Delaware Museum of Natural History; FMNH = Field
Museum of Natural History; MCZ = Museum of Comparative Zoology, Harvard; MMZ = Michigan
Museum of Zoology; NMNH = National Museum of Natural History; UGA = University of Georgia
Museum of Natural History; VMNH = Virginia Museum of Natural History. * denotes specimens
collected on Little Cumberland Island.

ID	Genus	Species	Date	Collector	Collection
20038	*Accipiter*	*striatus*	29-Dec-1904	Helme	VMNH
20069	*Accipiter*	*cooperii*	15-Apr-1903	Helme	VMNH
385953	*Agelaius*	*phoeniceus*	26-Dec-1902	Helme	AMNH
385954	*Agelaius*	*phoeniceus*	26-Dec-1902	Helme	AMNH
385983	*Agelaius*	*phoeniceus*	16-Jan-1894	Helme	AMNH
385984	*Agelaius*	*phoeniceus*	3-Apr-1903	Helme	AMNH
385985	*Agelaius*	*phoeniceus*	28-Apr-1903	Helme	AMNH
008369	*Agelaius*	*phoeniceus*	28-Apr-1903	Helme	DMNH
103237	*Agelaius*	*phoeniceus*	4-Aug-1897	Brown	MCZ
18100	*Agelaius*	*phoeniceus*	29-Apr-1903	Helme	VMNH
18387	*Agelaius*	*phoeniceus*	28-Apr-1903	Helme	VMNH
18388	*Agelaius*	*phoeniceus*	28-Apr-1903	Helme	VMNH
564053	*Agelaius*	*phoeniceus*	7-Apr-1903	Helme	NMNH
564054	*Agelaius*	*phoeniceus*	24-Apr-1903	Helme	NMNH
564051	*Agelaius*	*phoeniceus*	29-Apr-1903	Helme	NMNH
564052	*Agelaius*	*phoeniceus*	28-Apr-1903	Helme	NMNH
19756	*Aix*	*sponsa*	28-Dec-1904	Helme	VMNH
19853	*Aix*	*sponsa*	9-Jan-1905	Helme	VMNH
19855	*Aix*	*sponsa*	8-Jun-1903	Helme	VMNH
19860	*Aix*	*sponsa*	8-Jun-1903	Helme	VMNH
19861	*Aix*	*sponsa*	8-Jun-1903	Helme	VMNH
19862	*Aix*	*sponsa*	4-Jun-1903	Helme	VMNH
19864	*Aix*	*sponsa*	23-Jun-1909	Helme	VMNH
19865	*Aix*	*sponsa*	7-Jun-1903	Helme	VMNH
009248	*Ammodramus*	*sandwichensis*	19-Dec-1904	Helme	DMNH
009326	*Ammodramus*	*savannarum*	8-Apr-1902	Helme	DMNH
009327	*Ammodramus*	*savannarum*	20-Apr-1903	Helme	DMNH
009377	*Ammodramus*	*nelsoni*	16-Jan-1903	Helme	DMNH
009379	*Ammodramus*	*caudacutus (s.s.)*	27-Apr-1903	Helme	DMNH
009399	*Ammodramus*	*maritimus*	12-Jan-1903	Helme	DMNH
009400	Ammodramus	maritimus	5-Apr-1902	Helme	DMNH
009401	Ammodramus	maritimus	1-Mar-1902	Helme	DMNH

009402	*Ammodramus*	*maritimus*	23-Jan-1905	Helme	DMNH
009403	*Ammodramus*	*maritimus*	10-Feb-1903	Helme	DMNH
009404	*Ammodramus*	*maritimus*	20-Apr-1905	Helme	DMNH
009405	*Ammodramus*	*maritimus*	10-Mar-1902	Helme	DMNH
009409	*Ammodramus*	*maritimus*	10-Apr-1902	Helme	DMNH
009410	*Ammodramus*	*maritimus*	28-Jan-1903	Helme	DMNH
111895	*Ammodramus*	*caudacutus*	18-May-1916	Worthington	FMNH
148900	*Ammodramus*	*maritimus*	18-May-1916	Worthington	FMNH
103270	*Ammodramus*	*maritimus*	12-Dec-1904		MCZ
152295	*Ammodramus*	*maritimus*	12-Nov-1931	Greenway	MCZ
152296	*Ammodramus*	*maritimus*	12-Sep-1931	Greenway	MCZ
257948	*Ammodramus*	*maritimus*	12-Oct-1931	Greenway	MCZ
14915	*Ammodramus*	*savannarum*	21-Apr-1903	Helme	VMNH
15114	*Ammodramus*	*savannarum*	18-Apr-1903	Helme	VMNH
15115	*Ammodramus*	*savannarum*	4-Apr-1903	Helme	VMNH
107995	*Ammodramus*	*maritimus*	12-Mar-1903	Helme	MMZ
401038	*Ammospiza*	*maritima*	12-Mar-1902	Helme	AMNH
350524	*Anas*	*rubripes*	24-Dec-1904	Helme	AMNH
565	*Anas*	*acuta*	10-Dec-1903		UGA
19571	*Anas*	*discors*	4-Apr-1903	Helme	VMNH
19695	*Anas*	*discors*	28-Dec-1904	Helme	VMNH
19698	*Anas*	*acuta*	28-Dec-1909	Helme	VMNH
19717	*Anas*	*clypeata*	28-Dec-1904	Helme	VMNH
19738	*Anas*	*rubripes*	23-Dec-1902	Helme	VMNH
19741	*Anas*	*rubripes*	31-Dec-1902	Helme	VMNH
	Anas	*strepera*	30-Mar-1903	Helme	VMNH
*2670	*Anous*	*stolidus*	9-Sep-1965	Richardson	UGA
378131	*Anthus*	*spraguei*	27-Mar-1903	Helme	AMNH
378132	*Anthus*	*spraguei*	28-Mar-1903	Helme	AMNH
378133	*Anthus*	*spraguei*	28-Mar-1903	Helme	AMNH
378134	*Anthus*	*spraguei*	30-Mar-1903	Helme	AMNH
005656	*Ardea*	*herodias*	3-Jan-1905	Helme	DMNH
349668.00	*Ardea*	*alba*	25 Apr 1893	Helme	AMNH
355458	*Ardea*	*alba*	14-Apr-1903	Helme	DNMH
355459	*Arenaria*	*interpres*	16-Jan-1903	Helme	AMNH
316378	*Arenaria*	*interpres*	27-Mar-1903	Helme	AMNH
4360	*Arenaria*	*interpres*	11-Oct-1931	Greenway	MCZ
4361	*Arenaria*	*interpres*	22-May-1971	Wharton	UGA

4365	*Arenaria*	*interpres*	22-May-1971	Wharton	UGA
21599	*Arenaria*	*interpres*	28-Nov-1970	Candler	UGA
21632	*Arenaria*	*interpres*	29-Apr-1903	Helme	VMNH
360970	*Arenaria*	*interpres*	16-Jan-1903	Helme	VMNH
360971	*Asio*	*flammeus*	14-Dec-1904	Helme	AMNH
504	*Asio*	*flammeus*	30-Dec-1904	Helme	AMNH
351044	*Asio*	*flammeus*	30-Dec-1904	Helme	UGA
351161	*Aythya*	*valisneria*	17-Dec-1904	Helme	AMNH
351162	*Aythya*	*affinis*	25-Mar-1902	Helme	AMNH
351163	*Aythya*	*affinis*	9-Apr-1903	Helme	AMNH
351164	*Aythya*	*affinis*	20-Dec-1904	Helme	AMNH
566	*Aythya*	*affinis*	9-Jan-1905	Helme	AMNH
567	*Aythya*	*affinis*	31-Mar-1904		UGA
587	*Aythya*	*affinis*	19-Mar-1904		UGA
4257	*Aythya*	*americana*	28-Oct-1903		UGA
19868	*Aythya*	*affinis*	19-Feb-1972	Wharton	UGA
19883	*Aythya*	*americana*	17-Dec-1904	Helme	VMNH
19966	*Aythya*	*americana*	17-Dec-1904	Helme	VMNH
20010	*Aythya*	*affinis*	18-Apr-1903	Helme	VMNH
20017	*Aythya*	*affinis*	20-Dec-1904	Helme	VMNH
20018	*Aythya*	*affinis*	21-Apr-1905	Helme	VMNH
21341	*Aythya*	*affinis*	18-Apr-1903	Helme	VMNH
22323	*Bartramia*	*longicauda*	6-Apr-1903	Helme	VMNH
19549	*Bartramia*	*longicauda*	27-Apr-1903	Helme	VMNH
19570	*Botaurus*	*lentiginosus*	4-Apr-1903	Helme	VMNH
20019	*Botaurus*	*lentiginosus*	29-Apr-1903	Helme	VMNH
352360	*Bucephala*	*albeola*	24-Mar-1902	Helme	VMNH
21972	*Buteo*	*jamaicensis*	16-Dec-1904	Helme	AMNH
356575	*Calidri*	*pusilla*	13-Mar-1902	Helme	VMNH
356576	*Calidris*	*melanotos*	1-Apr-1903	Helme	AMNH
356577	*Calidris*	*melanotos*	3-Apr-1903	Helme	AMNH
357046	*Calidris*	*melanotos*	3-Apr-1903	Helme	AMNH
357047	*Calidris*	*alpina*	10-Mar-1902	Helme	AMNH
357047	*Calidris*	*alpina*	9-Apr-1902	Helme	AMNH
356776	*Calidris*	*alpina*	21-Apr-1903	Helme	AMNH
005854	*Calidris*	*minutilla*	10-Mar-1902	Helme	ANMH
005901	*Calidris*	*pusilla*	25-Apr-1905	Helme	DMNH
486	*Calidris*	*melanotos*	1-Apr-1903	Helme	DMNH
491	*Calidris*	*alba*	2-Sep-1903		UGA

496	*Calidris*	*melanotos*	21-Apr-1903		UGA
591	*Calidris*	*mauri*	2-Sep-1903		UGA
4378	*Calidris*	*alba*	2-Sep-1903		UGA
4379	*Calidris*	*canutus*	28-Nov-1970	Candler	UGA
4380	*Calidris*	*canutus*	28-Nov-1970	Candler	UGA
4381	*Calidris*	*canutus*	22-May-1971	Wharton	UGA
4385	*Calidris*	*canutus*	22-May-1971	Wharton	UGA
4386	*Calidris*	*alpina*	3-May-1970	Wharton	UGA
4387	*Calidris*	*alpina*	28-Nov-1970	Wharton	UGA
4388	*Calidris*	*alpina*	22-May-1971	Wharton	UGA
4389	*Calidris*	*mauri*	28-Nov-1970	Wharton	UGA
4390	*Calidris*	*alba*	28-Nov-1970	Wharton	UGA
4391	*Calidris*	*alba*	22-May-1971	Wharton	UGA
5926	*Calidris*	*alba*	22-May-1971	Wharton	UGA
21835	*Calidris*	*alpina*	28-Nov-1970	Wharton	UGA
21850	*Calidris*	*pusilla*	25-Apr-1905	Helme	VMNH
21854	*Calidris*	*himantopus*	19-Apr-1905	Helme	VMNH
21867	*Calidris*	*melanotos*	1-Apr-1903	Helme	VMNH
21884	*Calidris*	*alpina*	10-Mar-1902	Helme	VMNH
21885	*Calidris*	*alpina*	28-Mar-1902	Helme	VMNH
21913	*Calidris*	*minutilla*	29-Apr-1903	Helme	VMNH
21916	*Calidris*	*minutilla*	10-Mar-1902	Helme	VMNH
21933	*Calidris*	*minutilla*	30-Mar-1903	Helme	VMNH
21950	*Calidris*	*melanotos*	19-Apr-1905	Helme	VMNH
21974	*Calidris*	*pusilla*	10-Apr-1903	Helme	VMNH
22448	*Calidris*	*alba*	22-Apr-1903	Helme	VMNH
22518	*Calidris*	*alpina*	25-Apr-1905	Helme	VMNH
22531	*Calidris*	*alpina*	22-Dec-1902	Helme	VMNH
22567	*Calidris*	*alpina*	9-Apr-1902	Helme	VMNH
203420	*Calidris*	*alpina*			VMNH
3313	*Calidris*	*alba*	6-Jun-1902	Helme	MMZ
602130	*Calonectris*	*diomedea*	2-Sep-1973	Hudick	UGA
6016.00	*Calonectris*	*diomedea*	22-Aug-2008	Ruckdeschel	NMNH
006017	*Caprimulgus*	*carolinensis*	9-Apr-1902	Helme	DMNH
89264	*Caprimulgus*	*carolinensis*	18-Apr-1903	Helme	DMNH
178359	*Caprimulgus*	*carolinensis*	1-Apr-1903	Helme	MMZ
103220	*Cardinalis*	*cardinalis*	28-Mar-1903		FMNH
103221	*Cardinalis*	*cardinalis*	4-Jul-1897	Brown	MCZ
103222	*Cardinalis*	*cardinalis*	4-Jul-1897	Brown	MCZ

103240	*Cardinalis*	*cardinalis*	4-May-1897	Brown	MCZ
5442	*Cardinalis*	*cardinalis*	4-Mar-1897	Brown	MCZ
15726	*Cardinalis*	*cardinalis*	25-Mar-1992		UGA
15908	*Cardinalis*	*cardinalis*	17-Apr-1902	Helme	VMNH
15909	*Cardinalis*	*cardinalis*	17-Apr-1902	Helme	VMNH
386822	*Cardinalis*	*cardinalis*	1-Jan-1905	Helme	VMNH
18410	*Cassidix*	*mexicanus*	22-Dec-1902	Helme	AMNH
18537	*Cassidix*	*major*	2-Apr-1902	Helme	VMNH
18538	*Cassidix*	*major*	10-Jan-1903	Helme	VMNH
18542	*Cassidix*	*major*	31-Mar-1903	Helme	VMNH
18545	*Cassidix*	*major*	12-Mar-1903	Helme	VMNH
18546	*Cassidix*	*major*	16-Apr-1903	Helme	VMNH
18548	*Cassidix*	*major*	23-Dec-1902	Helme	VMNH
18549	*Cassidix*	*major*	23-Apr-1903	Helme	VMNH
18551	*Cassidix*	*major*	1-Apr-1903	Helme	VMNH
18552	*Cassidix*	*major*	25-Apr-1905	Helme	VMNH
18554	*Cassidix*	*major*	7-Apr-1903	Helme	VMNH
18555	*Cassidix*	*major*	18-Apr-1905	Helme	VMNH
602092	*Cassidix*	*major*	10-Jan-1903	Helme	VMNH
63275	*Catharacta*	*maccormicki*	14-Sep-2006	Ruckdeschel	NMNH
148078	*Catoptrophorus*	*semipalmatus*	18-Mar-1931	Greenway	MCZ
152309	*Catoptrophorus*	*semipalmatus*	11-Oct-1931	Greenway	MCZ
182278	*Catoptrophorus*	*semipalmatus*	19-Mar-1931	Greenway	MCZ
64824	*Catoptrophorus*	*semipalmatus*	19-Mar-1931	Greenway	MCZ
21701	*Catoptrophorus*	*semipalmatus*	30-Mar-1903	Helme	MMZ
21769	*Catoptrophorus*	*semipalmatus*	24-Mar-1902	Helme	VMNH
21771	*Catoptrophorus*	*semipalmatus*	2-Jan-1903	Helme	VMNH
21781	*Catoptrophorus*	*semipalmatus*	27-Mar-1903	Helme	VMNH
21782	*Catoptrophorus*	*semipalmatus*	30-Mar-1903	Helme	VMNH
21783	*Catoptrophorus*	*semipalmatus*	1-Apr-1903	Helme	VMNH
64825	*Catoptrophorus*	*semipalmatus*	1-Apr-1903	Helme	VMNH
354887	*Catoptrophorus*	*semipalmatus*	1-Apr-1903	Helme	MMZ
354888	*Charadrius*	*semipalmatus*	10-Apr-1902	Helme	AMNH
354889	*Charadrius*	*semipalmatus*	30-Mar-1903	Helme	AMNH
355041	*Charadrius*	*semipalmatus*	30-Mar-1903	Helme	AMNH
355042	*Charadrius*	*wilsonia*	27-Mar-1903	Helme	AMNH
355043	*Charadrius*	*wilsonia*	25-Mar-1902	Helme	AMNH
355044	*Charadrius*	*wilsonia*	27-Mar-1903	Helme	AMNH
005762	*Charadrius*	*wilsonia*	18-Apr-1905	Helme	AMNH

005763	*Charadrius*	*wilsonia*	27-Mar-1903	Helme	DMNH
005764	*Charadrius*	*wilsonia*	27-Mar-1903	Helme	DMNH
406969	*Charadrius*	*melodus*	6-Apr-1903	Helme	DMNH
152310	*Charadrius*	*semipalmatus*	30-Mar-1903	Helme	FMNH
254636	*Charadrius*	*wilsonia*	18-Mar-2002		MCZ
64501	*Charadrius*	*wilsonia*	4-Jan-1902	Helme	MCZ
532	*Charadrius*	*wilsonia*	27-Mar-1903	Helme	MMZ
4353	*Charadrius*	*wilsonia*	21-Apr-1903		UGA
21496	*Charadrius*	*semipalmatus*	28-Nov-1970	Candler	UGA
21539	*Charadrius*	*wilsonia*	27-Mar-1903	Helme	VMNH
21541	*Charadrius*	*wilsonia*	18-Apr-1905	Helme	VMNH
21570	*Charadrius*	*semipalmatus*	10-Apr-1902	Helme	VMNH
203390	*Charadrius*	*melodus*	12-Jan-1903	Helme	VMNH
203392	*Charadrius*	*semipalmatus*	10-Apr-1903	Helme	MMZ
007415	*Charadrius*	*wilsonia*	1-Apr-1902	Helme	MMZ
007416	*Cistothorus*	*palustris*	11-Jun-1905	Helme	DMNH
007417	*Cistothorus*	*palustris*	12-Dec-1904	Helme	DMNH
007418	*Cistothorus*	*palustris*	12-Mar-1902	Helme	DMNH
3260	*Cistothorus*	*palustris*	23-Dec-1904	Helme	DMNH
103262	*Colaptes*	*auratus*	21-Mar-1970	Dopson	UGA
103267	*Columbigallina*	*passerina*	4-May-1897	Brown	MCZ
359920	*Columbigallina*	*passerina*	14-Jan-2003	Bangs	MCZ
005970	*Columbina*	*passerina*	26-Dec-1902	Helme	AMNH
005971	*Columbina*	*passerina*	14-Jan-1903	Helme	DMNH
005972	*Columbina*	*passerina*	17-Jan-1908	Helme	DMNH
005973	*Columbina*	*passerina*	17-Jan-1908	Helme	DMNH
016911	*Columbina*	*passerina*	26-Dec-1902	Helme	DMNH
*3280	*Columbina*	*passerina*	14-Jan-1903	Helme	DMNH
*3282	*Columbina*	*passerina*	18-Mar-1970	Richardson	UGA
203468	*Columbina*	*passerina*	18-Mar-1970	Richardson	UGA
4296	*Contopus*	*virens*	27-Apr-1905	Helme	MMZ
13873	*Coragyps*	*atratus*	22-May-1971	Wharton	UGA
21216	*Corvus*	*brachyrhynchos*	4-Jan-1902	Helme	VMNH
387657	*Coturnicops*	*noveboracensis*	/ / /no date	Helme	VMNH
387658	*Crocethia*	*alba*	21-Apr-1903	Helme	AMNH
387659	*Crocethia*	*alba*	21-Apr-1903	Helme	AMNH
103202	*Crocethia*	*alba*	21-Apr-1903	Helme	AMNH
103203	*Dendrocopos*	*pubescens*	3-Aug-1897		MCZ
103207	*Dendrocopos*	*pubescens*	4-Aug-1897	Brown	MCZ

007987	*Dendrocopos*	*pubescens*	9-Sep-1897	Brown	MCZ
008009	*Dendroica*	*caerulescens*	24-Apr-1903	Helme	DMNH
008010	*Dendroica*	*dominica*	20-Apr-1903	Helme	DMNH
008150	*Dendroica*	*dominica*	27-Mar-1902	Helme	DMNH
017223	*Dendroica*	*striata*	24-Apr-1903	Helme	DMNH
103013	*Dendroica*	*dominica*	11-Apr-1902	Helme	DMNH
103216	*Dendroica*	*discolor*	4-Apr-1897	Brown	MCZ
103244	*Dendroica*	*caerulescens*	9-Sep-1897	Brown	MCZ
103248	*Dendroica*	*palmarum*	4-Mar-1897	Brown	MCZ
103249	*Dendroica*	*palmarum*	13-Apr-1905		MCZ
103250	*Dendroica*	*discolor*	4-Apr-1897	Brown	MCZ
103251	*Dendroica*	*dominica*	9-Sep-1897	Brown	MCZ
103258	*Dendroica*	*discolor*	4-Apr-1897	Brown.	MCZ
182635	*Dendroica*	*palmarum*	4-Mar-1897	Brown	MCZ
16505	*Dendroica*	*discolor*	4-May-1897	Brown	MCZ
16553	*Dendroica*	*petechia*	24-Apr-1903	Helme	VMNH
16555	*Dendroica*	*petechia*	24-Apr-1903	Helme	VMNH
16642	*Dendroica*	*tigrina*	28-Apr-1903	Helme	VMNH
16707	*Dendroica*	*caerulescens*	8-Apr-1902	Wayne	VMNH
16708	*Dendroica*	*caerulescens*	/ / /1902	Helme	VMNH
16711	*Dendroica*	*caerulescens*	27-Apr-1903	Helme	VMNH
16713	*Dendroica*	*caerulescens*	27-Apr-1905	Helme	VMNH
17029	*Dendroica*	*dominica*	14-Apr-1903	Helme	VMNH
17030	*Dendroica*	*dominica*	30-Mar-1903	Helme	VMNH
17034	*Dendroica*	*dominica*	7-Apr-1902	Helme	VMNH
17039	*Dendroica*	*dominica*	14-Apr-1903	Helme	VMNH
17182	*Dendroica*	*pinus*	14-Apr-1903	Helme	VMNH
17183	*Dendroica*	*pinus*	24-Apr-1903	Helme	VMNH
17185	*Dendroica*	*pinus*	24-Mar-1902	Helme	VMNH
17257	*Dendroica*	*discolor*	9-Apr-1903	Helme	VMNH
17258	*Dendroica*	*discolor*	22-Apr-1903	Helme	VMNH
17304	*Dendroica*	*palmarum*	29-Mar-1902	Helme	VMNH
17305	*Dendroica*	*palmarum*	8-Apr-1903	Helme	VMNH
17306	*Dendroica*	*palmarum*	2-Apr-1903	Helme	VMNH
17307	*Dendroica*	*palmarum*	12-Mar-1903	Helme	VMNH
17308	*Dendroica*	*palmarum*	7-Apr-1903	Helme	VMNH
17309	*Dendroica*	*palmarum*	10-Jan-1903	Helme	VMNH
17310	*Dendroica*	*palmarum*	11-Apr-1902	Helme	VMNH
17311	*Dendroica*	*palmarum*	16-Dec-1904	Helme	VMNH

17312	*Dendroica*	*palmarum*	3-Apr-1903	Helme	VMNH
17313	*Dendroica*	*palmarum*	16-Dec-1904	Helme	VMNH
17314	*Dendroica*	*palmarum*	3-Apr-1903	Helme	VMNH
17316	*Dendroica*	*palmarum*	14-Dec-1904	Helme	VMNH
564372	*Dendroica*	*palmarum*	2-Apr-1903	Helme	VMNH
564373	*Dendroica*	*kirtlandii*	12-Apr-1902	Helme	NMNH
008550	*Dendroica*	*kirtlandii*	26-Apr-1905	Helme	NMNH
008551	*Dolichonyx*	*oryzivorus*	27-Apr-1903	Helme	DMNH
332	*Dolichonyx*	*oryzivorus*	25-Apr-1905	Helme	DMNH
18014	*Dolichonyx*	*oryzivorus*	21-Apr-1903		UGA
349688	*Dolichonyx*	*oryzivorus*	25-Apr-1905	Helme	VMNH
349748	*Egretta*	*thula*	15-Apr-1903	Helme	AMNH
349749	*Egretta*	*tricolor*	5-Apr-1902	Helme	AMNH
349750	*Egretta*	*tricolor*	3-Apr-1902	Helme	AMNH
349751	*Egretta*	*tricolor*	28-Mar-1903	Helme	AMNH
349752	*Egretta*	*tricolor*	7-Apr-1903	Helme	AMNH
349810	*Egretta*	*tricolor*	1-Jan-1903	Helme	AMNH
005649	*Egretta*	*caerulea*	22-Dec-1902	Helme	AMNH
005650	*Egretta*	*caerulea*	26-Feb-1908	Helme	DMNH
005651	*Egretta*	*caerulea*	17-Apr-1902	Helme	DMNH
005655	*Egretta*	*caerulea*	1-Feb-1902	Helme	DMNH
005657	*Egretta*	*thula*	13-Apr-1903	Helme	DMNH
005658	*Egretta*	*tricolor*	4-Apr-1902	Helme	DMNH
005659	*Egretta*	*tricolor*	5-Apr-1902	Helme	DMNH
71422	*Egretta*	*tricolor*	11-Apr-1903	Helme	DMNH
4974	*Egretta*	*caerulea*	18-May-1916	Worthington	FMNH
18621	*Egretta*	*rufescens*	26-Jul-1979	Selb	UGA
19525	*Egretta*	*caerulea*	13-Apr-1903	Helme	VMNH
20110	*Egretta*	*caerulea*	22-Dec-1902	Helme	VMNH
20576	*Falco*	*columbarius*	5-Jan-1905	Helme	VMNH
20580	*Falco*	*columbarius*	9-Jan-1905	Helme	VMNH
20594	*Falco*	*columbarius*	23-Apr-1903	Helme	VMNH
20658	*Falco*	*sparverius*	6-Jan-1903	Helme	VMNH
349811	*Falco*	*sparverius*	22-Dec-1902	Helme	VMNH
579	*Florida*	*caerulea*	29-Mar-1902	Helme	AMNH
580	*Fulica*	*americana*	12-Oct-1903		UGA
581	*Fulica*	*americana*	28-Oct-1903		UGA
21142	*Fulica*	*americana*	26-Oct-1903		UGA
355639	*Fulica*	*americana*	28-Dec-1904	Helme	VMNH

355640	*Gallinago*	*delicata*	16-Jan-1903	Helme	AMNH
355641	*Gallinago*	*delicata*	18-Apr-1903	Helme	AMNH
005788	*Gallinago*	*delicata*	14-Dec-1904	Helme	AMNH
21639	*Gallinago*	*delicata*	22-Dec-1902	Helme	DMNH
21690	*Gallinago*	*gallinago*	21-Mar-1902	Helme	VMNH
354615	*Gallinago*	*gallinago*	11-Apr-1902	Helme	VMNH
21131	*Gallinula*	*chloropus*	3-Jan-1905	Helme	AMNH
4261	*Gallinula*	*chloropus*	17-Dec-1909	Helme	VMNH
4262	*Gavia*	*immer*	28-Nov-1970	Wharton	UGA
*A883273	*Gavia*	*stellata*	15-May-1971	Candler	UGA
4315	*Gavia*	*stellata*	8-Dec-1970	Richardson	UGA
17317	*Geochelidon*	*nilotica*	22-May-1971	Wharton	UGA
17549	*Geothlypis*	*trichas*	19-Dec-1904	Helme	VMNH
17551	*Geothlypis*	*trichas*	4-Apr-1903	Helme	VMNH
17553	*Geothlypis*	*trichas*	16-Apr-1903	Helme	VMNH
148076	*Geothlypis*	*trichas*	14-Apr-1902	Helme	VMNH
148077	*Haematopus*	*ostralegus*	30-Nov-1931	Greenway	MCZ
4352	*Haematopus*	*ostralegus*	12-Aug-1931	Greenway	MCZ
008199	*Haematopus*	*palliatus*	24-May-1905	Candler	UGA
008200	*Helmitheros*	*vermivorus*	17-Apr-1903	Helme	DMNH
16303	*Helmitheros*	*vermivorus*	27-Apr-1903	Helme	DMNH
386216	*Helmitheros*	*vermivorus*	23-Apr-1903	Helme	VMNH
386217	*Icterus*	*spurius*	27-Apr-1903	Helme	AMNH
008338	*Icterus*	*spurius*	25-Apr-1905	Helme	AMNH
18389	*Icterus*	*spurius*	22-Apr-1903	Helme	DMNH
18408	*Icterus*	*spurius*	21-Apr-1905	Helme	VMNH
18409	*Icterus*	*spurius*	26-Apr-1905	Helme	VMNH
007747	*Icterus*	*spurius*	25-Apr-1903	Helme	VMNH
007748	*Lanius*	*ludovicianus*	12-Apr-1902	Helme	DMNH
007749	*Lanius*	*ludovicianus*	9-Jan-1903	Helme	DMNH
358482	*Lanius*	*ludovicianus*	13-Dec-1904	Helme	DMNH
358483	*Larus*	*philadelphia*	5-Jan-1905	Helme	AMNH
358484	*Larus*	*philadelphia*	5-Jan-1905	Helme	AMNH
358485	*Larus*	*philadelphia*	10-Mar-1902	Helme	AMNH
358486	*Larus*	*philadelphia*	14-Mar-1902	Helme	AMNH
006125	*Larus*	*philadelphia*	10-Apr-1903	Helme	AMNH
563	*Larus*	*atricilla*	10-Apr-1903	Helme	DMNH
4301	*Larus*	*atricilla*	1-Apr-1903		UGA
4302	*Larus*	*delawarensis*	28-Nov-1970	Wharton	UGA

4306	*Larus*	*delawarensis*	28-Nov-1970	Wharton	UGA
4307	*Larus*	*atricilla*	28-Nov-1970	Wharton	UGA
494	*Larus*	*atricilla*	22-May-1971	Wharton	UGA
21864	*Limnodromus*	*griseus*	27-Oct-1903		UGA
576769	*Limnodromus*	*griseus*	17-Feb-1905	Helme	VMNH
008196	*Limnodromus*	*scolopaceus*	12-Mar-1903	Helme	NMNH
008197	*Limnothlypis*	*swainsonii*	2-Apr-1905	Helme	DMNH
19897	*Limnothlypis*	*swainsonii*	15-Mar-1902	Helme	DMNH
103205	*Lophodytes*	*cucullatus*	25-Dec-1902	Helme	VMNH
103206	*Melanerpes*	*erythrocephalus*	9-Sep-1897	Brown	MCZ
103239	*Melanerpes*	*erythrophthalmus*	9-Sep-1897	Brown	MCZ
103247	*Melanerpes*	*erythrophthalmus*	9-Sep-1897	Brown.	MCZ
152307	*Melanerpes*	*carolinus*	9-Sep-1897	Brown	MCZ
586	*Melanerpes*	*erythrocephalus*	9-Sep-1897	Brown	MCZ
588	*Melanitta*	*americana*	17-Nov-1903		UGA
589	*Melanitta*	*perspicillata*	19-Mar-1904	Arnow	UGA
*3352	*Melanitta*	*perspicillata*	17-Nov-1903	Arnow	UGA
556914	*Melanitta*	*americana*	28-Nov-1969	Dopson	UGA
751411	*Melanitta*	*perspicilata*	22-Jun-1978	Rudkdeschel	NMNH
751412	*Meleagris*	*gallopavo*	Winter	Helme	AMNH
19959	*Meleagris*	*gallopavo*	Winter	Helme	AMNH
375363	*Mergus*	*serrator*	3-Apr-1903	Helme	VMNH
375364	*Mimus*	*polyglottos*	17-Apr-1905	Helme	AMNH
103261	*Mimus*	*polyglottos*	7-Jan-1905	Helme	AMNH
182279	*Mimus*	*polyglottos*	15-Apr-1897	Brown	MCZ
4267	*Mimus*	*polyglottos*	4-Aug-1897	Brown	MCZ
5301	*Morus*	*bassanus*	2-May-1970	Wharton	UGA
369266	*Morus*	*bassanus*	2-Feb-1986	Haney	UGA
006967	*Myiarchus*	*crinitus*	31-Mar-1902	Helme	AMNH
355733	*Myiarchus*	*crinitus*	17-Apr-1903	Helme	DMNH
355734	*Numenius*	*phaeopus*	29-Apr-1903	Helme	AMNH
21784	*Numenius*	*phaeopus*	25-Apr-1905	Helme	AMNH
005666	*Numenius*	*phaeopus*	25-Apr-1905	Helme	VMNH
542	*Nycticorax*	*nycticorax*	4-Apr-1903	Helme	DMNH
19526	*Nycticorax*	*nycticorax*	21-Apr-1903		UGA
*3343	*Nycticorax*	*violaceus*	27-Apr-1903	Helme	VMNH
*5463	*Oceanites*	*oceanicus*	1-Jul-1972	Richardson	UGA
608564	*Oceanodroma*	*leucorhoa*	26-May-1991	Sciple	UGA
22253	*Oceanodroma*	*leucorhoa*	1-May-1991	Ruckdeschel	NMNH

007935	*Otus*	*asio*	4-Jan-1905	Helme	VMNH
007936	*Parula*	*americana*	12-Apr-1902	Helme	DMNH
147505	*Parula*	*americana*	21-Apr-1905	Helme	DMNH
148899	*Parula*	*americana*	17-May-1916	Worthington	FMNH
103238	*Parula*	*americana*	17-May-1916	Worthington	FMNH
256517	*Parula*	*americana*	4-Apr-1897	Brown	MCZ
256896	*Parula*	*americana*	4-Mar-1897	Brown	MCZ
302218	*Parula*	*americana*	4-Mar-1902	Helme	MCZ
16305	*Parula*	*americana*	4-Apr-1897	Brown	MCZ
16491	*Parula*	*americana*	22-Apr-1905	Helme	VMNH
16493	*Parula*	*americana*	27-Apr-1905	Helme	VMNH
16499	*Parula*	*americana*	9-Apr-1903	Helme	VMNH
16504	*Parula*	*americana*	4-Apr-1902	Helme	VMNH
312278	*Parula*	*americana*	22-Apr-1905	Helme	VMNH
14526	*Parus*	*carolinensis*	15-Apr-1897	Brown	MCZ
	Parus	*carolinensis*	25-Dec-1900	Maynard	MCZ
14905	*Passerculus*	*sandwichensis*	20-Mar-1902	Helme	VMNH
14906	*Passerculus*	*sandwichensis*	1-Apr-1902	Helme	VMNH
14907	*Passerculus*	*sandwichensis*	13-Jan-1903	Helme	VMNH
14908	*Passerculus*	*sandwichensis*	12-Mar-1903	Helme	VMNH
14909	*Passerculus*	*sandwichensis*	30-Mar-1903	Helme	VMNH
14910	*Passerculus*	*sandwichensis*	3-Apr-1903	Helme	VMNH
14911	*Passerculus*	*sandwichensis*	4-Apr-1903	Helme	VMNH
14912	*Passerculus*	*sandwichensis*	4-Apr-1903	Helme	VMNH
14913	*Passerculus*	*sandwichensis*	2-Apr-1903	Helme	VMNH
14914	*Passerculus*	*sandwichensis*	3-Apr-1905	Helme	VMNH
14314	*Passerculus*	*sandwichensis*	16-Apr-1905	Helme	VMNH
008637	*Passerculus*	*sandwichensis*	4-Apr-1903	Helme	VMNH
008638	*Passerina*	*ciris*	24-Apr-1903	Helme	DMNH
017393	*Passerina*	*ciris*	28-Apr-1905	Helme	DMNH
71243	*Passerina*	*ciris*	29-Apr-1903	Helme	DMNH
15913	*Passerina*	*ciris*	17-May-1916	Worthington	FMNH
16061	*Passerina*	*cyanea*	24-Apr-1903	Helme	VMNH
16062	*Passerina*	*cyanea*	22-Apr-1905	Helme	VMNH
16086	*Passerina*	*ciris*	21-Apr-1905	Helme	VMNH
16087	*Passerina*	*ciris*	27-Apr-1905	Helme	VMNH
16088	*Passerina*	*ciris*	24-Apr-1903	Helme	VMNH
16089	*Passerina*	*ciris*	2-Apr-1905	Helme	VMNH
16090	*Passerina*	*ciris*	27-Apr-1905	Helme	VMNH

16091	*Passerina*	*ciris*	27-Apr-1905	Helme	VMNH
16092	*Passerina*	*ciris*	20-Apr-1903	Helme	VMNH
16093	*Passerina*	*ciris*	25-Apr-1905	Helme	VMNH
16094	*Passerina*	*ciris*	21-Apr-1903	Helme	VMNH
16095	*Passerina*	*ciris*	27-Apr-1903	Helme	VMNH
16096	*Passerina*	*ciris*	30-Apr-1903	Helme	VMNH
16097	*Passerina*	*ciris*	30-Apr-1903	Helme	VMNH
16098	*Passerina*	*ciris*	20-Apr-1903	Helme	VMNH
16099	*Passerina*	*ciris*	20-Apr-1903	Helme	VMNH
16100	*Passerina*	*ciris*	14-Apr-1902	Helme	VMNH
16101	*Passerina*	*ciris*	27-Apr-1905	Helme	VMNH
16102	*Passerina*	*ciris*	22-Apr-1905	Helme	VMNH
103224	*Passerina*	*ciris*	21-Apr-1905	Helme	VMNH
4268	*Pelecanus*	*occidentalis*	//	Shaw	MCZ
*5212	*Phalacrocorax*	*auritus*	2-May-1970	Wharton	UGA
008708	*Phalacrocorax*	*auritus*	23-May-1980	Rappole	UGA
008709	*Pipilo*	*erythrophthalmus*	1-Apr-1903	Helme	DMNH
008710	*Pipilo*	*erythrophthalmus*	25-Feb-1905	Helme	DMNH
103227	*Pipilo*	*erythrophthalmus*	16-Jun-1903	Helme	DMNH
15375	*Pipilo*	*erythrophthalmus*	4-Mar-1897	Brown	MCZ
15722	*Pipilo*	*erythrophthalmus*	8-Apr-1905	Helme	VMNH
15723	*Pipilo*	*erythrophthalmus*	2-Jan-1905	Helme	VMNH
008575	*Pipilo*	*erythrophthalmus*	2-Feb-1905	Helme	VMNH
008576	*Piranga*	*rubra*	8-Apr-1902	Helme	DMNH
017296	*Piranga*	*rubra*	17-Apr-1902	Helme	DMNH
103212	*Piranga*	*rubra*	14-Apr-1903	Helme	DMNH
103213	*Piranga*	*rubra*	4-May-1897	Brown	MCZ
103214	*Piranga*	*rubra*	4-Aug-1897	Brown	MCZ
152308	*Piranga*	*rubra*	4-Aug-1897	Brown	MCZ
16103	*Piranga*	*rubra*	4-Aug-1897	Brown	MCZ
16148	*Piranga*	*rubra*	14-Apr-1903	Helme	VMNH
16149	*Piranga*	*rubra*	16-Apr-1903	Helme	VMNH
16150	*Piranga*	*rubra*	27-Apr-1903	Helme	VMNH
16151	*Piranga*	*rubra*	18-Apr-1903	Helme	VMNH
16152	*Piranga*	*rubra*	28-Apr-1905	Helme	VMNH
16153	*Piranga*	*rubra*	14-Apr-1903	Helme	VMNH
16154	*Piranga*	*rubra*	22-Apr-1905	Helme	VMNH
16155	*Piranga*	*rubra*	14-Apr-1903	Helme	VMNH
16156	*Piranga*	*rubra*	14-Apr-1903	Helme	VMNH

16157	*Piranga*	*rubra*	20-Apr-1903	Helme	VMNH
454637	*Piranga*	*rubra*	27-Apr-1905	Helme	VMNH
355284	*Piranga*	*rubra*	15-Apr-1902	unknown	NMNH
355285	*Pluvialis*	*squatarola*	6-Apr-1903	Helme	AMNH
005775	*Pluvialis*	*squatarola*	29-Apr-1903	Helme	AMNH
544	*Pluvialis*	*squatarola*	9-Apr-1902	Helme	DMNH
596	*Podiceps*	*auritus*	18-Feb-1902		UGA
597	*Podiceps*	*auritus*	18-Feb-1904		UGA
4263	*Podiceps*	*grisegena*	18-Feb-1904		UGA
546	*Podiceps*	*auritus*	12-Mar-1971	Wharton	UGA
74439	*Podilymbus*	*podiceps*	26-Oct-1903		UGA
146596	*Polioptila*	*caerulea*	17-May-1916	Worthington	FMNH
103215	*Polioptila*	*caerulea*	17-May-1916	Worthington	FMNH
103236	*Polioptila*	*caerulea*	4-Mar-1897	Brown	MCZ
15116	*Polioptila*	*caerulea*	4-May-1897	Brown	MCZ
354589	*Pooecetes*	*gramineus*	11-Jan-1905	Helme	VMNH
20668	*Porphyrio*	*martinica*	16-Apr-1913	Helme	AMNH
354442	*Porphyrula*	*martinica*	11-Apr-1903	Helme	VMNH
354443	*Porzana*	*carolina*	27-Apr-1903	Helme	AMNH
354444	*Porzana*	*carolina*	10-Apr-1903	Helme	AMNH
005934	*Porzana*	*carolina*	27-Apr-1903	Helme	AMNH
005936	*Porzana*	*carolina*	1-Mar-1902	Helme	DMNH
21166	*Porzana*	*carolina*	20-Mar-1902	Helme	DMNH
21207	*Porzana*	*carolina*	10-Mar-1902	Helme	VMNH
21209	*Porzana*	*carolina*	8-Apr-1902	Helme	VMNH
307735	*Porzana*	*carolina*	13-Mar-1902	Helme	VMNH
103253	*Protonotaria*	*citrea*	24-Apr-1903		FMNH
16158	*Protonotaria*	*citrea*	4-Mar-1897	Brown	MCZ
16297	*Protonotaria*	*citrea*	/ / /1905	Helme	VMNH
16298	*Protonotaria*	*citrea*	/ / /1905	Helme	VMNH
3312	*Protonotaria*	*citrea*	/ / /1902	Swann	VMNH
*2833	*Puffinus*	*lherminieri*	27-Sep-1973	Hudick	UGA
*3311	*Puffinus*	*lherminieri*	25-Jul-1966	Richardson	UGA
*3344	*Puffinus*	*gravis*	10-Jun-1973	Richardson	UGA
*3345	*Puffinus*	*gravis*	1-Jul-1972	Richardson	UGA
559131	*Puffinus*	*gravis*	1-Jul-1972	Richardson	UGA
559131	*Puffinus*	*gravis*	24-Jun-1983	Ruckdeschel	NMNH
008470	*Puffinus*	*gravis*	24-Jun-1983	Potter, Pruitt	NMNH
008471	*Quiscalus*	*major*	10-Jun-1903	Helme	DMNH

008472	*Quiscalus*	*major*	14-Apr-1903	Helme	DMNH
008474	*Quiscalus*	*major*	10-Jan-1903	Helme	DMNH
008481	*Quiscalus*	*major*	7-Apr-1902	Helme	DMNH
18556	*Quiscalus*	*quiscula*	12-Mar-1903	Helme	DMNH
751525	*Quiscalus*	*quiscula*	2-Aug-1902	Rice	VMNH
751526	*Rallus*	*longirostris*		Helme	AMNH
005926	*Rallus*	*longirostris*		Helme	AMNH
005927	*Rallus*	*longirostris*	11-Jan-1905	Helme	DMNH
005928	*Rallus*	*longirostris*	5-Jan-1905	Helme	DMNH
308634	*Rallus*	*longirostris*	18-Apr-1905	Helme	DMNH
103201	*Rallus*	*longirostris*	13-Dec-1904	Helme	FMNH
103208	*Rallus*	*longirostris*	22-Dec-1904	Helme	MCZ
21217	*Rallus*	*longirostris*	12-Dec-1904	Helme	MCZ
21243	*Rallus*	*longirostris*	22-Dec-1904	Helme	VMNH
21251	*Rallus*	*longirostris*	13-Dec-1904	Helme	VMNH
21253	*Rallus*	*longirostris*	13-Dec-1904	Helme	VMNH
21264	*Rallus*	*longirostris*	27-Apr-1903	Helme	VMNH
21266	*Rallus*	*longirostris*	/ / /1903	Helme	VMNH
21278	*Rallus*	*longirostris*	27-Apr-1903	Helme	VMNH
21281	*Rallus*	*longirostris*	10-Jan-1903	Helme	VMNH
21282	*Rallus*	*longirostris*	24-Dec-1902	Helme	VMNH
21283	*Rallus*	*longirostris*	26-Dec-1902	Helme	VMNH
21284	*Rallus*	*longirostris*	1-Jan-1903	Helme	VMNH
21285	*Rallus*	*longirostris*	24-Apr-1903	Helme	VMNH
21286	*Rallus*	*longirostris*	1-Jan-1903	Helme	VMNH
21287	*Rallus*	*longirostris*	1-Jan-1903	Helme	VMNH
21290	*Rallus*	*longirostris*	2-Jan-1903	Helme	VMNH
21296	*Rallus*	*longirostris*	1-Jan-1903	Helme	VMNH
21303	*Rallus*	*longirostris*	18-Apr-1903	Helme	VMNH
21309	*Rallus*	*longirostris*	24-Dec-1902	Helme	VMNH
21310	*Rallus*	*longirostris*	1-Jan-1903	Helme	VMNH
21311	*Rallus*	*longirostris*	1-Jan-1903	Helme	VMNH
21312	*Rallus*	*longirostris*	10-Jan-1903	Helme	VMNH
21315	*Rallus*	*longirostris*	24-Apr-1903	Helme	VMNH
21337	*Rallus*	*longirostris*	1-Jan-1903	Helme	VMNH
21338	*Rallus*	*longirostris*	1-Jan-1903	Helme	VMNH
21339	*Rallus*	*longirostris*	/ / /1902	Helme	VMNH
359219	*Rallus*	*longirostris*	7-Mar-1902	Helme	VMNH
359220	*Rynchops*	*niger*	14-Mar-1902	Helme	AMNH

359221	*Rynchops*	*niger*	14-Mar-1902	Helme	AMNH
359222	*Rynchops*	*niger*	16-Jan-1903	Helme	AMNH
359223	*Rynchops*	*niger*	14-Mar-1902	Helme	AMNH
006145	*Rynchops*	*niger*	27-Mar-1903	Helme	AMNH
006146	*Rynchops*	*niger*	22-Dec-1902	Helme	DMNH
558	*Rynchops*	*niger*	22-Dec-1902	Helme	DMNH
007615	*Rynchops*	*niger*	3-Feb-1904		UGA
14248	*Sialia*	*sialis*	16-Apr-1903	Helme	DMNH
14313	*Sialia*	*sialis*	6-Jan-1903	Helme	VMNH
103002	*Sialia*	*sialis*	16-Apr-1903	Helme	VMNH
111894	*Sitta*	*carolinensis*	25-Dec-2000	Maynard	MCZ
152294	*Sitta*	*carolinensis*	25-Dec-2000	Maynard	MCZ
103268	*Spizella*	*passerina*	4-Feb-1897	Brown	MCZ
152306	*Squatarola*	*squatarola*	11-Oct-1931	Brown	MCZ
007123	*Squatarola*	*squatarola*	16-Mar-1931	Greenway	MCZ
007124	*Stelgidopteryx*	*serripennis*	24-Apr-1903	Helme	DMNH
358746	*Stelgidopteryx*	*serripennis*	17-Apr-1905	Helme	DMNH
358747	*Sterna*	*forsteri*	10-Mar-1902	Helme	AMNH
358748	*Sterna*	*forsteri*	10-Apr-1902	Helme	AMNH
358749	*Sterna*	*forsteri*	7-Apr-1903	Helme	AMNH
358750	*Sterna*	*forsteri*	24-Apr-1905	Helme	AMNH
006130	*Sterna*	*forsteri*	10-Mar-1902	Helme	AMNH
006131	*Sterna*	*forsteri*	24-Apr-1905	Helme	DMNH
006133	*Sterna*	*forsteri*	27-Mar-1903	Helme	DMNH
553	*Sterna*	*maxima*	18-Apr-1905	Helme	DMNH
554	*Sterna*	*forsteri*	3-Feb-1904		UGA
555	*Sterna*	*forsteri*	3-Feb-1904		UGA
556	*Sterna*	*forsteri*	3-Feb-1904		UGA
4316	*Sterna*	*forsteri*	3-Feb-1904		UGA
4317	*Sterna*	*forsteri*	28-Nov-1970	Wharton	UGA
*2834	*Sterna*	*forsteri*	28-Nov-1970	Wharton	UGA
359038	*Sterna*	*fuscata*	8-Jul-1966	Richardson	UGA
385652	*Sternula*	*antillarum*	21-Jun-1915	Helme	AMNH
385653	*Sturnella*	*magna*	31-Dec-1902	Helme	AMNH
385654	*Sturnella*	*magna*	13-Jan-1903	Helme	AMNH
385655	*Sturnella*	*magna*	13-Dec-1904	Helme	AMNH
385656	*Sturnella*	*magna*	5-Jan-1905	Helme	AMNH
385657	*Sturnella*	*magna*	27-Jan-1905	Helme	AMNH
008430	*Sturnella*	*magna*	27-Jan-1905	Helme	AMNH

18082	*Sturnella*	*magna*	14-Dec-1904	Helme	DMNH
18095	*Sturnella*	*magna*	22-Dec-1904	Helme	VMNH
18096	*Sturnella*	*magna*	13-Jan-1903	Helme	VMNH
18099	*Sturnella*	*magna*	10-Apr-1902	Helme	VMNH
359050	*Sturnella*	*magna*	2-Jan-1905	Helme	VMNH
359051	*Thalasseus*	*maximus*	25-Mar-1902	Helme	AMNH
359052	*Thalasseus*	*maximus*	25-Mar-1902	Helme	AMNH
359053	*Thalasseus*	*maximus*	14-Apr-1902	Helme	AMNH
359054	*Thalasseus*	*maximus*	25-Mar-1902	Helme	AMNH
359066	*Thalasseus*	*maximus*	25-Mar-1902	Helme	AMNH
359067	*Thalasseus*	*sandvicensis*	14-Apr-1902	Helme	AMNH
557	*Thalasseus*	*sandvicensis*	14-Apr-1902	Helme	AMNH
007382	*Thalasseus*	*maximus*	21-Apr-1903		UGA
356364	*Thryothorus*	*ludovicianus*	11-Apr-1902	Helme	DMNH
356365	*Totanus*	*flavipes*	24-Mar-1902	Helme	AMNH
356366	*Totanus*	*flavipes*	16-Apr-1902	Helme	AMNH
356367	*Totanus*	*flavipes*	30-Mar-1903	Helme	AMNH
356368	*Totanus*	*flavipes*	19-Apr-1905	Helme	AMNH
356114	*Totanus*	*flavipes*	19-Apr-1905	Helme	AMNH
356115	*Tringa*	*semipalmata*	1-Apr-1902	Helme	AMNH
356116	*Tringa*	*semipalmata*	10-Apr-1902	Helme	AMNH
356117	*Tringa*	*semipalmata*	12-Apr-1902	Helme	AMNH
356118	*Tringa*	*semipalmata*	1-Apr-1903	Helme	AMNH
356168	*Tringa*	*semipalmata*	30-Mar-1903	Helme	AMNH
356230	*Tringa*	*semipalmata*	16-Jan-1903	Helme	AMNH
22532	*Tringa*	*melanoleuca*	19-Mar-1902	Helme	AMNH
22543	*Tringa*	*melanoleuca*	4-Apr-1902	Helme	VMNH
22552	*Tringa*	*flavipes*	24-Apr-1903	Helme	VMNH
22553	*Tringa*	*flavipes*	27-Mar-1902	Helme	VMNH
22555	*Tringa*	*flavipes*	24-Apr-1905	Helme	VMNH
22560	*Tringa*	*flavipes*	25-Apr-1903	Helme	VMNH
300880	*Tringa*	*flavipes*	18-Apr-1905	Helme	VMNH
506	*Tyrannus*	*tyrannus*	4-Feb-1897	Brown	MCZ
21987	*Tyto*	*alba*	4-Mar-1904		UGA
378775	*Tyto*	*alba*	8-Feb-1900	Arnow	VMNH
007803	*Vireo*	*griseus*	08-Mar-1897	Helme	AMNH
007804	*Vireo*	*griseus*	17-Apr-1902	Helme	DMNH
146597	*Vireo*	*griseus*	16-Apr-1903	Helme	DMNH
103252	*Vireo*	*griseus*	17-May-1916	Worthington	FMNH

103257	*Vireo*	*olivaceus*	16-Apr-1897	Brown	MCZ
17702	*Vireo*	*solitarius*	4-May-1897	Brown	MCZ
17874	*Vireo*	*olivaceus*	/ / /1903	Helme	VMNH
17931	*Vireo*	*flavifrons*	20-Apr-1903	Helme	VMNH
17932	*Vireo*	*flavifrons*	16-Apr-1902	Helme	VMNH
17994	*Vireo*	*solitarius*	9-Apr-1903	Helme	VMNH
18009	*Vireo*	*griseus*	17-Apr-1902	Helme	VMNH
18012	*Vireo*	*griseus*	20-Mar-1902	Helme	VMNH
18013	*Vireo*	*griseus*	17-Apr-1905	Helme	VMNH
008261	*Vireo*	*griseus*	17-Apr-1902	Helme	VMNH
17557	*Wilsonia*	*citrina*	7-Apr-1902	Helme	DMNH
17683	*Wilsonia*	*citrina*	8-Apr-1902	Helme	VMNH
17684	*Wilsonia*	*citrina*	17-Apr-1905	Helme	VMNH
17685	*Wilsonia*	*citrina*	17-Apr-1902	Helme	VMNH
17686	*Wilsonia*	*citrina*	27-Apr-1905	Helme	VMNH
17688	*Wilsonia*	*citrina*	14-Apr-1903	Helme	VMNH
17689	*Wilsonia*	*citrina*	28-Apr-1903	Helme	VMNH
17690	*Wilsonia*	*citrina*	15-Apr-1905	Helme	VMNH
17691	*Wilsonia*	*citrina*	22-Apr-1905	Helme	VMNH
17693	*Wilsonia*	*citrina*	7-Apr-1902	Helme	VMNH
17694	*Wilsonia*	*citrina*	11-Apr-1903	Helme	VMNH
17695	*Wilsonia*	*citrina*	6-Apr-1903	Helme	VMNH
17696	*Wilsonia*	*citrina*	15-Apr-1903	Helme	VMNH
17697	*Wilsonia*	*citrina*	12-Apr-1902	Helme	VMNH
17698	*Wilsonia*	*citrina*	8-Apr-1902	Helme	VMNH
17699	*Wilsonia*	*citrina*	29-Mar-1902	Helme	VMNH
17700	*Wilsonia*	*citrina*	27-Apr-1905	Helme	VMNH
17701	*Wilsonia*	*citrina*	17-Apr-1902	Helme	VMNH
103271	*Wilsonia*	*citrina*	17-Apr-1902	Helme	VMNH
426391	*Zonotrichia*	*albicollis*	15-Apr-1897	Brown	MCZ

APPENDIX V. MAMMALS OF CUMBERLAND ISLAND, GEORGIA.

Order	Family	Scientific Name	Common Name
Didelphi-morphia	Didelphidae	*Didelphis virginiana*	Virginia Opossum
Cingulata	Dasypodidae	*Dasypus novemcinctus*	Nine-banded Armadillo
Soricomorpha	Taplidae	*Scalopus aquaticus*	Eastern Mole
	Sorcidae	*Blarina carolinensis*	Southern Short-tailed Shrew
		Cryptotis parva	North American Least Shrew
Chiroptera	Vespertilionidae	*Perimyotis subflavus*	Eastern Pipistrelle
		Eptesicus fuscus	Big Brown Bat
		Lasiurus borealis	Eastern Red Bat
		Lasiurus intermedius	Northern Yellow Bat
		Lasiurus seminolus	Seminole Bat
		Nycticeius humeralis	Evening Bat
Carnivora	Canidae	*Canis latrans*	Coyote
		Urocyon cinereoargenteus	Gray Fox
	Ursidae	*Ursus americanus*	American Black Bear
	Procyonidae	*Procyon lotor*	Raccoon
	Mustelidae	*Neovison vison*	American Mink
		Lontra canadensis	North American River Otter
	Felidae	*Lynx rufus*	Bobcat
Pinnipedia	Phocidae	*Cystophora cristata*	Hooded Seal
		Monachus tropicalis	Caribbean Monk Seal
		Phoca vitulina	Harbor Seal
Cetacea	Delphinidae	*Steno bredanensis*	Rough-toothed Dolphin
		Feresa attenuata	Pygmy Killer Whale
		Globicephala macrorhynchus	Short-finned Pilot Whale
		Stenella longirostris	Spinner Dolphin
		Stenella frontalis	Atlantic Spotted Dolphin
		Lagenorhynchus acutus	Atlantic White-sided Dolphin
		Tursiops truncatus	Bottlenose Dolphin

	Physeteridae	*Kogia breviceps*	Pygmy Sperm Whale
		Kogia sima	Dwarf Sperm Whale
	Ziphiidae	*Mesoplodon densirostris*	Blainville's Beaked Whale
		Mesoplodon europaeus	Gervais' Beaked Whale
		Ziphius cavirostris	Cuvier's Beaked Whale
	Balaenopteridae	*Megaptera novaeangliae*	Humpback Whale
	Balaenidae	*Eubalaena glacialis*	North Atlantic Right Whale
Sirenia	Trichechidae	*Trichechus manatus*	West Indian Manatee
Perissodactyla	Equidae	*Equus caballus*	Horse
Artiodactyla	Suidae	*Sus scrofa*	Wild Boar
	Cervidae	*Odocoileus virginianus*	White-tailed Deer
Rodentia	Sciuridae	*Sciurus carolinensis*	Eastern Gray Squirrel
		Sciurus niger	Eastern Fox Squirrel
	Geomyidae	*Geomys pinetis*	Southeastern Pocket Gopher
	Castoridae	*Castor canadensis*	American Beaver
	Cricetidae	*Oryzomys palustris*	Marsh Oryzomys
		Peromyscus gossypinus	Cotton Deermouse
		Peromyscus polionotus	Oldfield Deermouse
		Reithrodontomys humulis	Eastern Harvest Mouse
		Sigmodon hispidus	Hispid Cotton Rat
	Muridae	*Rattus rattus*	Roof Rat
Lagomorpha	Leporidae	*Sylvilagus palustris*	Marsh Rabbit

APPENDIX VIA. PARASITES ON AMPHIBIANS AND REPTILES OF
CUMBERLAND ISLAND, GEORGIA.
Class = Arachnida. Order = Acarina. NW = N. Wilson; JOW = J. O. Whitaker; W+D = Wilson and
Durden, 2003; NVS = National Veterinary Services Laboratory.

Family	Genus and Species	Host Common Name	Host Scientific Name	Source
Ixodidae	*Amblyomma americana* Linnaeus, 1758	Gopher Tortoise	*Gopherus polyphemus*	NVS
	Ixodes scapularis Say, 1821	Broad-headed Skink	*Plestiodon laticeps*	W+D, NVS
		Eastern Fence Lizard	*Sceloporus undulatus*	NW, W+D
		Eastern Glass Lizard	*Ophisaurus ventralis*	NW, W+D, NVS
		Southeastern Five-lined Skink	*Plestiodon inexpectatus*	NW, W+D
Ixodorhynchidae	*Hemilaelaps triangulus* (Ewing, 1923)	Coachwhip	*Masticophis flagellum*	NVS
Trombiculidae	*Eutrombicula alfreddugesi* (Oudemans, 1910)	Broad-headed Skink	*Plestiodon laticeps*	NVS
		Coachwhip	*Masticophis flagellum*	W+D, NVS
		Eastern Fence Lizard	*Sceloporus undulatus*	NW, W+D
		Green Anole	*Anolis carolinensis*	NVS
	Eutrombicula splendens (Ewing, 1913)	Coachwhip	*Masticophis flagellum*	W+D
		Eastern Glass Lizard	*Ophisaurus ventralis*	W+D
	Hannemania sp.	Southern Leopard Frog	*Lithobates sphenocephalus*	JOW
	Parasecia gurneyi (Ewing, 1937)	Broad-headed Skink	*Plestiodon laticeps*	NVS
	Microtrombicula trisetica (Loomis and Crossley, 1953)	Broad-headed Skink	*Plestiodon laticeps*	NVS

APPENDIX VIB. PARASITES ON BIRDS OF CUMBERLAND ISLAND, GEORGIA.
Class = Arachnida. Order = Acarina. NW = N. Wilson; JOW = J. O. Whitaker; W+D = Wilson and Durden, 2003; NVS = National Veterinary Services Laboratory.

Family	Genus and Species	Host Common Name	Host Scientific Name	Source
Analgidae	*Analges* sp.	Northern Cardinal	*Cardinalis cardinalis* (Linnaeus, 1758)	W+D
	Pterodectes sp. Robin,1877	Northern Cardinal	*Cardinalis cardinalis* (Linnaeus, 1758)	W+D
	Trouessartia spp.	Gray Catbird	*Dumatella carolinensis* (Linnaeus, 1758)	W+D
		Northern Cardinal	*Cardinalis cardinalis* (Linnaeus, 1758)	W+D
Laelapidae	*Androlaelaps casalis* (Berlese, 1887)	Pileated Woodpecker	*Dryocopus pileatus* (Linnaeus, 1766)	NW, W+D
Ixodidae	*Amblyomma americanum* (Linnaeus, 1758)	Northern Cardinal	*Cardinalis cardinalis* (Linnaeus, 1758)	NW, W+D
	Ixodes brunneus Koch, 1844	Barred Owl	*Strix varia* (Barton, 1799)	NW, W+D
		Gray Catbird	*Dumatella carolinensis* (Linnaeus, 1758)	NW, W+D
		Great Crested Flycatcher	*Myiarchus crinitus* (Linnaeus, 1758)	NW, W+D
		Northern Cardinal	*Cardinalis cardinalis* (Linnaeus, 1758)	NVS
		Wild Turkey	*Meleagris gallopavo* (Linnaeus, 1758)	NW, W+D
Mallophaga	*Chelopistes meleagridis* (Linnaeus, 1758)	Wild Turkey	*Meleagris gallopavo* (Linnaeus, 1758)	NW, W+D
	Cummingsiella ambigua (Burmeister, 1838)	Common Snipe	*Gallinago gallinago* (Linnaeus, 1758)	NW, W+D
	Menacanthus stramineus (Nitzsch, 1818)	Wild turkey	*Meleagris gallopavo* (Linnaeus, 1758)	NW, W+D
	Oxylipeurus polytrapezius (Burmeister, 1838)	Wild Turkey	*Meleagris gallopavo* (Linnaeus, 1758)	NW, W+D
	Penenirmus auritus (Scopoli, 1763)	Pileated Woodpecker	*Dryocopus pileatus* (Linnaeus, 1766)	NW, W+D
	Philopterus sp.	Northern Cardinal	*Cardinalis cardinalis* (Linnaeus, 1758)	NW, W+D
Trombiculidae	*Eutrombicula alfreddugesi* (Oudemans, 1910)	Barred Owl	*Strix varia* (Barton, 1799)	NW, W+D
	Eutrombicula liposkyana (Wolfenbarger, 1952)	Barred Owl	*Strix varia* (Barton, 1799)	NW, W+D
	Eutrombicula splendens (Ewing, 1913)	Barred Owl	*Strix varia* (Barton, 1799)	NW, W+D
	Neotrombicula whartoni (Ewing, 1929)	Hermit Thrush	*Catharus guttatus* (Pallas, 1811)	NW, W+D

| Parasecia gurneyi (Ewing, 1937) | Barred Owl | Strix varia (Barton, 1799) | NW, W+D |

APPENDIX VI C. PARASITES ON MAMMALS OF CUMBERLAND ISLAND, GEORGIA.
NW = N. Wilson; JOW = J. O. Whitaker; LD = L. Durden; W+D = Wilson and Durden, 2003; NVS = National Veterinary Services Laboratory.

Family	Genus and Species	Host Common Name	Host Scientific Name	Source
CLASS ARACHNIDA, ORDER ACARINA				
Ascidae	*Proctolaelaps pygmaeus* (Müller, 1860)	Southern Short-tailed Shrew	*Blarina carolinensis*	NVS
Atopomelidae	*Didelphilichus serrifer* Fain, 1970	Virginia Opossum	*Didelphis virginiana*	JOW, LD
Crytolaelapidae	*Crytolaelaps* sp.	Southern Short-tailed Shrew	*Blarina carolinensis*	JOW
Glycyphagidae	*Marsupialichus brasiliensis* Fain, 1969	Virginia Opossum	*Didelphis virginiana*	JOW
	Scalopacarus obesus Fain and Whitaker, 1973	Eastern Mole	*Scalopus aquaticus*	JOW
	Xenoryctes latiporus Fain and Whitaker, 1973	Southern Short-tailed Shrew	*Blarina carolinensis*	NVS
Histiostomatidae	*Prowichmannia spinifera* (Michael, 1901)	Southern Short-tailed Shrew	*Blarina carolinensis*	NVS
Laelapidae	*Androlaelaps casalis* (Berlese, 1887)	Eastern Gray Squirrel	*Sciurus carolinensis*	NW, W+D
	Androlaelaps fahrenholzi (Berlese, 1911)	Cotton Deermouse	*Peromyscus gossypinus*	JOW, NW, W+D
		Eastern Gray Squirrel	*Sciurus carolinensis*	JOW
		Marsh Oryzomys	*Oryzomys palustris*	NW, W+D
		Marsh Rabbit	*Sylvilagus palustris*	W+D
		Southern Short-tailed Shrew	*Blarina carolinensis*	JOW
	Androlaelaps morlani (Strandtmann, 1949)	Eastern Gray Squirrel	*Sciurus carolinensis*	JOW
	Eulaelaps stabularis (Koch, 1836)	Cotton Deermouse	*Peromyscus gossypinus*	NW, W+D
		Eastern Mole	*Scalopus aquaticus*	W+D
		Southern	*Blarina*	JOW

		Short-tailed Shrew	*carolinensis*	
	Haemogamasus harperi (Keegan, 1951)	Eastern Mole	*Scalopus aquaticus*	NW, W+D
	Hypoaspis sp. (Koch and Berendt, 1854)	Southern Short-tailed Shrew	*Blarina carolinensis*	JOW
Listrophoridae	*Olistrophorus blarinae* McDaniel and Whitaker, 1972	Southern Short-tailed Shrew	*Blarina carolinensis*	JOW, NVS
	Prolistrophorus bakeri (Radford, 1949)	Hispid Cotton Rat	*Sigmodon hispidus*	NVS
	Prolistrophorus grassii (Radford, 1954)	Marsh Oryzomys	*Oryzomys palustris*	NVS
Macrochelidae	*Macrochelys sp.*	Eastern Gray Squirrel	*Sciurus carolinensis*	JOW
Macronyssidae	*Ornithonyssus bacoti* (Hirst, 1913)	Cotton Deermouse	*Peromyscus gossypinus*	NW, JOW, LD. W+D
		Eastern Gray Squirrel	*Sciurus carolinensis*	W+D
		Hispid Cotton Rat	*Sigmodon hispidus*	LD, W+D
		Marsh Oryzomys	*Oryzomys palustris*	NW, W+D
		Virginia Opossum	*Didelphis virginiana*	NVS
	Ornithonyssus wernecki (Fonseca, 1935)	Virginia Opossum	*Didelphis virginiana*	JOW, LD, W+D
Myobiidae	*Archemyobia inexpectatus* Jameson, 1955	Virginia Opossum	*Didelphis virginiana*	JOW
	Blarinobia simplex (Ewing, 1938)	Southern Short-tailed Shrew	*Blarina carolinensis*	JOW, NVS
	Protomyobia americana McDaniel, 1967	Southern Short-tailed Shrew	*Blarina carolinensis*	NVS
	Protomyobia blarinae Lukoschus, Jencken, and Whitaker, 1988	Southern Short-tailed Shrew	*Blarina carolinensis*	NVS
	Radfordia palustris (Fain and Lukoschus, 1977)	Marsh Oryzomys	*Oryzomys palustris*	JOW, NVS
	Radfordia subliger Ewing, 1938	Cotton Deermouse	*Peromyscus gossypinus*	JOW
Psoroptidae	*Psoroptes cuniculi* Delafond, 1859	White-tailed Deer	*Odocoileus virginanus*	NW, W+D
Pygmephoridae	*Bakerdania sp.*	Southern Short-tailed Shrew	*Blarina carolinensis*	JOW
	Pygmephorus brevicadae	Southern	*Blarina*	JOW

	Smiley and Whitaker, 1979	Short-tailed Shrew	*carolinensis*	
	Pygmephorus designatus (Mahunka, 1973)	Southern Short-tailed Shrew	*Blarina carolinensis*	JOW
	Pygmephorus moreohorridus Mahunka, 1975	Southern Short-tailed Shrew	*Blarina carolinensis*	NVS
	Pygmephorus mustelae Rack, 1975	Eastern Mole	*Scalopus aquaticus*	JOW
		Southern Short-tailed Shrew	*Blarina carolinensis*	JOW
	Pygmephorus tamiasi Mahunka, 1975	Southern Short-tailed Shrew	*Blarina carolinensis*	JOW
Trombiculidae	*Euschoengastia* sp.	Marsh Oryzomys	*Oryzomys palustris*	NVS
	Euschoengastia peromysci (Ewing, 1929)	Cotton Deermouse	*Peromyscus gossypinus*	NW, JOW, W+D. NVS
		Hispid Cotton Rat	*Sigmodon hispidus*	JOW
		Marsh Oryzomys	*Oryzomys palustris*	NW, W+D
	Euschoengastia setosa (Ewing, 1937)	Marsh Oryzomys	*Oryzomys palustris*	NW, W+D, NVS
	Eutrombicula alfreddugesi (Oudemans, 1910)	Eastern Gray Squirrel	*Sciurus carolinensis*	NW, JOW, W+D, NVS
		Hispid Cotton Rat	*Sigmodon hispidus*	JOW
		Marsh Oryzomys	*Oryzomys palustris*	JOW, NW, LD, W+D, NVS
		Raccoon	*Procyon lotor*	NVS
		Virginia Opossum	*Didelphis virginiana*	JOW
	Eutrombicula batatas (Linnaeus, 1758)	White-tailed Deer	*Odocoileus virginianus*	NW, W+D
	Eutrombicula splendens (Ewing, 1913)	Hispid Cotton Rat	*Sigmodon hispidus*	NW, W+D, NVS
	Lepiotrombidium peromysci (Vercammen-grandjean and Langston, 1976)	Hispid Cotton Rat	*Sigmodon hispidus*	JOW
	Neotrombicula microti (Ewing, 1928)	Eastern Gray Squirrel	*Sciurus carolinensis*	JOW
	Neotrombicula whartoni (Ewing, 1929)	Eastern Gray Squirrel	*Sciurus carolinensis*	NW, W+D

Ixodidae	*Amblyomma americanum* (Linnaeus, 1758)	Cotton Deermouse	*Peromyscus gossypinus*	NW, LD, W+D
		Eastern Gray Squirrel	*Sciurus carolinensis*	NW, LD, W+D, NVS
		Horse (feral)	*Equus caballus*	W+D, NVS
		Marsh Oryzomys	*Oryzomys palustris*	W+D
		Marsh Rabbit	*Sylvilagus palustris*	NW, W+D
		Nine-banded Armadillo	*Dasypus novemcinctus*	W+D, NVS
		Raccoon	*Procyon lotor*	NW, W+D
		Virginia Opossum	*Didelphis virginiana*	W+D, NVS
		White-tailed Deer	*Odocoileus virginianus*	NW, W+D
		Wild Boar (feral)	*Sus scrofa*	NW, W+D
	Amblyomma auricularium (Conil, 1878)	Eastern Gray Squirrel	*Sciurus carolinensis*	NVS
	Amblyomma maculatum (Koch, 1844)	Hispid Cotton Rat	*Sigmodon hispidus*	NVS
		Marsh Rabbit	*Sylvilagus palustris*	W+D
		Wild Boar (feral)	*Sus scrofa*	NW, W+D
	Dermacentor variabilis (Say, 1821)	Bobcat	*Lynx rufus*	W+D
		Cotton Deermouse	*Peromyscus gossypinus*	NW, W+D
		Eastern Gray Squirrel	*Sciurus carolinensis*	NW, W+D
		Hispid Cotton Rat	*Sigmodon hispidus*	NW, W+D
		Marsh Oryzomys	*Oryzomys palustris*	NW, W+D, NVS
		Marsh Rabbit	*Sylvilagus palustris*	NW, W+D
		Raccoon	*Procyon lotor*	NW, W+D
		Southern Short-tailed Shrew	*Blarina carolinensis*	NVS
		Virginia Opossum	*Didelphis virginiana*	LD, W+D, NVS
		Wild Boar (feral)	*Sus scrofa*	NW, W+D

Haemaphysalis leporispalustris (Packard, 1869)	Eastern Gray Squirrel	*Sciurus carolinensis*	W+D
	Marsh Rabbit	*Sylvilagus palustris*	NW, W+D
Ixodes affinis (Neumann, 1899)	Cotton Deermouse	*Peromyscus gossypinus*	NW, W+D
	Eastern Gray Squirrel	*Sciurus carolinensis*	NW, W+D
	Eastern Mole	*Scalopus aquaticus*	NW, W+D
	Hispid Cotton Rat	*Sigmodon hispidus*	NVS
	Marsh Oryzomys	*Oryzomys palustris*	NW, W+D
	Southern Short-tailed Shrew	*Blarina carolinensis*	NVS
	White-tailed Deer	*Odocoileus virginianus*	W+D
Ixodes scapularis (Say, 182)	Cotton Deermouse	*Peromyscus gossypinus*	W+D
	Eastern Gray Squirrel	*Sciurus carolinensis*	NW, W+D
	Horse (feral)	*Equus caballus*	W+D
	Marsh Oryzomys	*Oryzomys palustris*	NVS
	Nine-banded Armadillo	*Dasypus novemcinctus*	W+D, NVS
	Southern Short-tailed Shrew	*Blarina carolinensis*	JOW, NVS
	Virginia Opossum	*Didelphis virginiana*	LD, W+D, NVS
	White-tailed Deer	*Odocoileus virginianus*	NW, W+D
	Wild Boar (feral)	*Sus scrofa*	NW, W+D
Ixodes texanus (Banks, 1909)	Raccoon	*Procyon lotor*	NVS

CLASS INSECTA, ORDER ANOPLURA

Haematopinidae	*Solenopotes binipilosus* (Fahrenholz, 1916)	White-tailed Deer	*Odocoileus virginianus*	JOW
Hoplopleuridae	*Hoplopleura hirsuta* (Ferris, 1916)	Hispid Cotton Rat	*Sigmodon hispidus*	LD, W+D

	Hoplopleura oryzomydis (Pratt and Lane, 1951)	Marsh Oryzomys	*Oryzomys palustris*	NW, W+D, NVS
	Neohaematopinus sciuri (Jancke, 1931)	Eastern Gray Squirrel	*Sciurus carolinensis*	NW, JOW W+D
	Haematopinus suis (Linnaeus, 1758)	Wild Boar (feral)	*Sus scrofa*	NW, W+D
Trichodectidae	*Damalinia sp.* (Mjöberg, 1910)	White-tailed Deer	*Odocoileus virginianus*	W+D, NVS
	Damalinia (Cervicola) sp. (Kéler,)	White-tailed Deer	*Odocoileus virginianus*	NVS
	Damalinia (*Tricholipeurus*) sp. (Bedford, 1936)	White-tailed Deer	*Odocoileus virginianus*	NVS
	Damalinia (*Tricholipeurus*) *lipeuroides* (Mégnin, 1884)	White-tailed Deer	*Odocoileus virginianus*	NVS
	Damalinia (*Tricholipeurus) parallela* (Osborn, 1896)	White-tailed Deer	*Odocoileus virginianus*	NVS
	Stachiella (Trichodectes) *octomaculatus* (Paine, 1912)	Raccoon	*Procyopn lotor*	NW, JOW, W+D
Leptinidae	*Leptinus americana* (LeConte, 1866)	Southern Short-tailed Shrew	*Blarina carolinensis*	JOW
Cuterebridae	*Cuterebra* sp.	Cotton Deermouse	*Peromyscus gossypinus*	JOW
		Marsh Oryzomys	*Oryzomys palustris*	JOW
Hippoboscidae	*Lipotena mazamae* (Rondani, 1878)	White-tailed Deer	*Odocoileus virginianus*	NW. LD, W+D
Ceratophyllidae	*Orchopeas leucopus* (Baker, 1904)	Cotton Deermouse	*Peromyscus gossypinus*	W+D
Pulicidae	*Cediopsylla simplex* (Baker, 1895)	Bobcat	*Lynx rufus*	LD, W+D
	Ctenocephalides felis (Bouché, 1835)	Marsh Oryzomys	*Oryzomys palustris*	NW, W+D
		Raccoon	*Procyon lotor*	NVS
		Virginia Opossum	*Didelphis virginiana*	LD, W+D, NVS
	Echidnophaga gallinacean (Westwood, 1875)	Cotton Deermouse	*Peromyscus gossypinus*	NW
		Eastern Gray Squirrel	*Sciurus carolinensis*	NW, W+D
		Raccoon	*Procyon lotor*	NVS

| | | Roof Rat | *Rattus rattus* | NW, W+D |
| Rhopalopsyllidae | *Polygenis gwyni* (Fox, 1914) | Hispid Cotton Rat | *Sigmodon hispidus* | NW, LD, W+D |

INDEX

Aedes solicitans, 84
Aleurites fordii, 40
Ambrosia beetle, 58
Amelia Island, 17, 20, 51, 52, 65, 88, 95, 97, 98, 99, 100, 102, 103, 104, 105, 112, 119, 120, 121, 124, 125, 126, 127, 128, 129, 139, 143, 144, 216, 221, 224, 228, 229, 234, 236, 261, 267, 270, 273, 275, 276
Amphipod, 223
Aquifer, 11
Artesian well, 13
Babesia, 279
Ballmoss, 57
Banded birds, 161, 162, 180, 183
Besnoitia sp., 215, 268
Bird nesting, 73
Blackbeard Island, 7, 224, 227, 257
Black drink, 24
Bricks, 9, 36
Carpenter Bee, 116
Cattle fever, 279
Centruroides hentzi, 62
Christmas Bird Count, 148
Chrysops spp., 84
Clay, 9, 28, 36, 81
Cochinel insect, 29-30
Cotton, 38-39
Crayfish, 75, 104, 231, 235
Cricket, 118
Culicoides spp., 84, 254
Cypress, 80
Dactylopius coccus, 29-30
Deer fly, 84
Dike, 39-40
Ditches, 39
Dividings, 14-15, 37, 81
Epiphytes, 56-58
Euglandina rosea, 84
Feral livestock, 27, 37, 50, 52, 57, 61, 76, 77, 78, 80, 85-86, 88, 93-94, 101, 103, 106, 120, 129, 133, 135, 142, 182, 254, 246, 269, 271, 275-282
Fire, 42-45, 53-54, 55, 60-62, 64-67, 77, 94, 95, 96, 98, 104, 107, 113, 115, 116, 120, 121, 122, 127, 128, 130, 131, 145, 149, 160, 166, 169, 186, 190, 258, 259, 260, 269, 270, 271, 275
Fire 1981, 42-43, 67, 71, 107, 259, 271

Fire ants, 75
Fort Prince William, 31
Fort St. Andrews, 31
Gemma gemma, 140
Geukensia demissa, 84-85
Ghost Crab, 135
Green, Nathanael, 32
Green-fly orchid, 58
Heartworm, 84
Hodges, M., 148
Horse fly, 84
Humate, 10, 54, 81
Hunter Tract, 41
Hunting, 40-41, 108, 110, 150, 152, 153, 156, 165, 167, 170, 186, 230, 232, 234, 237, 244, 250, 252-253, 255, 258-259, 275,
Hurricane, 16-17
Indigo, 39
Intercoastal waterway, 13-15
Introduced species, 30, 36, 64, 77, 89, 91, 92, 93, 145-146, 150, 156, 168, 185, 211, 214, 216, 222, 256, 260, 262, 263, 275
Jekyll Island, 88, 116
Jetty, 8, 52, 132, 177, 280
Johnston, D.W., 148
Kissing bug, 62, 232
Liberty County, 13
Little Cumberland Island, 7, 17, 95, 100, 101, 107, 116, 117, 124, 125, 126, 128, 129, 146, 168, 185, 222, 227, 233, 240, 249, 257
Little St. Simons Island, 7, 116, 217, 227, 253
Littorina irrorata, 84
Live oak, 32
Lyme disease, 268
Lyon, John, 30
Marine mammal, 23
Missions, 25-27
Mosquitos, 84
Narceus americanus, 50, 217, 232
Nemobius sp., 118
Nephila sp., 224
No-see-ums, 84
Opossum, 120
Ossabaw Island, 97, 99, 100, 101, 102, 105, 106, 116, 117, 118, 121, 125, 128, 129, 139, 225, 227, 236, 257, 259
Palmetto, 44, 59

Parasite, 24, 103, 104, 108, 113, 114, 116, 119-120, 122, 125, 128, 129, 130, 131, 145, 147, 156, 158, 160, 187, 190, 191, 197, 198, 208, 215, 232, 237, 241, 244, 245, 254, 261, 266, 268, 273, 274
Periwinkle, 84
Phellinus pini, 35, 62
Pine, 35, 45, 60, 62-63
Plant adaptations, 46, 48, 53, 54, 57, 58, 65, 72, 82
Prickly-pear, 29
Procambarus paeninsulanus, 75
Procambarus talpoides, 75
Red bay, 58-59
Red-heart disease, 35, 62
Resurrection fern, 57
Ribbed mussel, 84-85
Rice, 37-38, 40
Roadkill, 71, 88, 95, 96, 116, 117, 119, 120, 121, 122, 124, 125-126, 127, 128, 129, 130, 131, 145, 147, 182, 187, 193, 209, 255
Rosy glandina, 84
Sapelo Island, 17, 55, 77, 95, 97, 98, 99, 100, 101, 102, 104, 106, 112, 116, 117, 118, 121, 123, 124, 125, 127, 128, 129, 132, 139, 190, 216, 224, 225, 226, 227, 230, 244, 257, 259
Sassafras, 28-29, 59
Saw palmetto, 59
Sawmill, 36
Scorpion, 62
Screwworm, 254-255

Shell mounds, 83
Shoestring fern, 57
Skidaway Island, 224
Slough, 12, 51, 68, 71
Snail, Amber, 50
Soils, 9-11
Southern needleleaf, 57
Spanish moss, 56-57, 225
St. Catherines Island, 26, 97, 99, 100, 101, 104, 105, 106, 116, 117, 118, 121, 128, 129, 132, 139, 144, 216, 217, 221, 224, 230, 233, 277
St. Simons Island, 13, 17, 88, 144, 185, 236, 277
Succinea campestris, 50
Tabanus spp., 84
Talitroides topitotum, 222
Tar kiln, 33-34
TED, 133, 137
Tornados, 16-18, 52
Triatoma sanguisuga, 232
Trypanosoma cruzi, 218
Tung tree, 40
Turpentine, 33-35
Turtle excluder device (TED), 133
Tybee Island, 88, 101, 144, 257
Wassaw Island, 116, 118, 121, 139, 194, 257
Water wells, 13
Wax myrtle, 70-71, 76, 193
Wells, 13
Willis, S., 148
Wiregrass, 61
Xylocopa sp., 116

INDEX TO VERTEBRATE SPECIES

Acadian Flycatcher, 190
Accipiter cooperii, 167
Accipiter gentiles 168
Accipiter striatus, 167
Acris gryllus, 95
Actitis macularia, 174
Agelaius phoeniceus, 209
Agkistrodon piscivorus, 117, 127, 129-130, 223
Aix sponsa, 150
Alca torda, 185
Alle alle, 185
Alligator mississippiensis, 22, 79, 104, 106-111,
    129, 219, 233, 244, 255, 275
Ambystoma talpoideum, 103
Americal Eel, 89
American Alligator, 22, 79, 104, 106-111, 129,
    219, 233, 244, 255, 275
American Avocet, 174
American Back Duck, 151
American Beaver, 79, 212, 213, 262-265
American Bittern, 162
American Black Bear, 109, 135, 229-230
American Coot, 171
American Crow, 193
American Golden-Plover, 172
American Goldfinch, 211
American Kestrel, 169, 271
American Mink 109, 233-234, 238
American Oystercatcher, 173
American Pipit, 198
American Redstart, 201
American Robin, 197
American White Pelican, 161
American Wigeon, 151
American Woodcock, 178
Ammodramus caudacutus, 206
Ammodramus martimus, 206-207
Ammodramus nelsoni, 206
Ammodramus savannarum, 206
Amphiuma means, 103-105
Anas acuta, 152
Anas americana, 151
Anas clypeata, 152
Anas crecca, 152
Anas discors, 152
Anas fulvigula, 151
Anas penelope, 151
Anas platyrhynchos, 151
Anas rubripes, 151
Anas strepera, 151

Anaxyrus quercicus, 94
Anaxyrus terrestris, 94-95
Anguilla rostrata, 89
Anhinga, 161
Anhinga anhinga, 161
Anolis carolinensis, 112-113, 122, 215
Anoüs stolidus, 181
Anthus spinoletta, 198
Anthus spragueii, 198
Apalone ferox, 146
Aquila chrysaetos, 168--169
Archilochus colubris, 188
Arctic Tern, 183
Ardea alba, 163
Ardea Herodias, 162
Arenaria interpres, 176
Armadillo, 113, 117, 128, 212, 213, 216-220
Asio flammeus, 187
Asio otus, 187
Aspidoscelis sexlineata, 117-118, 125
Atlantic Spotted Dolphin, 242-243
Atlantic White-sided Dolphin, 243
Audubon's Shearwater, 159
Avocet, 174
Aythya affinis, 153
Aythya americana, 153
Aythya collaris, 153
Aythya marila, 153
Aythya valisineria, 152-153
Bachman's Sparrow, 205
Baeolophus bicolor 194
Bald Eagle, 167
Baltimore Oriole, 211
Band-rumped Storm Petrel, 159
Banded Water Snake, 126-127
Bank Swallow, 194
Barking Treefrog, 97
Barn Owl, 186
Barn Swallow, 194
Barred Owl, 187
Bartramia longicauda, 175
Bass 92
Bats, 224-227
Bay-breasted Warbler, 202
Bear, 109, 135, 229-230
Beaver, 79, 212, 213, 262-265
Belted Kingfisher, 188-189
Bewick's Wren, 195
Bicknell's Thrush, 197
Big Brown Bat, 225

Black-and-White Warbler, 200
Black Crappie, 92
Black Racer, 119-120
Black Rail, 170
Black Scoter, 154
Black Skimmer, 184
Black Tern, 182
Black Vulture, 109, 165-166
Black-bellied Plover, 171-172
Black-billed Cuckoo, 186
Blackburnian Warbler, 202
Black-crowned Night Heron, 164
Black-legged Kittywake, 179
Black-necked Stilt, 173-174
Blackpoll Warbler, 203
Black-throated Blue Warbler, 203
Black-throated Green Warbler, 204
Blainville's Beaked Whale, 247
Blarina carolinensis, 222-223, 268
Blue Grosbeak, 208
Blue Jay, 192
Bluebird 196
Bluegill, 91-92
Blue-gray Gnatcatcher, 196
Blue-winged Teal, 152
Blue-winged Warbler, 199-200
Boat-tailed Grackle, 210
Bobcat, 120, 212, 213, 232, 233, 235-238, 255, 271
Bobolink, 209
Bombycilla cedrorum, 198
Bonaparte's Gull, 179-180
Botaurus lentiginosus, 162
Bottlenose Dolphin, 243-245
Brant, 150
Branta bernicla, 150
Branta canadensis, 150
Bridled Tern, 182
Broad-headed Skink, 115-116, 130
Broad-winged Hawk, 168
Brown Booby, 160
Brown Creeper, 195
Brown Noddy, 181
Brown Pelican, 161-162
Brown Thrasher, 198
Brown-headed Cowbird, 210-211
Brown-headed Nuthatch, 195
Bubo virginianus, 187
Bubulcus ibis, 164
Bucephala albeola, 154
Bucephala clangula, 155
Buff-breasted Sandpiper 178
Bufflehead, 154
Buteo jamaicensis, 168

Buteo lagopus, 168
Buteo lineatus, 168
Buteo platypterus, 168
Butorides virescens, 164
Calidris alba, 176
Calidris alpina, 177
Calidris canutus, 176
Calidris fuscicollis, 177
Calidris himantopus, 177-178
Calidris maritima, 177
Calidris mauri, 176
Calidris melanotos, 177
Calidris minutilla, 177
Calidris pusilla, 176
Calonectris diomedea, 158
Calonectris edwardsii, 158
Canada Goose, 150
Canebrake Rattlesnake, 132
Canis latrans, 212, 213, 227-228, 255
Cantopus virens, 190
Canvasback, 152-153
Cape May Warbler, 202
Cape Verde Shearwater, 158
Caprimulgus carolinensis, 187-188
Caprimulgus vociferous, 188
Cardellina pusilla, 204
Cardinalis cardinalis, 208
Caretta caretta, 133, 134-135
Caribbean Monk Seal, 239
Carolina Chickadee, 194
Carolina Wren, 195
Carpodacus mexicanus, 211
Carpodacus purpureus, 211
Caspian Tern, 182
Castor Canadensis, 79, 212, 213, 262-265
Cathartes aura, 166
Catharus bicknelli, 197
Catharus fuscesens, 196
Catharus guttatus, 197
Catharus minimus, 196-197
Catharus ustulatus, 197
Cattle Egret, 164
Cave Swallow, 194
Cedar Waxwing, 198
Cemophora coccinea, 118-119, 231
Certhia americana, 195
Chaetura pelagica, 188
Charadrius melodus, 173
Charadrius nivosus, 172
Charadrius semipalmatus, 172
Charadrius vociferous, 173
Charadrius wilsonia, 172
Chelonia mydas, 135-136
Chelydra serpentina, 138-139

Chen caerulescens, 150
Chestnut-sided Warbler, 203
Chicken Snake, 113, 121-122
Chicken Turtle, 139
Chlidonias niger, 182
Chimney Swift, 188
Chipping Sparrow, 205
Chondestes grammacus, 206
Chordeiles minor, 187
Chroicocephalus Philadelphia, 179-180
Chuck-will's-widow, 187-188
Circus cyaneus, 167
Cistothorus palustris, 196
Cistothorus platensis, 195-196
Clangula hyemalis, 154
Clapper Rail, 170
Clay-colored Sparrow, 205
Cliff Swallow, 194
Coachwhip, 118, 124-125
Coccothraustes vespertinus, 212
Coccyzus americanus, 186
Coccyzus erythropthalmus, 186
Cochliomyia, 254-55
Colapes auratus, 190
Colinus virginianus, 156
Coluber constrictor, 119-120
Columba livia, 185
Columbina passerina, 186
Condylura cristata, 221-222
Connecticut Warbler, 201
Common Eider, 154
Common Garter Snake, 128-129, 130
Common Goldeneye, 155
Common Grackle, 210
Common Ground-dove, 186
Common Kingsnake, 123
Common Loon, 157
Common Merganser, 155
Common Moorhen, 171
Common Nighthawk, 187
Common Snipe, 178
Common Tern, 182-183
Common Yellowthroat, 201
Connecticut Warbler, 201
Contopus virens, 190
Cooper's Hawk, 167
Coot, 171
Cope's Gray Treefrog, 98
Coragyps atratus, 109, 165-166
Coral Snake, 118, 123-124
Corn Snake, 120-121, 259
Corvus brachyrhynchos, 193
Corvus ossifragus, 193
Cory's Shearwater, 158

Cotton Deermouse, 266-269
Cottonmouth, 117, 127, 129-130, 223
Cottontail rabbit, 214
Coturnicops noveboracensis, 169-170
Cowbird, 204
Coyote, 135, 212, 213, 227-228, 255
Crappie, 92
Crotalus adamanteus, 131-132
Crotalus horridus, 132
Cryptotis parva, 213, 223-224
Cuvier's Beaked Whale, 248-249
Cyanocitta cristata, 192
Cygnus columbianus, 150
Cyprinodon variegatus, 90
Cystophora cristata, 238
Dark-eyed Junco, 207
Dasypus novemcinctus, 113, 117, 128, 212, 213,
     216-220
Deer, 30-31, 237, 253-256
Deirochelys reticularia, 139
Dendrocygna bicolor, 150
Dermochelys coriacea, 137-138
Desmognathus auriculatus, 105
Diadophis punctatus, 120
Diamond-backed Terrapin, 85, 139-141
Didelphis virginiana, 120, 212, 213, 214-216
Dolichonyx oryzivorus, 209
Dormitator maculatus, 93
Double-crested Cormorant, 161
Dovekie, 185
Downy Woodpecker, 189
Dryocopus pileatus, 190
Dumetella carolinensis, 197-198
Dunlin, 177
Dwarf Salamander, 105-106
Dwarf Sperm Whale, 246-247
Eagle, Bald, 167
Eagle, Golden, 168
Eastern Bluebird, 196
Eastern Cottontail, 214, 275
Eastern Diamondback Rattlesnake, 131-132
Eastern Fence Lizard, 113-114
Eastern Fox Squirrel, 213, 260
Eastern Glass Lizard, 111-112
Eastern Gray Squirrel, 122, 213, 237, 256-260
Eastern Harvest Mouse, 213, 270
Eastern Kingbird, 191
Eastern Meadowlark, 209
Eastern Mole, 220-222
Eastern Mud Turtle, 143-144
Eastern Narrow-mouthed Frog, 100
Eastern Newt, 106
Eastern Phoebe ***
Eastern Pipistrelle, 224

Eastern Red Bat, 225
Eastern Ribbon Snake, 95, 96, 127-128
Eastern Screech Owl, 186-187
Eastern Spadefoot, 100-101, 129, 130
Eastern Towhee, 205
Eastern Wood Pewee, 190
Egretta caerulea, 163
Egretta rufescens, 164
Egretta thula, 163
Egretta tricolor, 163
Elanoides forficatus, 166
Empidonax minimus, 190
Empidonax virescens, 190
Eptesicus fuscus, 225
Equus caballus, 213, 275-282
Eremophila alpestris, 193
Eretmochelys imbricata, 136
Eubalaena glacialis, 249-251
Eucinostomus sp., 92
Eudocimus albus, 165
Euphagus carolinus, 210
Eurasian Collared-dove, 185
Eurasian Wigeon, 151
European Starling, 198
Eurycea quadrigitata, 105-106
Evening Bat, 226-227
Evening Grosbeak, 212
Falco columbarius, 169, 271
Falco peregrinus, 169
Falco sparverius, 169
Farancia abacura, 104, 122-123
Fat Sleeper, 93
Fence Lizard, 113-114, 215
Feral animals, 27, 275-282
Feresa attenuata, 240-241
Field Sparrow, 205
Fish Crow, 193
Five-lined Skink, 94
Florida Pine Snake, 94
Florida Red-bellied Cooter, 141-142
Florida Red-bellied Snake, 127, 130
Florida Softshell, 146
Forster's Tern, 183
Fox Sparrow, 207
Fox Squirrel, 213, 260
Franklin's Gull, 180
Fregata magnificens, 160
Fulica Americana, 171
Fulvous Whistling Duck, 150
Fundulus confluentus, 90
Fundulus heteroclitus, 90
Gadwall, 151
Gallinago gallinago, 178
Gallinula chloropus, 171

Gambusia affinis, 90-91
Garter Snake, 95, 128-129, 130
Gastrophryne carolinensis, 100
Gavia immer, 157
Gavia stellata, 156
Gelochelidon nilotica, 182
Geomys pinetis, 260-262
Geothlypis trichas, 201
Gervais' Beaked Whale, 247-248
Glass Lizard, 111-112
Glaucous Gull, 181
Globicephala macrorhynchus, 241
Glossy Ibis, 165
Golden Eagle, 168-169
Golden-crowned Kinglet, 196
Goldfinch, 211
Gopher Tortoise, 50, 144-146
Gopherus polyphemus, 50, 144-146
Goshawk, Northern, 168
Grasshopper Sparrow, 206
Gray Catbird, 197-198
Gray Fox, 228-229
Gray Kingbird, 191
Gray Squirrel, 122, 256-260
Gray-cheeked Thrush, 196
Great Black-backed Gull, 181
Great Blue Heron, 162
Great Crested Flycatcher, 191
Great Egret, 163
Great Horned Owl, 187
Great Shearwater, 158
Greater Scaup, 153
Greater Yellowlegs, 174
Green Anole, 57, 112-113, 122, 215
Green Sea Turtle, 133, 135-136
Green Treefrog, 95-96, 128
Green Heron, 164
Green-winged Teal, 152
Ground-Dove, 186
Ground Skink, 116-117, 130, 191
Grus Canadensis, 171
Gull-billed Tern, 182
Haematopus palliatus, 173
Hairy Woodpecker, 189
Haliaeetus leucocephalus, 167
Harbor Seal, 239-240
Harvest Mouse, 213
Hawk, Broad-winged, 168
Hawk, Cooper's, 167
Hawk, Red-shouldered, 168
Hawk, Red-tailed, 168
Hawk, Rough-legged, 168
Hawk, sharp-shinned, 167
Hawksbill Sea Turtle, 133, 136

Helmitheros vermivorus, 199
Hermit Thrush, 197
Herring Gull, 180-181
Himantoppus mexicanus, 173-174
Hirundo rustica, 194
Hispid Cotton Rat, 237, 270-272
Hog, 27, 275-282
Hooded Merganser, 155
Hooded Seal, 238
Hooded Warbler, 201
Horned Grebe, 157
Horned Lark, 193
Horse, 213, 275-282
House Finch, 211
House Wren, 195
Humpback Whale, 249
Hydroprogne caspia, 182
Hyla chrysoscelis, 98
Hyla cinerea, 95-96, 128
Hyla femoralis, 96-97
Hyla gratiosa, 97
Hyla squirella, 97-98
Hylocichla mustelina, 197
Iceland Gull, 181
Ictalurus natalis, 89
Icteria virens, 204
Icterus galbula, 211
Icterus spurius, 211
Ictinia mississippiensis, 166-167
Indigo Bunting, 208-209
Island Glass Lizard, 112
Ixobrychus exilis, 162
Junco hyemalis, 207
Kemp's Ridley Sea Turtle, 133, 136-137
Kentucky Warbler, 201
Kestrel, American, 169, 271
Killdeer, 173
King Eider, 153
King Rail, 170
Kingsnake, 123
Kinosternon baurii, 144
Kinosternon subrubrum, 143-144
Kirtland's Warbler, 202
Kite, Swallow-tailed, 166-167
Kite, Mississippi, 166
Kogia breviceps, 245-246
Kogia sima, 246-247
Lagenorhynchus acutus, 243
Lampropeltis elapsoides, 123-124
Lampropeltis getula, 123
Lanius ludovicianus, 192
Largemouth Bass, 92
Lark Sparrow, 206
Larus argentatus, 180-181

Larus delawarensis, 180
Larus fuscus, 181
Larus glaucoides, 181
Larus hyperboreus, 181
Larus marinus, 181
Lasiurus borealis, 225
Lasiurus intermedius, 225-226
Lasiurus seminolus, 226
Laterallus jamaicensis, 170
Laughing Gull, 180
Leach's Storm Petrel, 159
Least Bittern, 162
Least Flycatcher, 190
Least Sandpiper, 177
Least Shrew, 213, 223-224
Least Tern, 182
Leatherback Sea Turtle, 133, 137-138
Leopard Frog, 102-103, 129
Lepidochelys kempii, 133, 136-137
Lepomis gulosus, 91
Lepomis macrochirus, 91-92
Lesser Black-backed Gull, 181
Lesser Scaup, 153
Lesser Yellowlegs, 175
Leucophaeus atricilla, 180
Leucophaeus pipixcan, 180
Limnodromus griseus, 178
Limnodromus scolopaceus, 178
Limnothlypis swainsonii, 200
Limosa fedoa, 175-176
Lithobates grylio, 101-102
Lithobates sphenocephalus, 102-103
Little Blue Heron, 163
Little Grass Frog, 99
Loggerhead Sea Turtle, 133, 134-135
Loggerhead Shrike, 192
Long-billed Curlew, 175
Long-billed Dowitcher, 178
Long-eared Owl, 187
Long-tailed Duck, 154
Long-tailed Jaeger, 184-185
Lontra Canadensis, 234-235
Lophodytes cucullatus, 155
Louisiana Waterthrush, 199
Lynx rufus, 120, 212, 213, 232, 233, 235-238.
    255, 271
Magnificent Frigatebird, 160
Magnolia Warbler, 202
Malaclemys terrapin, 85, 139-141
Mallard, 151
Manatee, 251-253
Marbled Godwit, 175-176
Marsh Killifish, 90
Marsh Oryzomys, 107, 265-266

Marsh Rabbit, 237, 273-275
Marsh Wren, 196
Marine mammals, 240-251
Masked Booby, 160
Masticophis flagellum, 118, 124-125
Megaceryle alcyon, 188-189
Megaptera novaeangliae, 249
Megascops asio, 186-187
Melanerpes carolinus, 189
Melanerpes erythrocephalus, 189
Melanitta fusca, 154
Melanitta nigra, 154
Melanitta perspicillata, 154
Meleagris gallopavo, 156
Melospiza georgiana, 207
Melospiza melodia, 207
Mergus merganser, 155
Mergus serrator, 155
Merlin, 169, 271
Mesoplodon densirostris, 247
Mesoplodon europaeus, 247-248
Micropterus salmoides, 92
Micrurus fulvius, 118
Mimus polyglottos, 198
Mink, 109, 233-234, 238
Mississippi Kite, 166-167
Mniotilta varia, 200
Mockingbird, 198
Mojarras, 92
Mole Salamander, 103
Mole Skink, 114-115
Molothrus bonariensis, 210
Molothus ater, 210-211
Mole, 215, 220-222
Monachus tropicalis, 239
Moorhen, 171
Morus bassanus, 160
Mosquitofish, 90-91
Mottled Duck, 151
Mourning Dove, 186
Mugil cephalus, 93
Mud Snake, 104, 122-123
Mummichog, 90
Mycteria Americana, 159
Myiarchus crinitus, 191
Narrow-mouthed Frog, 100
Nashville Warbler, 200-201
Nelson's Sparrow, 206
Neovison vison, 233-234. 238
Nerodia fasciata, 126-127
Nighthawk, 187
Nine-banded Armadillo, 113, 117, 128, 212, 213, 216-220
North American Least Shrew, 213, 223-224

North American River Otter, 234-235
North Atlantic Right Whale, 249-251
Northern Bobwhite, 156
Northern Cardinal, 208
Northern Flicker, 190
Northern Gannet, 160-161
Northern Harrier, 167
Northern Mockingbird, 198
Northern Parula, 202
Northern Pintail, 152
Northern Rough-winged Swallow, 193
Northern Shoveler, 152
Northern Waterthrush, 199
Northern Yellow Bat, 225-226
Norway Rat, 272
Notophthalmus viridescens, 106
Numenius americanus, 175
Numenius phaeopus, 175
Nyctanassa violacea, 164
Nycticeius humeralis, 226-227
Nycticorax nycticorax, 164
Oak Toad, 94
Oceanites oceanicus, 159
Oceanodroma castro, 159
Oceanodroma leucorhoa, 159
Odocoileus virginianus 30-31, 237, 253-256
Oldfield Deermouse, 213, 269
Onychoprion anaethetus, 182
Onychoprion fuscata, 181
Opheodrys aestivus, 125-126
Ophisaurus compressus, 112
Ophisaurus ventralis, 111-112
Oporornis agilis, 201
Oporornis formosus, 201
Opossum, 120, 212, 213, 214-216
Orange-crowned Warbler, 200
Orchard Oriole, 211
Oreothlypis celata, 200
Oreothlypis peregrina, 200
Oreothlypis ruficapilla, 200-201
Oryzomys palustris, 107, 265-266
Osprey, 166
Otter, 234-235
Ovenbird, 199
Oxyura jamaicensis, 155
Oystercatcher, 173
Painted Bunting, 209
Palm Warbler, 203
Pandion haliaetus, 166
Pantherophis guttatus, 120-121
Pantherophis obsoletus, 121-122, 259
Parasitic Jaeger, 184
Parkesia motacilla, 199
Parkesia noveboracensis, 199

Parula, 202
Passerculus sandwichensis, 206
Passerella iliaca, 207
Passerina caerulea, 208
Passerina ciris, 209
Passerina cyanea, 208-209
Pectoral Sandpiper, 177
Pelecanus erythrorhynchos, 161
Pelecanus occidentalis, 161-162
Pelican, American White, 161
Pelican, Brown, 161-162
Peregrine Falcon, 169
Perimyotis subflavus, 224
Peromyscus gossypinus, 266-269
Peromyscus polionotus, 213, 269
Peucaea aestivalis, 205
Phaethon lepturus, 159
Phalacrocorax auritus, 161
Phalaropus fulicaria, 179
Phalaropus lobatus, 179
Phalaropus tricolor, 179
Pheucticus ludovicianus, 208
Phoca vitulina, 239-240
Picoides borealis, 189-190
Picoides pubescens, 189
Picoides villosus, 189
Pied-billed Grebe, 157
Pig Frog, 101-102
Pileated Woodpecker, 190
Pine Siskin, 211
Pine Warbler, 203
Pine Woods Littersnake, 126
Pine Woods Treefrog, 96-97
Pipilo erythrophthalmus, 205
Piping Plover, 173
Piranga olivacea, 208
Piranga rubra, 207-208
Pituophis melanoleucus, 94
Platalea ajaja, 165
Plectrophenax nivalis, 199
Plegadis falcinellus, 165
Plestiodon egregious, 114-115
Plestiodon fasciatus, 94
Plestiodon inexpectatus, 115
Plestiodon laticeps, 115-116, 130
Pluvialis dominica, 172
Pluvialis squatarola, 171-172
Pocket Gopher, 260-262
Podiceps auritus, 157
Podiceps grisegena, 157
Podilymbus podiceps, 157
Poecile carolinensis, 194
Poecilia latipinna, 91
Polioptila caerulea, 196

Pomarine Jaeger, 184
Pomoxis nigromaculatus, 92
Pooecetes gramineus, 205
Porphyrio martinica, 171
Porzana Carolina, 170-171
Prairie Warbler, 204
Procyon lotor, 96, 104, 107, 109, 119, 135, 230-233, 238
Progne subis, 193
Prothonotary Warbler, 200
Protonotaria citrea, 200
Pseudacris crucifer, 98-99
Pseudacris nigrita, 99-100
Pseudacris ocularis, 99
Pseudemys nelsoni, 141-142
Pterochelidon fulva, 194
Pterochelidon pyrrhonota, 194
Puffinus gravis, 158
Puffinus griseus, 158
Puffinus lherminieri, 159
Purple Finch, 211
Purple Gallinule, 171
Purple Martin, 193
Purple Sandpiper, 177
Pygmy Killer Whale, 240-241
Pygmy Sperm Whale, 245-246
Pyrocephalus rubinus, 190
Quiscalus major, 210
Quiscalus quiscula, 210
Raccoon, 96, 104, 107, 109, 119, 135, 230-233, 238
Racerunner, 117-118, 125
Rallus elegans, 170
Rallus limicola, 170
Rallus longirostris, 170
Rattus norvegicus, 272
Rattus rattus, 214, 272-273
Razorbill, 185
Recurvirostra americana, 174
Red Corn Snake, 120-121
Red Knot, 176
Red Phalarope, 179
Red-bellied Woodpecker, 189
Red-breasted Merganser, 155
Red-breasted Nuthatch, 194
Red-cockaded Woodpecker, 189-190
Reddish Egret, 164
Red-eyed Vireo, 192
Redhead, 153
Red-headed Woodpecker, 189
Red-necked Grebe, 157
Red-necked Phalarope, 179
Red-shouldered Hawk, 168
Red-tailed Hawk, 168

Red-throated Loon, 156
Red-winged Blackbird, 209
Regulus calendula, 196
Regulus satrapa, 196
Reithrodontomys humulis, 213, 270
Rhadinea flavilata, 126
Ribbon Snake, 95, 96, 127-128
Rice Rat, 107, 265-266
Right Whale, 249-251
Ring-billed Gull, 180
Ring-necked Snake, 120
Ring-necked Duck, 153, 215
Riparia riparia, 194
Rissa tridactyla, 179
Robin, 197
Rock Dove, 185
Roof Rat, 214, 272-273
Roseate Spoonbill, 165
Rose-breasted Grosbeak, 208
Rough Green Snake, 125-126
Rough-legged Hawk, 168
Rough-toothed Dolphin, 240
Rough-winged Swallow, 193
Royal Tern, 183
Ruby-crowned Kinglet, 196
Ruby-throated Hummingbird, 188
Ruddy Duck, 155
Ruddy Turnstone, 176
Rufous Hummingbird, 188
Rusty Blackbird, 210
Rynchops niger, 184
Sabine's Gull, 179
Sailfin Molly, 91
Saltmarsh Sparrow, 206
Sanderling, 176
Sandhill Crane, 171
Sandwich Tern, 183-184
Savannah Sparrow, 206
Sayornis phoebe ***
Scalopus aquaticus, 215, 220-222
Scaphiopus holbrookii, 100-101, 129, 130
Scarlet Kingsnake, 123-124
Scarlet Snake, 118-119, 231
Scarlet Tanager, 208
Sceloporus undulatus, 113-114
Scincella lateralis, 116-117, 130, 191
Scissor-tailed Flycatcher, 191-192
Sciurus carolinensis, 122, 213, 237, 256-260
Sciurus niger, 213, 260
Scolopax minor, 178
Seals, 238-240
Sea turtles, 132-138
Seaside Sparrow, 206-207
Sedge Wren, 195-196

Seiurus aurocapillus, 199
Selasphorus rufus, 188
Seminole Bat, 226
Semipalmated Plover, 172
Semipalmated Sandpiper, 176
Setophaga americana, 202
Setophaga caerulescens, 203
Setophaga castanea, 202
Setophaga citrine, 201
Setophaga coronata, 203-204
Setophaga discolor, 204
Setophaga dominica, 204
Setophaga fusca, 202
Setophaga kirtlandii, 202
Setophaga magnolia, 202
Setophaga palmarum, 203
Setophaga pensylvanica, 203
Setophaga petechia, 202-203
Setophaga pinus, 203
Setophaga ruticilla, 201
Setophaga striata, 203
Setophaga tigrina, 202
Setophaga virens, 204
Sharp-shinned Hawk, 167
Sheepshead Minnow, 90, 125
Shiny Cowbird, 210
Short-billed Dowitcher, 178
Short-eared Owl, 187
Short-finned Pilot Whale, 241
Shrew, 222-224
Siala sialis, 196
Sigmodon hispidus, 270-272
Sitta Canadensis, 194
Sitta carolinensis, 194-195
Sitta pusilla, 195
Six-lined Racerunner, 117-118, 125
Snapping Turtle, 138-139
Snipe, 178
Snow Bunting, 199
Snow Goose, 150
Snowy Egret, 163
Snowy Plover, 172
Solitary Sandpiper, 174
Solitary Vireo, 192
Somateria mollissima, 154
Somateria spectabilis, 153-154
Song Sparrow, 207
Sooty Shearwater, 158
Sooty Tern, 181
Sora, 170-171
South Polar Skua, 184
Southeastern Five-lined Skink, 115
Southeastern Pocket Gopher, 260-262
Southern Chorus Frog, 99-100

Southern Cricket frog, 95
Southern Dusky Salamander, 105
Southern Leopard Frog, 102-103
Southern Short-tailed Shrew, 130, 222-223, 268
Southern Toad, 94-95, 129
Sphyrapicus varius, 189
Spinner Dolphin, 242
Spinus pinus, 211
Spinus tristis, 211
Spizella pallida, 205
Spizella passerina, 205
Spizella pusilla, 205
Spotted Sandpiper, 174
Sprague's Pipit, 198
Spring Peeper, 98-99
Squirrel Treefrog, 97-98
Star-nosed Mole, 221-222
Stelgidopteryx serripennis, 193
Stenella frontalis, 242-243
Stenella longirostris, 242
Steno bredanensis, 240
Stercorarius maccormicki, 184
Stercorarius longicaudus, 184-185
Stercorarius parasiticus, 184
Stercorarius pomarinus, 184
Sterna forsteri, 183
Sterna hirundo, 182-183
Sterna paradisaea, 183
Sternula antillarum, 182
Stilt Sandpiper, 177-178
Storeria occipitomaculata, 127, 130
Streptopelia decaocto, 185
Striped Mud Turtle, 144
Striped Mullet, 93
Strix varia, 187
Sturnella magna, 209
Sturnus vulgaris, 198
Sula dactylatra, 160
Sula leucogaster, 160
Summer Tanager, 207-208
Surf Scoter, 154
Sus scrofa, 27, 275-282
Swainson's Thrush, 197
Swainson's Warbler, 200
Swallow-tailed Kite, 166
Swamp Sparrow, 207
Sylvilagus floridanus, 214, 275
Sylvilagus palustris, 237, 273-275
Tachycineta bicolor, 193
Tennessee Warbler, 200
Thalasseus maximus, 183
Thalasseus sandvicensis, 183-184
Thamnophis sauritus, 95, 96, 127-128
Thamnophis sirtalis, 95, 128-129, 130

Thyromanes bewickii, 195
Thyrothorus ludovicianus, 195
Timber/Canebrake Rattlesnake, 132
Towhee, 205
Toxostoma rufum, 198
Trachemys scripta, 142-143
Tree Swallow, 193
Trichechus manatus, 251-253
Tricolored Heron, 163
Tringa flavipes, 175
Tringa melanoleuca, 174
Tringa semipalmatus, 174-175
Tringa solitaria, 174
Troglodytes aedon, 195
Troglodytes troglodytes, 195
Tropicbird, 159
Tryngites subruficollis, 178
Tufted Titmouse, 194
Tundra Swan, 150
Turdus migratorius, 197
Turkey Vulture, 166
Tursiops truncatus, 243-245
Two-toed Amphiuma, 103-105
Tyrannus dominicensis, 191
Tyrannus forficatus, 191-192
Tyrannus tyrannus, 191
Tyrannus verticalis, 191
Tyto alba, 186
Upland Sandpiper, 175
Urocyon cinereoargenteus, 228-229
Ursus americanus, 109, 135, 229-230
Veery, 196
Vermillion Flycatcher, 190
Vermivora cyanoptera, 199-200
Vesper Sparrow, 205
Vireo flavifrons, 192
Vireo griseus, 192
Vireo olivaceus, 192
Vireo solitarius, 192
Virginia Opossum, 120, 212, 213, 214-216
Virginia Rail, 170
Vulture, 109, 165-166
Warmouth, 91
Water turkey, 161
West Indian Manatee, 251-253
Western Kingbird, 191
Western Sandpiper 176
Whimbrel, 175
Whip-poor-will, 188
White Ibis, 165
White-breasted Nuthatch, 194-195
White-eyed Vireo, 192
White-rumped Sandpiper, 177
White-tailed Deer, 253-256

White-tailed Tropicbird, 159
White-throated Sparrow, 207
White-winged Scoter, 154
White-winged Dove, 185
Wild Turkey, 156
Willet, 174
Wilson's Phalarope, 179
Wilson's Plover, 172
Wilson's Storm Petrel, 159
Wilson's Warbler, 204
Winter Wren, 195
Woodcock, 178
Wood Duck, 150
Wood Stork, 159
Wood Thrush, 197
Worm-eating Warbler, 199
Xanthocephalus xanthocephalus, 210
Xema sabini, 179
Yellow Bullhead, 89
Yellow Rail, 169-170
Yellow Rat Snake, 121-122, 259
Yellow Warbler, 202-203
Yellow-bellied Pond Slider, 142-143
Yellow-bellied Sapsucker, 189
Yellow-billed Cuckoo, 186
Yellow-breasted Chat, 204
Yellow-crowned Night Heron, 164
Yellow-headed Blackbird, 210
Yellow-rumped Warbler, 203-204
Yellow-throated Vireo, 192
Yellow-throated Warbler, 204
Zenaida asiatica, 185
Zenaida macroura, 186
Ziphius cavirostris, 248-249
Zonotrichia albicollis, 207